> There is a season fo[...]
> purpose under the heaven.

—Ecclesiastes

Scientists have long felt that this ancient wisdom about life's cyclical nature also applies to the human body and its many, varied functions. Now, after centuries of experimentation, here is an intriguing report on man's inner time clocks and the new scientific discoveries about them that could revolutionize our lives.

BODY TIME

the book that tells you

● How our highs and lows can be predicted—our peaks of strength and productivity, and our valleys of stress and illness.

● The importance of body time in medical treatment. Timing may have a vital influence on the success of X-ray therapy, surgery, and even psychotherapy.

● How the new knowledge of body time may be put to work in the future. There are applications in space travel . . . teaching and study methods . . . the planning of health programs . . . the prevention of industrial accidents . . . the arrangement of work shifts . . . fatigue control—and many other practical, important and humane areas of life.

Body Time

PHYSIOLOGICAL RHYTHMS
AND SOCIAL STRESS

Gay Gaer Luce

A NATIONAL GENERAL COMPANY

BODY TIME

*A Bantam Book / published by arrangement with
Pantheon Books, Inc.*

PRINTING HISTORY
Pantheon edition published November 1971
Bantam edition published January 1973

Published simultaneously in the United States and Canada

*Bantam Books are published by Bantam Books, Inc., a National
General company. Its trade-mark, consisting of the words "Bantam
Books" and the portrayal of a bantam, is registered in the United
States Patent Office and in other countries. Marca Registrada.
Bantam Books, Inc., 666 Fifth Avenue, New York, N.Y. 10019.*

PRINTED IN THE UNITED STATES OF AMERICA

To

ALAIN REINBERG

There is a season for everything
And a time for every purpose under the heaven:
A time to be born, and a time to die;
A time to plant and a time to reap . . .

ECCLESIASTES

PREFACE

MODERN MAN HAS SET THE TIME OUT OF JOINT. As a result we now live at a pace that is dissonant with our inner needs. We no longer act in harmony with natural cycles as did our ancestors throughout the millennia, working by day, resting by night, abiding the seasons, and traveling no faster than animal feet or sails could carry them. So man lived for perhaps 30,000 generations. Suddenly, only fifty years ago, the exponential surge of technology began to fling us out of all former concepts of time and space. Today we travel at the speed of sound, and with media such as television it is possible to compress the information of several lifetimes into a month or two. It is an exciting time to be alive, but a disturbing one, for our bodies and brains have not changed so much from those of our primitive ancestors, yet we must adapt to constant change. Acceleration is the thrust of our technology. Competition sets the pace for the economy. Coveting the affluence of technology we conform to the kind of social scheduling that is economically efficient, and which optimizes the use of machines. But it is not necessarily a beneficial pacing for human beings. In biological systems, time is represented in a metabolic process that is cyclic, in which we eat and digest, inhale and exhale, absorbing and using energy in a rhythmic way. These time sequences in us are often dissonant with the social machine, and many victims of this disparity suffer from emotional and somatic illnesses.

Deep within us, the seething commotion of our cells is organized. Intermeshed cycles of timing may be the glue that holds us together.

This is a book about the role of biological time cycles in our health and enjoyment of life. It is an admittedly crude and early look at a most overlooked dimension of our lives—time. However, it seems urgent to describe this dimension now, using whatever information is available, in language and analogies that everyone can understand. A book of this kind has many defects, for it anticipates the maturation of research. Scientific purists would wait for clearer understanding, more adequate information, a theory. But time structure is a matter of personal importance to everyone. Most people do not know about their own biological time cycles and do not realize that they have a time-structure. If they are distressed and unhappy at the pacing of urban life, they think that it is their fault. Swept along in the concepts of their business-oriented culture, many people berate themselves if they are not as consistent and productive as machines.

Time is the most intimate and pervasive aspect of our lives, yet the language of our self-expectations is static. We traverse the life cycle from birth to maturity, aging, and death. We observe the round of seasons, the ceaseless alternation of day and night. We are touched by inner cycles of sleepiness and hunger, yet our self-image is as fixed as a photograph. We expect consistent feeling and behavior in family and friends. We aspire to undeviating performance at work, and measure our state of health against some static norm. Our habitual language imposes the expectations of a steady state. All of this hinders us from feeling our rhythmic nature. Indeed, cyclic change is so unexpected even among medical doctors and scientists that it is often mistaken for abnormality.

We are aware of our physical structure, skeleton,

fingers and toes, yet unaware that we are organized of time as well. Most people are faintly conscious of some rhythmic interaction between respiration and heartbeat when they run, or they recognize their rhythm of sleep and waking, or of fluctuations of hunger and energy each day. If a person were to maintain a systematic diary of his life, he would be startled to see how many moods and periods of illness or strength were predictable. Were he to look inside himself, he might note that his body, like a most complex factory, operates on something analogous to an elaborate production schedule. How else could millions of biochemicals arrive at the nerve ends or organs that needed them in the right quantities at precisely the right time? Without a surge of activity among liver and kidney enzymes, we might be poisoned rather than nourished by the food we eat, for these enzymes must be manufactured and ready when the food arrives. Some production schedule must govern this manufacturing and inventory in the body, a schedule that is also synchronized by the timing of our sleep and activity each day.

Although the study of time structure in human beings has just begun, it is likely to effect revolutionary changes in medicine, for the timing of an action can be as potent as a drug or surgery. A study of human time structure will certainly force technologically advanced nations to reconsider the ways in which they schedule work and rest, meals and recreation. Even though the fluctuations that transform us each day seem relatively small, these biological cycles will become essential information to scientific experimenters in many fields of biology and medicine, in developing and testing drugs, in the study of human physiology, in understanding brain function and the keenness of human perception and performance.

Knowledge of time structure means a revolution in self-insight, a change in our image and use of ourselves as drastic as that of Freudian insight. We live in an era when man is undergoing several revolutions in his concept of himself, changing his ideas of who he is, how he functions, and what his limits may be. The psychological revolution caused us to pay attention to the way in which experience early in life could shape later behavior and feeling. Today, laboratory instruments are being used to teach people how to control their own autonomic nervous system and bodily functions once believed to be involuntary. Man's sensory range has been expanded by X-rays, radio, microwaves. Psychedelic drugs have meanwhile expanded the range of consciousness. To subsequent generations, we will seem as underdeveloped as cavemen seem today, for we are still people who cannot control our own nervous systems, who do not know the range of our conscious experience, and who are not intimate with our own timing, our own structure of rhythmic change. In some respects we may seem more primitive than tribal peoples who live in nature, for we, without understanding it, live outside of the tempo of the natural world around us and are out of touch with the natural rhythms of our own selves.

Human rhythmicity has been studied relatively little, but there is a vast and fascinating literature on biological cycles in plants, animals, and insects. This book is not about the many studies of paramecia, plant life, birds, or fish, nor does it cover migration and the navigation of birds and fish. No single book could cover the entire range of studies in biological rhythms that will undoubtedly prove valuable for all biological science, for agriculture, medicine, transportation, and education, and which will enhance our ability to live within the natural world without destroying it. Nor does this book touch on theories of biological cycles or mathematical models of the kinds of mechanisms that may regulate our various rhythms; references to some of these can be found in the bibliography. This book focuses upon human time structure and primarily on the daily rhythms of man that may be important for health and comfort.

This book evolved during many nights when I stood looking over the shoulders of scientists as the brain wave tracings from sleeping experimental subjects unfolded on the electroencephalograph machine. Roughly every ninety minutes throughout the night there appeared the pinched quick brain waves and rapid eye movements of a special dreaming state. One cannot observe these rhythmic changes, corollaries of profoundly different states of mind, without becoming acutely aware of one's own cycles of change, of dreams, heartbeat, drives, and mood. These are the waves of change under a surface we call constant.

In 1967 I began to collect data for a monograph on rhythms for the National Institute of Mental Health. I had underestimated the difficulty and breadth of the project. Men and women from diverse disciplines— mathematics and biology, psychiatry and psychology— were at work in the United States, the Soviet Union, Germany, France, Italy, Ireland, England, Japan, Africa, and throughout the world. Their findings were published in so many kinds of journals that it was possible for people to explore the same problem without hearing of each other. Only late in 1970 did the *Journal of Interdisciplinary Cycle Research* come into being, to be followed in 1971 by the *Journal of Chronobiology*. The field was expanding rapidly, and as I began to read the studies applicable to human beings, the project seemed hopeless. Taken alone, many studies were unexciting: often they indicated merely that there was a little more of some substance in the urine at one hour than at another hour. The task of collating seemed tedious at first, but slowly it dawned on me that there must be some integrated pattern in the appearance around the clock of these substances of life. A startling picture began to emerge, for it became clear that we must be constructed out of time as certainly as we are constructed of bones and flesh. In some nebulous way we all sense that there is an exchange between body weight and rate of metabolism, between matter and time.

Warning

There is no formula, no simplification that can make human time structure easily visible. I have tried to arrange the huge morass of data in a particular sequence so that readers would finally see the totality.

For many readers there will be too much new information to ingest at one time. The author took several years to absorb the information, and no reader should be embarrassed to skip the sections that are difficult. Indeed, the book was written with the hope that people would select the areas that particularly interest them. There is no theory to describe time structure, only the weight of the evidence. I have eliminated mountains of data, but interested readers will find it in my monograph, cited in the bibliography.

This book is circular. Its order was designed to build the reader's comprehension as painlessly as possible. It begins and ends with an ecological view of man in nature, a humankind profoundly suffused with rhythmic changes related to those of the cosmos, changes that are little known and mysterious. The second chapter introduces some of the ways in which work schedules and travel alter our basic rhythms of sleep and activity, offering studies of the sleep–and–activity rhythm during isolation. The third chapter discusses the cyclic states of sleep, suggesting that these rhythms of night actually pervade the day, and that they have several possible meanings in infancy and old age. Chapters four and five are difficult! Here is basic physiological information about changes that permeate body and mind each twenty-four hours. For many readers the names of hormones and other body chemicals will be unfamiliar. It is not necessary to read and remember it all. However, by selectively skimming through chapters four and five, it will be possible to understand why a person feels different at different hours of day and night, why his symptoms of illness fluctuate, and why drugs affect him differently depending upon the hour. With this glimpse of a time map of twenty-four hours in the body, one may begin to understand how stress and trauma may generate illness by shifting body timing. Experiments in what we would call psychological stress have done just that, producing mental and physical illness in animals akin to those of people. This is the topic of chapter seven. In chapter eight, one sees how slight shifts in normal cycles might appear in the form of periodic illnesses. Little attention has been paid to weekly, monthly, and yearly cycles in human beings. These begin to seem more comprehensible if one looks at the "external" forces that gently synchronize our daily activity cycle, our hormonal changes, and our seasonal rhythms. One dominant synchronizer—light—is the subject of the last chapter, which describes very briefly how its biological potence synchronizes flowering in plants and mating in birds, and how it may be guiding us. For those who want to probe more deeply into the literature there is an extensive bibliography, grouped by subject and listing popular books and general articles, as well as technical papers and books. An appendix describes methods and problems of collecting and analyzing physiological changes in time.

Time is difficult to write about, to read about, and to think about—for we are part of its process. Although this is a slow book to read, and one that may not be easy to gulp whole, I hope that every reader will ultimately share the author's electric sense of recognition upon seeing and sensing the internal rhythms that bind us in time, with the rhythms of earth and cosmos.

Gay Gaer Luce
New York, February 1971

ACKNOWLEDGMENTS

I SHOULD LIKE TO THANK ALL OF YOU WHO HAVE contributed substance and shape to this book and its earlier versions. But no scientific contributor should be held responsible for mistakes that are mine, for a popular phraseology that many would eschew, and for my own interpretations of data and dramatic speculations. Without impugning their reputation for rigor, I am grateful to all the contributors, especially Dr. Charles F. Stroebel and Dr. Arne Sollberger, for their invaluable corrections and imaginative advice, and Dr. James Meyerhoff, whose critical suggestions have helped to render the medical material intelligible. Everyone who consults the bibliography will be grateful to Diane Deitchman and Barbara Milliken. However, the readability of the book is largely due to the skilled editing of Jean Houston and Paula McGuire.

CONTENTS

PREFACE vii

ACKNOWLEDGMENTS XV

1 TIDES OF LIFE: CONCEPTS OF CULTURE 1

2 TRAVEL, WORK SCHEDULES, AND ISOLATION 27

3 SLEEP, DREAMS, AND THE BIOLOGICAL HOUR 65

4 DAILY CHANGES 121

5 RHYTHMS OF SYMPTOMS AND CELLS 149

6 HOURS OF VULNERABILITY AND RESISTANCE
   TO DRUGS AND ILLNESS 173

7 TIME AND THE CONSEQUENCES OF STRESS 197

8 PERIODIC SYMPTOMS IN SICKNESS AND
   HEALTH 233

9 LIGHT—A LINK WITH THE RHYTHMS OF
   EARTH 263

APPENDIX: NOTES ON THE VOCABULARY AND
   ANALYSIS OF RHYTHMS 297

BIBLIOGRAPHY 319

INDEX 397

CHARTS AND GRAPHS

1. Amplitude, Period, and Frequency   29

2. Harmonic Analysis   30, 306

3. Circadian System of the Rat   144

4. Circadian System of the Mouse   177

5. Human Circadian System:
   Birth, Death, Morbidity, Susceptibility, and
   Reactivity   192

6. Wave Forms   304

7. Wave-length Phase Difference   308

8. Analysis of 17-Ketosteroid Rhythm: Annual and
   Weekly Rhythms   312

9. Circadian Rhythms in Duration of Diastole and
   Heart Rate of Men Experiencing Weightlessness
   for Several Days in Extraterrestrial Space   315

1 TIDES OF LIFE: CONCEPTS OF CULTURE

Man is subject to certain rules prescribed by his own nature, which must be known if he is to live correctly in health and recover properly from illness.

Werner Jaeger,
PAIDEIA

This succession of the seasons provides us with the great cycle we call the year. The next most important biological cycle would appear to be the twenty-eight-day lunar month. Though we moderns reckon our calendars by solar months, that is really only a bookkeeping convenience. Many animal behaviors are dominated by the phases of the moon, by the cycles of its waxing and waning; more and more human behaviors and biological processes are now considered to be affected either directly or indirectly by lunar periods. Of course the smallest and most dramatic cycle which dominates our behavior is the diurnal period, the rotation of the earth, the alternation of night and day.

Yet we don't live our lives in accordance with this knowledge of the importance of cycles in our physiological well-being.

John Bleibtreu,
THE PARABLE OF THE BEAST

1 Tides of Life: Concepts of Culture

MOST OF US MOVE FROM DAY TO DAY IN A measured circle of time. Slaves to the clock on the wall, we progress like somnambulists in deep trance, unaware, out of contact, oblivious to the clocks inside us. We treat ourselves mechanically, ignoring the ceaseless process within our cells. We heed the gross demands of the flesh that our skeletons carry, but what principle gives order to the endless activity within this flesh? What force prevents utter anarchy?

Time structure gives this seething life a shape. Yet nobody teaches us about our body's time in school. Body time is rarely mentioned by doctors and even more rarely considered by leaders of business and government who set the schedules by which we work and live. Time is the most overlooked dimension in human nature. Astronomers know more about the timing of pulses from distant radio stars than we know about the pulses of our own body. Children in school will learn how a water clock or a pendulum works, and how to program an intricate timer into a computer—but they will not learn how to sense or regulate their own body rhythms. We learn about the tuning fork resonance that drives an atomic wristwatch, but we have hardly begun to study the inner clocks that allow a human being to awaken himself from sleep at a certain hour. Time cycles may provide the epoxy that melds the fragments of our substance into a coherent whole, yet we are strangely lacking in curiosity about this fundamental aspect of our nature. Perhaps we are afraid. Our culture has bathed our minds with its own special views of time. We may not want to discover that our culture

3

and our nature are in conflict. Even the first fumbling
discoveries about human "body time" are jolting, cast-
ing doubt on our comfortably ingrained daily habits,
the way we perform research, or more important, the
way we treat people who are sick. No aspect of our
existence is beyond time, so even the earliest and most
primitive discoveries about human "clocks" must pene-
trate every pore and every gesture, every avenue of
behavior. Perhaps as knowledge increases, it will begin
to give us back to ourselves. At present, most of us
have become living anomalies, victims of a profound
dissonance between our culture and our natural rhythmicity.

If there is a paucity of knowledge about human
rhythms, the literature of biology is replete with elegant
studies of rhythms in animals, plants, insects, and birds.
These are scarcely touched upon here since they are
precisely and artfully described in many other books.
Still, when exploring human time structure, it is well to
remember that we are not unlike the other creatures
with whom we share this planet. As we begin to venture
into our own cyclic nature, to examine our sense of
time and our cultural time concepts, a few images from
animals and insects will suggest urgent questions about
ourselves.

RHYTHMS IN SEA CREATURES, INSECTS, ANIMALS

Invisible rhythms underlie most of what we assume to be constant in ourselves and the world around
us. Life is in continual flux and the change is not
chaotic.

Though we can neither see nor feel them, we are
nevertheless surrounded by rhythms of gravity, electromagnetic fields, light waves, air pressure, and sound.
Each day, as earth turns on its axis, we experience the
alternation of light and darkness. The moon's revolution also pulls our atmosphere into a cycle of change.
Night follows day. Seasons change. The tides ebb and
flow. These rhythms are evident in animals and man.
Walk along a beach at midday and tiny holes at the

water's edge reveal the tunnels of the almost transparent, shrimplike creature, the sand hopper. Only by digging would one find them. But at sunset they migrate in droves up the beach. Again at sunrise they return to the water's edge. Since they eat plankton that wash into their tunnels, the nightly migration does not appear to be a search for food. The migrations are not well understood, for we are at a disadvantage studying so different a creature. Perhaps from a distant planet the rhythmic migrations of human beings to beaches by day and their evening evacuation would seem quite as mysterious. Like the human being who will travel a long distance to return home, the sand hopper also has a sense of orientation. When Dr. Floriano Papi, a zoologist, transported some of them across the boot of Italy to the eastern shore and released them, the tiny creatures turned away from the water and headed overland in the direction from which they had come.

These little crustaceans, like the bees gathering honey, or the migrating birds, seem to contain an internal clock that orients them in space from referents such as the sun and moon. To the sand hopper, the beaches must seem vast ever-changing landscapes with no reliable signposts; so are the seas, and the skies to those who navigate them, and these creatures are equipped with a system of orienting themselves by the more stable markers of moon, sun, and stars. Perhaps ancient man once migrated across vast desert-lands and arid mountains, using an inner sense of time to gauge his direction by the sun's position. If so, we seem to have lost that innate sense of time and space, and now need sextants, compasses, and elaborate star charts. Is there a vestigial time sense in us? It is interesting that people who lose track of time often experience panic and disorientation, for time is as crucial as place in human orientation.

Man has always found it easier to tell time by the sun than by the stars or moon, but many sea creatures listen to both voices. Vacationers along New England beaches have noticed crabs with a big claw shaped like a fiddle. During the daylight hours this fiddler crab is dark green, but at night it turns a pale yellowish tan.

The crabs spend most of their time in their burrows, but as the tide ebbs they come out to forage for food. When Dr. Frank Brown brought crabs to his laboratory at the University of Illinois, they continued to lighten and darken their skin color with the sunlight in a twenty-four-hour rhythm, even in constant light. But they grow active in rhythm with the tides of the eastern shore, a lunar rhythm of 24.8 hours. Next, a shipment of oysters from New Haven was brought one thousand miles to Evanston. Oysters filter nourishment from sea-water, opening their shells at high tide. At first, the oysters continued to open at the time of high tide on the New England coast, but after about two weeks they were opening at the times of the upper and lower transit of the moon which would have been high tide in Evanston, were Evanston near the sea. Like the crabs, the oysters did not seem to be reacting to changes in baro-metric pressure, for they were in special pressurized tanks. However, other rhythmic changes might pene-trate any tank—fluctuations of gravity, geomagnetic fields, and radiation—and might bring cycles of the moon into the "shielded" laboratory. Man is not shielded from these atmospheric changes, either. If we think of ourselves as creatures of the sun, we nonethe-less show strikingly lunar rhythms, such as the twenty-nine-day menstrual cycle, which is the period of the lunar month.

Much to the disgust of people who want to protect their wooden houses, pests such as termites usually appear in swarms. They hatch that way. Early on a spring morning one may see them emerging in a slow flow, crawling, and then like a fountain of insects, flying away from their pupal infancy. Fruit flies also emerge at dawn. As biologist Colin Pittendrigh and his asso-ciates have shown, the pupal flies are ready at twenty-four-hour intervals to be triggered into emergence, and even if kept in constant darkness, they can be triggered into birth by a single pulse of light at the right moment.

Human births and labor also show an unequal dis-tribution around the twenty-four hours. Most births come between midnight and 6:00 A.M. We probably know less about the timing of human births than we do about the timing of fruitfly eclosion.

Cotton growers in Mexico and the southwestern states can predict exactly the date when they will see the destructive pink bollworm, for the changing summer light appears to affect a flow of hormones necessary for growth in the dormant worm. Annual rhythms of plants, insects, and animals make spring and summer a festival of rebirth. What signals set the time of migration and breeding, of dormancy, blooming and fruiting? Biologists and botanists have been studying the ways in which plants and insects and birds anticipate the seasons, but little has been said about man. We too seem to show annual rhythms in our reproductive activity. In Denmark it is said that sex crimes increase notably during summer, and almost disappear in winter. Births are not distributed evenly over the year, and for the northern hemisphere, the peak birth rate is in March. Children show spurts of growth in spring. And we all secrete a thyroid hormone known as summer hormone, which reduces body heat during the hot months. How our bodies anticipate the hot weather is not understood; we have looked more at the flowering rhythm of plants, the migration and mating of birds.

CIRCADIAN RHYTHMS: "CIRCA" "DIES"

Of the many rhythms we casually observe in the creatures around us, the most familiar is the daily rhythm of activity and rest. Even the city dweller who never visits "nature" has seen the nocturnal rhythms of the cockroach. Turn on a kitchen light at night in an old building and the roaches scurry for cover, yet in the darkest buildings, one can turn on the light before noon and rarely see a creature. Dogs, diurnally active like man, will follow their owners to bed. But cats, lazy by day, find the onset of darkness stimulating, and then begin to play. Mollusks, fish, birds, cats, chimpanzees, and man—most living organisms show a daily rhythm of activity and rest. Even plants slowly proceed through a daily dance, and at night many of them close their leaves, or allow them to droop, raising and opening their leaves by day.

Ordinarily, the cues of daylight and darkness help to keep plants and animals synchronized with the environment. But neither honey-bees, plants, nor man entirely depend upon such cues. All will continue to alternate between activity and rest, and to show their "time sense" even when isolated from the outside world. When placed out of touch, in a salt mine or deep cavern, the organism begins to "free run." Perhaps a more nearly inherent rhythm now appears. It is not precisely twenty-four hours, the cycle of a solar day. Nor is it usually a precise 24.8 hours, the period of a lunar day. It is approximately twenty-four hours, a rhythm usually called circadian, from the Latin *circa* (around) *dies* (day)—around a day.

If we were abandoned with some food and entertainment in a salt mine, we would settle down to a circadian cycle of sleep and rest—although we might oscillate at first. The circadian cycle seems to be an important organizing principle in our physiology. People may be unaware that their body temperature, blood pressure, respiration, pulse, blood sugar, hemoglobin levels, and amino acid levels change—rising and falling in circadian cycles. So do our adrenal hormones, our urine volume, and almost every function from the rate of cell division to mood. Many rhythms go unnoticed. For instance, the skin temperature, particularly of the hands and feet, changes in a circadian rhythm. During sleep temperature is usually higher on the left side, while during the day it is usually higher on the right.

A dramatic corollary of the circadian change is the extent to which strength and weakness vary with biological time of day. Life and death may depend on the balance of timing. Mortality has been decided experimentally, not by the amount, but by the time of day a rodent received X-radiation, an injection of pneumonia virus, or drugs. Translated into the events of human life, these experiments may indicate that early-morning exposure to infection or nuclear radiation would be far more lethal than exposure late in the day. Deaths, symptoms, and drug effects do not occur evenly around the clock, as women with morning sickness know well. Doctors receive most of their calls from patients with coronaries, or pregnant women in labor, during the wee hours of the morning. There is, in short, a rhythmicity to the most important events of our lives.

OTHER CYCLES: THEIR INTERMESHING

The longer the period of a rhythm, the more difficult it is to study. This means that we know very little about seasonal or annual rhythms in people. We have not, until very recently, studied the monthly menstruation rhythm of women. However, monthly rhythm may appear in both sexes, for a seventeenth-century doctor, Sanctorius, used a fine scale to weigh healthy men over long periods of time and discovered a monthly weight change of 1-2 pounds.

Very rapid rhythms of enzymes or brain cells lie at the other end of our spectrum. Brain wave rhythms, displayed by electroencephalography, show changes in the polarity of brain cells, which occur in fractions of seconds or microseconds. Next to them the heartbeat seems slow.

How do these various rhythms intermesh? There are only beginning to be hints of fragments of answers. One of the pertinent relationships for all people is the ratio between respiration and pulse. We are conscious of our hearts, for the heart works hard to pump 70 barrels of blood a day, alternating rhythmically between dilation (diastole) and contraction (systole). Listening to the beat of one's heart through the pressure changes at the wrist, one would hear roughly sixty to eighty beats a minute. The heart and lungs operate rhythmically together. At rest, respiration is four times slower than pulse, meaning about fifteen to twenty breaths a minute. Both pulse rate and respiration rate show a circadian rise and fall, reaching a peak during the day, and dropping to a low point during sleep.

Proper timing is a sign of health. Dr. Gunther Hildebrandt, at the University of Marburg, Germany, has concluded that a healthy person shows a four-to-one ratio of heartbeat to respiration. In Germany and throughout Europe, people with cardiac problems or other symptoms often recuperate in the famous health spas. These are not resorts. In a spa a patient will follow a rigid schedule of sleep and meals, of immersion in natural spring waters or carbon dioxide baths. One theory of balneology, as these bath treatments are called, is based on classic ideas of medicine, in which the disharmony of the sick body is restored to harmony by a very regular schedule. Dr. Hildebrandt, in his studies of patients at these spas, saw that cardiac patients often had a six-to-one heartbeat-to-respiration ratio before they began their treatments, but regained a four-to-one ratio after treatments.

The circulatory system is a very complicated closed hydraulic system. Many German scientists have searched the relationships between heart rate and motor activity for clues to the cause of arrhythmia. People who do not feel well may visit their physician, and show "normal" electrocardiograms. Yet they exhibit abnormal ratios of pulse to respiration, a sign of internal discord, that may one day offer a way of diagnosing cardiac problems at a very early stage.

Someday, when we begin to assemble a kind of time map of the body's various rhythms, everyone will be surprised and perhaps delighted to recognize rhythms already observed in themselves. Anyone with a bad head cold, for instance, knows that we do not breathe evenly through both our nostrils at once. We alternate. Yogic masters, who learn deliberately to alternate breathing through one nostril and then the other—perhaps rhythmically thereby to start the beat of ecstatic meditation—know about this normal breathing rhythm. Ordinarily a man will breath through one nostril for about three hours while the tissues of the other are slightly engorged. Then in a three-hour exchange, he will breathe predominantly through the other nostril. Three-hour rhythms may be among the basic sub-units of our physiology. Hunger contractions occur in roughly three-to-four-hour rhythms.

A PACEMAKER IN A SEA SLUG

Presumably these rhythms are generated by a pacemaker in the brain. Indeed, brain cells in certain regions of animal brains show rhythms of activity, in two-to-three-hour cycles. However, none of these would be considered pacemaker cells in any simple sense. Animal brains and human brains are hideously complex, so a scientist who hoped to find a pacemaker cell would have to examine a creature so simple that it only had relatively few nerve cells. This was the strategy of Dr. Felix Strumwasser, who has looked at the activity rhythms of a creature to which most people would impute no rhythm at all—it moves so slowly. This is a sea slug, found in the tidal pools of the California shore. However, its circadian activity rhythm is comically visible when twenty-four hours of film are speeded up and presented in a few minutes. Then the proverbially slow slug suddenly rouses to jump and dart around frenetically during his active period. One giant nerve cell in this simple creature would become very active at dawn and dusk. Thus Dr. Strumwasser was able to stimulate the cell at different times of day, and watch its response. This cell may be a kind of pacemaker for the creature's activity rhythm.

TIME SENSE

Some timing of activity must be learned. Dogs and cats can show an uncanny sense of the clock hour as they appear, demanding their deserved walk or meal. Many animals in experiments have shown that they have a time sense that can be trained, but which is probably "unconscious." Perhaps they are responding to internal signals, of which man is generally unaware. These signals from cycles within the brain might act as a subtle stimulus, giving us time information.

Perhaps, if a "sense" of time can be conditioned, we may teach all people to enjoy the kind of time sense that now only rare individuals seem to possess. These are people who can awaken at the precise hour they have elected beforehand, even though the time may be peculiar and irrelevant to their usual schedules. They can "set" their heads to awaken at 3:23 A.M., or to sleep for exactly ten minutes. There are many people, indeed, so consciously synchronized with the twenty-four-hour day of external clocks that they never need to wear a watch. They can tell the time within ten minutes. On the other hand, some of our time sense must depend upon the amount of attention given to clock time, and its importance in our lives. Dr. Irwin Pollack and his associates at Johns Hopkins Hospital in Baltimore surprised themselves when they gave standard tests of time estimation to patients, and found that there were more errors and inaccuracies among people from lower economic brackets. The expectation of promptness and obeisance to the clock that middle-class doctors, lawyers, or social workers might demand simply is not a faculty among people who haven't matured in a clock-sensitive environment. The ghetto child who at an early age has nowhere special to go or nothing to do, like the Navaho or Mexican, has no urgent need of hours and minutes.

TIME SENSE IN CHILDREN

In childhood the passage of time seems to be experienced differently than in maturity. Psychologists Jean Piaget and Paul Fraisse have explored this difference in their many studies. Until about age eight, time is generally experienced as being very expanded or seems to pass slowly. Most parents have heard their children make such statements as, "If I ever live to be nine . . ." in tones implying that it would take about a century.

Through repeated experience, adults have learned to measure units in estimating time and to apply reasoning. In young children, each day is its own universe. Tomorrow is a barely comprehensible concept. Moreover, until a certain age children do not seem to have a sense of the ordering of events, even after adults have tried to teach them about it. Piaget reports one typical instance:

"How old are you?"

"Seven years old."

"Do you have a friend who is older than you?"

"Yes, this one next to me is eight years old."

"Very good. Which one of you was born first?"

"I don't know. I don't know when his birthday is."

"But come on, think a little. You told me that you are seven years old and that he is eight, now which of you was born first?"

"You'll have to ask his mother. I can't tell you."

If children do not feel as adults do about the duration of time this may be, in part, because they function physiologically at a different rate. The speed of the transactions of neurons in our brains and bodies must be calibrated to the rhythms of the physical world we perceive. Our brains must respond at a certain rate to hear sounds of certain frequencies. A young person hears higher sounds than an old person, suggesting that his brain responses are faster. However, humans do not have receptors that respond as fast as those of the dog, which means that our pets can hear ultra-high sound which we cannot. We can see certain colors, but others are beyond our vision. We can see discrete movement until it becomes so fast that our brains no longer separate the frames of a moving picture but instead see continuous motion; when flashes of light occur swiftly enough we perceive only a beam.

PHYSIOLOGICAL AND PSYCHOLOGICAL FACTORS IN TIME SENSE

The role of physiological speed in perception has fascinated many scientists. Roland Fischer writes in *The Voices of Time:*

The relativity of our reference point can be demonstrated by taking a moving picture of a plant at one frame a minute, and then speeding it up to thirty frames a second. The plant will appear to behave like an animal, clearly perceiving stimuli and reacting to them. Why, then, do we call it unconscious? To organisms that react 1800 times as quickly as we react we might appear to be unconscious. They would in fact be justified in calling us unconscious since we would not normally be conscious of their behavior.

Albert Einstein once wrote, "When you sit with a nice girl for two hours you think it's only a minute. But when you sit on a hot stove for a minute you think it's two hours. That's relativity." Does our varying sense of time have a plausible explanation? Accurate estimates of short time intervals depend upon some internal pacemaker. Perhaps in a monotonous situation, the stimulus input is excessive relative to an internal pacemaker. But metabolic changes also may be involved.

The French speleologist Michel Siffre instigated interest in the circadian fluctuations of individual subjective time-perception, and he also demonstrated what strange misperceptions of time seem to occur during isolation. He spent sixty days in a cave, yet emerged thinking he had been there only thirty-five days. Many factors influence the perception of both long- and short-time intervals.

People demonstrably change their sense of time when they are under the influence of such hallucinogenic and excitatory drugs as LSD or psilocybin. If asked to tap on a Morse key at a self-chosen rate and instructed to tap as evenly as possible, they will tap fastest at the peak of the drug state. At the time of increased tapping, they experience "a flood of inner sensations" or time contraction. Under the influence of psychedelic drugs many people have felt as if months of experience were compressed into a few hours.

TRANCE STATES

Drs. Linn Cooper, Milton Erickson, Robert E. L. Masters, and Jean Houston have shown that learning can be intensely focused by using time distortion and hypnotic trance states; in their experiments they have enabled a student to improve graphic art skills in a few hours, skills that might normally take a semester of classroom work. In time-distortion experiments, people make judgments about their experiences with reference to some learned sense of time. There may be natural units of time and attention in the nervous system that are available to an individual, and only future research can tell whether or not they approximate the units of our clocks. Studies of time distortion emphasize how limited our cultural view of "time sense" can be, and may offer us ways of enriching the education of the young by compressing more learning into the early school years. A number of scientists have conjectured that any intelligent youngster could have the knowledge of today's college graduate by the age of ten. Children using time-distortion techniques might indeed accelerate their own study. One fact in their favor is a high rate of brain metabolism.

METABOLISM

If metabolism and temperature were high, two minutes of brain time might pass in only one minute of clock time—and we would think that time was dragging. As Dr. Hudson Hoagland relates in *The Voices of Time,* he began thinking about time sense, body temperature, and chemical kinetics in the early 1930s. He recalled his wife having a temperature of 104 degrees with influenza and asking him to go to the drugstore. Although he was gone only twenty minutes, she insisted that he had taken hours. Intrigued, Hoagland took a stopwatch and without telling her why, asked her to count to sixty, at about one number per second. His wife, a trained musician, had a good time-sense, but she counted to sixty in much less than a minute. Hoagland repeated the test some twenty-five times with a consistent result. When her body temperature was high she counted faster; when her body temperature was low, she counted slowly. Hoagland later used diathermy on student volunteers and tested the perceptions of short time intervals. The students counted faster when their body temperatures were high, suggesting that perception of short time intervals may be modulated by a metabolic-chemical pacemaker system in the brain. In the progression from childhood to maturity, there is a decline in the rate at which one consumes oxygen and a slowing of the metabolism. It may be possible that the higher metabolic rate of the child suggests why time seems to move so slowly for him, while time passes swiftly for the elderly person whose metabolism is low.

If Hoagland's physicochemical hypothesis of short-time intervals were correct, time should be a variable experience for snakes, lizards, and other cold-blooded animals. On warm summer days the time should seem to pass slowly for them, while on cold days it might seem to pass rapidly. Thus a winter's hibernation might seem like a night's sleep. There are, of course, more factors in general time perception, and in the experience of short intervals, than could be explained by metabolism. Nonetheless, in experiments, people have varied in their estimates of time intervals much as Hoagland predicted, in accordance with their daily rhythm of body temperature.

MENTAL ILLNESS

Distortions of time sense are also reported by many psychotic patients. In one study patients were asked to produce a specified short-time interval. Those in unhappy emotional states gave inaccurately brief intervals as if their nervous systems were running at an accelerated pace. Patients in pleasanter states gave more accurate intervals, and psychotic patients seemed to show a more distorted time sense than depressed or neurotic patients, estimating time more accurately as they improved.

IN THE LABORATORY

Psychologist Robert Ornstein has reviewed the literature of time estimation in his book, *On the Experience of Time*. He concludes that the sense of duration cannot be correlated with any physiological "clock," and that time sense must be more psychological than biological. Time durations seem long to us if we are conscious of a great deal of information. Ornstein performed nine ingenious experiments that demonstrated the role of awareness and memory in time experience.

Subjects reported feeling the assigned intervals as longer when the amount and complexity of the stimuli within the measured interval were increased. People judged intervals comparatively longer when they recalled the contents than when they did not, suggesting that our sense of duration may be related to memory as well as to information-processing. For instance, a subject saw a short film of a modern dancer going through twenty-six dance positions; the film was spliced up so that the movements could be seen almost separately, in eleven segments, or in six segments, or merely divided into two. With dance, design, sound, and images, the more a person had to "work" at remembering the information, the longer he believed his exposure to it.

This might explain the sense of expanded time in children, who have not yet learned how to code their experience in an abbreviated manner. It may also explain why a dull, disorganized lecture seems to last three hours instead of one—it is much harder to code.

Coding seems to affect a person's experience of time, even after the event is over. For example, think of the way a vacation feels from day to day. There are so many activities, pitching a tent, finding a rare fish, climbing rocks, diving in a still clear pool, trying to light a fire with sticks, and so on through the many unfamiliar and lovely events that make up a single day. The vacation seems to go on for much longer than two weeks, yet when you return to familiar office routine, you now describe the vacation by saying you drove to Nova Scotia, where you camped out and fished. Suddenly, summarized thus in your mind, the vacation shrinks to a short interval, in the long and familiar pattern of your usual life. The experience of time is related to the way we remember, and the way we remember is related to the way we learn to think. From the moment we are born parents, teachers, and friends are shaping our concept of time.

CULTURAL CONCEPTS OF TIME

The pace an individual keeps in work and recreation, his subjective sense of duration, and what he imagines he can accomplish within any specific interval are aspects of time that may be influenced by culture. Temporal attitudes pervade a culture to such an extent that they are almost invisible, yet they are probably more influential than we imagine. In subtle but powerful ways, cultural concepts of time have helped to mold the history of civilization.

Time concepts may help to explain the astonishing accuracy of early Chinese histories. Not only did the Chinese document events from earliest antiquity, but they also expressed an orderly respect for family tradition and rules of human conduct, qualities that appear to have been generated by a philosophy embodying respect for time cycles of considerable magnitude. Naturalists and astronomers saw that the cycles of the sun and moon were reflected in life, and this in turn influenced their philosophy: "The sun at noon is the sun declining; the creature born is the creature dying." In cycle-oriented Taoism time was divided into seasons and eras, considered part of an infinite chain of duration—past, present, and future.

Because it was an agrarian society, almost every Chinese mathematician and astronomer worked on calendars. Between 370 B.C. and A.D. 1742 about a hundred different calendars were developed, each one embodying astronomical events with ever-increasing accuracy.

In the first century A.D., Buddhism and a philosophy of continual metamorphosis spread through China. Naturalists and philosophers observed evolutionary transformations in living organisms, so sixteen centuries before Darwin they expressed an evolutionary naturalism that embodied a succession of phylogenetic unfoldings, rather than the concept of a single train of evolution with which Western science began. Complex concepts of time led to remarkably sophisticated theories that included accurate perception of astronomical change, views on the nature of fossils, and explanations of the unity of these vast time cycles in the development and history of each man. In the Chinese view, man's place was a humble and appropriate part of the time cycle. Morally and biologically he fit into the grand expanse of nature and history. Thus he saw his world and his future very differently than does any modern Westerner.

In the thirteenth century, the Chinese *Book of Changes* gave an estimate of phases in the evolution of life covering about 130,000 years. At that time the Chinese were calculating astronomical periods in millions of years. Western attitudes of that era were primitive by contrast. Judeo-Christian perception of time was linear. The flow of time was believed to begin with some specific point in space-time. In seventeenth-century Europe, people piously believed in Bishop Usher's calculation of the date of the Creation of the Universe —October 6, 4004 B.C. Time, it was thought, had to begin with some significant event.

This simple linearity dictated much of Western thought, custom, and philosophical egotism. It encouraged a self-centered concept of our place in the universe, our hustling individuality, and our philosophies of cause and effect. These notions have been instrumental in the development of Western science.

Westerners measure time by action and outstanding actions are recorded as history. In contrast, India has never produced a written history. The Hindustani never troubled to make detailed chronological records of their national development, for they lived in a time domain characterized by a changeless sense of ever-becoming. To Westerners, Indians may seem lacking in urgency. Their universe, world, and social order are eternal; personal life is only a sample of a succession of lives, repeating themselves endlessly. Transmigration of souls and perpetual rebirth make meaningless any quantitative view of a particular period of time. Life, infinitely recycled, makes history less significant, and an individual's biography is merely a transient moment in the process.

The Japanese Buddhist concept of the transience of the physical world has very different consequences: it has led to intuitive, sensitive admonitions that if all things are transient, one must appreciate but not cling to the moment. "Time flies more swiftly than an arrow and life is more transient than dew." The ultimate reality is what one sees and experiences. The urgency of Western action is a new phenomenon in Japan. In Japanese sensibility, time is not an absolute nor an objective set of categories but a process. It is the change of nature. Man is part of that change and able to appreciate it, feeling transience to be part of the eternal loveliness of the universe rather than a threat to the ego (as Western man sees mortality).

Even the briefest statement is sufficient to indicate that cultural concepts of time have a pervasive influence upon individuals and upon major social developments. In medicine, for instance, one can see why ancient peoples might have accepted notions of biological rhythmicity, connecting human life with natural cycles, and why such ideas are almost nonexistent in our own society.

MEDICINE IN ANCIENT GREECE

Cultic medicine is easy to dismiss. Man has long outlived the need to influence his fertility by rituals to the phases of the moon. Still, the shaman and the priest, the medicine man and the astrologer often worked together, or were the same person. From the most distant history in Africa to the sophisticated Egyptian physician, an interaction with the cosmos was considered potent in human events and human health. In ancient Egypt, medical cults were abundant, and dreams and stars were interpreted seriously, but in addition to the cults of Imhotep or Sekhmet, in addition to horoscopes and dreams, there were physicians with a vast empirical knowledge of the human body, shrewd observers and superb bone setters. While great, Egyptian medicine never became the consummate cultural influence that characterized medicine in Greece.

On the little island of Cos, at the end of the fifth century B.C. a medical school led by Hippocrates integrated medicine into the universal laws of nature as then conceived, joining medicine with philosophy into a way of life. The healthy state of man and of nature was considered to consist of an equivalence of basic elements—harmony. For the doctor, a patient's harmony was an adaptation to a context—geography, climate, the astronomical cycle. Medical students were advised to study the effects of the seasons upon health. "Then he must study warm and cold winds, chiefly those which affect all mankind, and then those which are particular to any one region." He was advised to examine the effects of different waters, having different tastes and weights. Using all his senses to measure and define the environment, a doctor, arriving in a new city, would examine its geographic position, in relation to sunrise and to the direction of the winds. He would note soil and water. In order to understand long-term climatic changes, he would see when the stars would rise and set, judging by astronomical patterns the kind of a year it would be. Astronomy helped to understand the patient because diseases were known to change in certain seasons, and weather cycles were related to the stars.

The Greek physician had a sense of the wholeness of things and did not look at disease as an isolated problem. Although medical knowledge was arcane, secret, kept within the family, and although there was little medical literature addressed to the laymen, doctors did not try to cure patients without educating them in the nature and origin of their own illness, how it developed, what to expect. Physicians saw their job as one of helping nature heal herself, restoring balance that was disturbed by disease, but not interfering with nature. Man's life was conceived to progress rhythmically, in seven-year cycles. Within each cycle there was a regimen of health. Physicians were more concerned with educating healthy people in the proper diet, exercise, and rest, than with focusing on illness. Treatises on diet and gymnastics were written for the laymen—very rich and detailed encyclopedias, indeed. As Greek medicine developed, it began to aim at treating a man before disease could begin, prophylactically.

Over 2,400 years ago Hippocrates instructed his followers that regularity was a sign of health, and that irregular body functions or habits promoted ill health. He advised them to observe closely good and bad days in their patients as well as in healthy people. Therapies involved cycles of treatment, metasyncrisis. Patients were not fed the same food and herbs, nor given the same exercise each day, but in rotations of three or seven days. One-to-three-week incubation periods were known, as were seven-day appearances of rashes and symptoms. Time periods of sevens were considered vitally important to mankind, perhaps underlying the seven-day week. In some illnesses, repeated episodes come every seven days.

In the fourth century B.C., medicine intermingled with philosophy. Regimens of health were part of the life of the citizen, who attempted to maintain his own physical existence in harmony with the balance of nature. Plato wrote that the three physical virtues—health, strength, and beauty—were joined with the spiritual virtues of courage, temperance, and justice. Social, physical, and emotional health were one. In no way did the ideals of medicine conflict with the ideals of classic culture, for health was a crucial factor, an ideal of the culture.

By the eighteenth and nineteenth centuries, medicine had moved from concepts of wholeness to greater concentration on the parts. Physicians still made observations about the relationship between illness and cosmic changes. In the early eighteenth century an extraordinary British physician, Richard Mead, wrote a discourse "concerning the Action of the Sun and the Moon on Animal Bodies," filled with case histories like the following:

> The Girl, who was of lusty full Habit of Body, continued well for a few days, but was at Full Moon again seized with a most violent Fit, after which, the Disease kept its Periods constant and regular with the tides; She lay always Speechless during the whole Time of Flood, and recovered upon the Ebb ...

However, the thrust of medical science was not to consider the patient in his context, for modern doctors were learning about the infections and germs that caused disease, which had been mysterious external forces to the ancients.

Ironically, by the end of the nineteenth century,

classical precepts were presented in a new manner, a fashion that became a fad and which is still popular, the calculation of "biorhythms."

BIORHYTHMS AND FLIESS

In 1887 Wilhelm Fliess published his formula for the use of biological rhythms. He asserted that everyone was bisexual. The male component (strength, endurance, courage) was keyed to a cycle of twenty-three days. The female cycle (not menstrual, but a cycle of sensitivity, intuition, love, and other feelings) had a period of twenty-eight days. Both cycles, he asserted, are present in every cell and play a dialectic role throughout life in the ups and downs of vitality, physical and mental, and eventually determine the day of one's death.

Fliess and his magnum opus, *The Rhythm of Life: Foundations of an Exact Biology,* might have faded into obscurity had he not been a close friend of Sigmund Freud and introduced the use of cocaine as an anesthetic. For many years Freud thought Fliess had made a great breakthrough in biology. Fliess linked twenty-three- and twenty-eight-day cycles with changes in the mucosal lining of the nose. He related nasal irritation to neurotic symptoms and sexual abnormalities. He diagnosed ills by inspecting the nose and applying cocaine to what he called "genital cells" in its interior. He operated on Freud's nose twice. Fliess had a blatantly unsophisticated understanding of simple mathematics, yet every year his formula is offered to the public in new books on biorhythms that promise a reader the ability to chart his own cycles of physical or emotional vulnerability and strength in advance. By predicting his strength and weakness, much as a woman might put menstrual dates on a calendar, a person should be able to plan his activities for maximum advantage. If the formula concocted by Fliess was childish, the underlying idea may not be so far-fetched. At least, it does not seem far-fetched for people to forecast their rhythms empirically. This is possible only by keeping very detailed diaries on feelings at different hours of

the day—mood, attention, weight, symptoms, vitality—
for months and years. It is not so easy as a simple
formula, for we are all rhythmic beings, but the slightly
different beat we walk to makes a huge difference in
monthly or yearly undulations. With the aid of computers, however, mankind can finally hope to learn
about these undulations. There is no denying that they
exist or that they play a formative role in our personalities and the timing of important life events, such as
birth or death, and that they bias our response to
danger, ability to wake, and health—which is the substance of the rest of this book. The book starts back-
wards, however, with problems and studies that are
familiar to everyone. The real nature of these studies
will become apparent only in later chapters. Still, our
lives are molded by the clock on the wall, and by the
notion that sidereal time should dictate our actions. For
a number of decades people have behaved as if external
clock time were identical to internal time. This is obviously untrue. A person who sleeps by day and works
by night is physiologically 180 degrees out of phase
with the people who work by day. In no sense can external clocks reveal "biological time of day."

Our forebears knew this. The conflict between social
time and man's nature is even written into our Declaration of Independence. King George III had harassed
the American colonists by calling assemblies at peculiar
locations and difficult hours. The colonies construed
this as a Machiavellian strategy to disrupt their sleep
schedules, thereby rendering them psychologically vulnerable, and these self-aware founders of our nation
listed this as one of their grievances in 1776.

> He has called together legislative bodies at places
> unusual, uncomfortable and distant . . . for the sole pur-
> pose of fatiguing them. . . .
>
> DECLARATION OF INDEPENDENCE

2 TRAVEL, WORK SCHEDULES, AND ISOLATION

During the two months I spent underground in the depths of the Scarasson Cavern, I kept a diary in which I noted down everything that happened during my physiological days. . . .loss of memory became so pronounced that it was sometimes hard for me to remember what I had done a few minutes before. . . .

We now know, as we learned in the physical checkup given me at the end of the experiment, that my metabolism was greatly slowed down and that my condition of torpor (hypothermia) was that of semihibernation. . . .

Most curious of all, time seemed to pass very quickly. . . . Time passed without my being aware of it in the darkness and silence. I felt I was on another planet: for the most part I dwelt neither in the past nor in the future, but in the hostile present. In that environment everything was against me: the rocks that crashed down from time to time; the damp chill atmosphere; the darkness.

Michel Siffre,
BEYOND TIME

2 Travel, Work Schedules, and Isolation

AT NO TIME IN OUR HISTORY WAS IT MORE important to try and understand our physiological timing, and to know what limits or guidance it might give us in the scheduling of work, medication, travel, and space exploration. Practical needs have always galloped ahead of knowledge. During World War II the military requirements for twenty-four-hour vigilance and twenty-four-hour production in defense industries made the scheduling of work shifts crucial to national efficiency. It brought us face to face with our own conflicting inner rhythms. Night work, rotating shifts in factories, and transportation schedules have since generated accidents and dangers that drew attention to safety precautions. The practical response was to limit the work week—which did not solve the real problem. Recently, police departments in large cities such as New York have found officers sleeping on night duty. Air traffic controllers in big airports have included rotating shifts in their list of stresses when they went on strike. Moreover, a whole population of diplomats, businessmen, and astronauts have become fully aware that scheduling profoundly affects body and mind. In the early 1960s the eminent biologist, Erwin Bünning, opened a conference with his colleagues, suggesting that disruptions caused by certain kinds of schedules and travel might result in serious consequences such as illness, even possibly cancer. Although this has not been proven, a decade later it is clear that shifts in the sleep-waking schedule are not superficial and do have a biological aftermath.

SOME BASIC TERMS: FREQUENCY, PHASE, PERIOD, AMPLITUDE

It is difficult to discuss east-west travel or rotating shifts in our usual colloquial vocabulary. People often refer to fatigue, and to local time, neither of which is helpful. When a person travels east or west or works on a night shift, his entire body enters a state of transition for many days. Like an immensely complex clock with a million hands, we are always "resetting" or synchronizing our sleep and activity with the world around us. Unlike a mechanical clock, however, our numerous physiological systems do not reset at once. Indeed, certain cardiac rhythms may take three or four days, while adrenal hormones may take two weeks to reset to a new schedule of sleep and rest. In the language of biological rhythms this change in schedule would be called a phase shift. It is a shift in the phase of our sleep-waking cycle with reference to day and night.

Any event that recurs at a predictable interval can be described as if it were a cycle. It may be the rise and fall of body temperature, the occurrence of nightly sleep or morning wakening, the monthly menses of women, recurring fevers or moods. This repeated event can be described as a circular process—a cycle. The interval of time that it takes to complete the cycle is known as the period, and is often represented by the Greek letter (τ). The period may be only a microsecond, or it may be a year. This period is the time elapsed between peaks of body temperature or nightly sleep. The period of a day is about twenty-four hours.

The frequency of a cycle is the reciprocal of the period $(\bar{\tau})$. Every twenty-four hours most mammals sleep for several hours, so that the frequency of this sleep rhythm is 1/24. This is the frequency of fluctuations in body temperature and many other body functions. While it is essential to know the period or frequency of a cycle, more information is needed to describe it. One needs to know how much temperature or hormone levels change in a day—the extent of daily change in body temperature is greater in some people than in others. This is a difference in the amplitude (C) of the rhythm. One person may show a change of 2.1 degrees, while another changes by only 1.5 degrees.

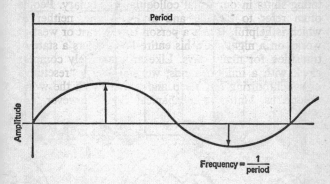

People tend to differ in the amplitudes of their physiological rhythms and also along another time dimension which may be a factor in temperamental differences. People may not show the peaks and troughs of their daily temperature rhythm simultaneously. If a person works at night, his temperature cycle should be about 180 degrees out of phase with that of a day worker. The placement of the peak or trough of a cycle, relative to some other cycle in the body or some external marker, is its phase, which is often denoted by the Greek letter (ϕ). The phase describes some part of the 360-degree cycle with reference to an external time point, which might be clock time, the hour at which a person went to sleep, or the peak of another body cycle.

In trying to study human beings as they traveled east or west or changed work shifts, scientists have actually been studying phase shifts. Manned space expeditions have raised questions about the period of man's cycle of sleep and activity. Must he live a circadian period of roughly twenty-four hours, or could he adapt to a twelve- or eighteen-hour day should circumstances ordain that this would be more convenient? Basically, the issues of travel involve phase shifts, although space ex-

Harmonic Analysis

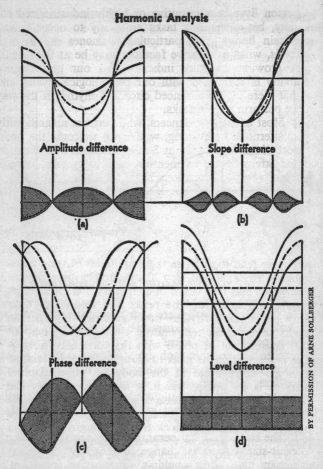

BY PERMISSION OF ARNE SOLLBERGER

ploration has raised interesting questions about the natural period of man's circadian rhythms and whether man is indeed bound to the cycle of a day.

PERFORMANCE: A CIRCADIAN RHYTHM

Many of our physiological functions are known to exhibit a pronounced circadian rhythm. Whether a person lives in a primitive or highly industrialized society, his demanding tasks are likely to occur during certain hours when particular hormones are at high levels, when integrative faculties may be at their peak. A growing literature indicates that our performance ability is correlated with our physiological cycles and that there is a pronounced circadian rhythm in the way we perform certain tasks.

Most athletes or dancers, who perform magnificently in afternoon or evening, would not welcome the prospect of having to play at 3 A.M. Muscular coordination and strength, not to mention time judgments, vary in the course of twenty-four hours. So does acuity. Many people like to postpone fine and exacting tasks, accounting, or writing, until afternoon. Radar operators are likely to make more errors and to have a harder time keeping alert, during hours when normally they would sleep.

BODY TEMPERATURE AND PERFORMANCE

Even before there were systematic, around-the-clock studies, it was suspected that body temperature and performance were related. Body temperature reaches a high point each day, falling to a nadir in late sleep. Individuals vary somewhat in their temperature rhythms, some showing a faster rise in the morning, others a steeper fall at night, but an individual's normal body temperature is not apt to change by more than 1.20 degrees each day.

The small daily temperature drop actually represents a fair-sized metabolic change, but not large enough that human motivation couldn't compensate for it. The subtle changes in ability that might recur each day, as temperature rises and declines, are particularly difficult to detect on performance tests. Most psychological tests are not designed to capture nuances; like gross sieves they detect only gross changes in behavior. However, an English scientific team with unusual patience has finally refined a series of tests so that they do indicate very small alterations in a person's performance.

Drs. Robert T. Wilkinson and Peter Colquhoun have tested Navy recruits on vigilance, arithmetic and other criteria after various schedules of sleep or sleep loss. Dr. Wilkinson had previously found that a highly motivated subject could compensate for sleep loss on short tests, but not if he spent a full eight- to ten-hour day in the laboratory doing various tasks such as listening to a train of beeps through earphones for the beep that was perhaps a fraction of a second shorter than the others. In one study, oral temperatures were taken hourly during waking and every two hours in sleep. Temperature rose on an average of 0.56 degree in the first three hours of waking, and remained stable, changing only 0.4 degree during 60 percent of the day. The most consistent improvement in performance efficiency occurred during the first three hours when temperature rose most. Peak performance coincided with the time of peak temperature, and low performance coincided with the interval of lowest temperature.

It has been thought that a metabolic rhythm may underlie the body temperature rhythm and that this may modulate activity in the central nervous system. Twenty-four-hour recordings of human brain waves do suggest that a circadian rhythm modulates the frequency and the amplitude of the brain-wave pattern. Thus, a twenty-four-hour record might show that a person had what is known as an alpha rhythm, a pattern seen in relaxed waking and meditation. It might be about 9.5 cycles per second at one hour, and 10 cps at another with a change in amplitude of several microvolts. There seems to be a parallel circadian rhythm in estimates of short-time intervals. A person may give a too-short estimate of a ten-second interval when his alpha rhythm is fast, but give a longer than ten-second estimate when his alpha rhythm is slower. Many researchers have looked at brain-wave responses at different hours around the clock. These brain-wave responses are the immediate pattern emitted by the person's brain after he has seen or heard or felt a test signal; they are recorded by an amplifier known as the electroencephalograph. Brain-wave responses change in a circadian rhythm as do vigilance, subjective fatigue, keenness of hearing, and sense of time.

TESTS OF AIRLINE PILOTS AND CREWS

As a person slowly and almost imperceptibly changes physiologically around the clock so, too, does the complexion of his performance. A group of researchers led by Dr. K. E. Klein at the Institute for Flight Medicine in Bad Godesberg, Germany, have begun to relate performance to biological change. They collected oral temperatures, cardiac output, levels of white blood cells, measured simple reaction time, and computed individual variance in reaction time, as well as taking many other measures. One group of volunteers was subjected to a series of complex tests, requiring coordination and continued performance for over ten minutes. They were given a physical exercise test on a bicycle with a voltimeter that measured the amount of work and also allowed the researchers to evaluate and predict the maximum oxygen uptake. Subjects were tilted to ninety degrees on a tilt table for about twenty minutes and tested while holding their breaths, then while breathing fast, or hyperventilating. Blood pressure and pulse responses were recorded. Altitude tolerance was tested in a low-pressure chamber.

Mental performances were at their peak between 2 and 4 P.M. This was the period of quickest reaction time and best psychomotor coordination. Poorest performances occurred between 2 and 4 A.M. In considering the capacities of a pilot who may have to fly both night and day shifts or travel east or west, one important clue to his adaptability may be the amplitude of his rhythm. The more he changes from night to day, the more difficulty he may encounter when he undergoes a phase shift. Dr. Klein's study indicated that maximum oxygen consumption, the pulse pressure of a man on a tilt table, and the length of time he could maintain useful consciousness despite too little oxygen all varied considerably depending upon time of day. In the course of the day there were also very large changes in blood constituents, such as plasma proteins and adrenal hormones, although body temperatures do not change considerably. Some kinds of test performance showed a marked rhythm, among them reaction time and psychomotor coordination. At certain hours motor performance became as poor as if the person had 0.09 percent alcohol in his blood.

The German flight institute studies have shown that between 1 and 7 P.M. people show the best mental performance, best tolerance for lying on a tilted table, and greatest physical fitness; they give their worst responses between 2 and 6 A.M. A healthy man is not equally resistant to all kinds of stresses at all hours; oxygen consumption may be lower at 3 A.M., for instance, making altitude adjustment easier then. A pilot with too little oxygen would be 50 percent more resistant to anoxia and to passing out at 3 A.M. than at 3 P.M., despite the fact that he does most tests better at 3 P.M.

As an individual's physiology changes around the clock, he becomes more adept at certain tasks, less adept at others, resistant to some stresses, vulnerable to others. For each challenge there is an hour at which a person will be best, and an hour when he will be worst. When further research delineates the details of this time map, many of us will probably rearrange our schedules so that we can optimize our abilities.

SHIFT WORK

In early surveys of work-rest shifts, researchers repeatedly uncovered signs of a circadian rhythm in performance, but did not know that all manner of behavioral and mental events, vulnerability to toxin, shock, infection, and drugs might be biased by biological time of day. They saw signs that phase shifts and non-circadian schedules might be unhealthy, but they did not yet know that a reversal of sleep and waking might be followed by a transition period as long as three weeks in which physiological rhythms were out of their usual phase relationship with the environment and each other. Even now, many people confuse phase shifts with fatigue.

Many of the early studies of accidents, ill health, and errors among night workers attributed the effects to night work itself, whereas they really stemmed from the workers' phase shifts on weekends and time off. Soviet scientists saw in night workers on the Moscow subway system abnormal physiological rhythms that could be attributed to a poorly organized routine of daytime rest rather than to working at night. Despite confusion, the early studies had an enormously beneficial effect on industry, producing safety regulations on railroads and generating an awareness that both human accidents and human ability are not distributed evenly over the twenty-four hours.

In Sweden, for instance, it was found that meter readers in a gasworks made the most errors on night shift, fewer during afternoon shifts, and fewest in the morning. Telephone operators answered incoming calls most slowly about 3 to 4 A.M. Industrial accidents have seemed to occur most frequently around 2 to 4 A.M. However, a French analysis of over 3,000 industrial accidents suggests that accidents are less frequent among night workers than among afternoon or early morning workers. The literature of such studies is vast, but uncontrolled for effects of monotony and phase shifts.

People have long suspected that rotating shifts might be detrimental to health. An unusually high incidence of ulcers has been found among shift workers. Air-traffic controllers usually rotate in shifts, as often as every few days in some airports or at intervals of two weeks in others. Men who cannot endure the schedule are screened out, but ulcers and hypertension are not too uncommon among those who remain. They also have the highest divorce rates in the country.

JET FATIGUE AND PHASE SHIFTS IN MICE

Recently, the public has heard about the symptoms known as "jet fatigue" that afflict flying crews and some travelers. One TWA pilot describes "jet syndrome" as a gradual progression with headaches, burning or unfocused eyes, gastrointestinal problems, loss of appetite, shortness of breath, sweating, and occasional nightmares. Stewardesses have also reported gastrointestinal problems, insomnia, elusive mental problems, and menstrual irregularities for which medical examination may reveal no official source. The "cure" may be to stop flying. Individuals vary in their adaptation to east-west flight and rotating shifts, yet in the long run this adaptation may be lower than anyone has assumed.

A recent survey of over 1,000 industrial workers in the Rhône valley showed that 45 percent of the workers could not adjust to a seven-day rotation, and 34 percent could not tolerate a two-day rotation. Body temperature rhythms did not adapt to either regimen, so that even the person who "felt" adjusted was actually living in a body that was not adapted. Even if a pilot or industrial worker adapts with reasonable comfort to phase shifts temporarily, the long-term effects on health may be worth considering.

In the mid-1960s a doctor, speaking to members of the Flying Physicians' Association, remarked that there might be signs of premature aging among pilots on east-west runs. Drs. Walter Nelson and Franz Halberg of the University of Minnesota have done preliminary studies that suggest it is possible to shorten the life span of mature rodents by merely inverting their light-dark cycle just once a week. Two groups of over ninety mice were observed throughout the study on a schedule of twelve hours darkness and twelve hours light. At age fifty-eight weeks, however, one group experienced a weekly inversion of the lighting schedule analogous to a jet flight halfway around the world. In many ways it was an easier schedule than that of a transatlantic pilot, who might have to make two phase shifts in a week. The control mice lived an average of 94.5 weeks, while the group subjected to weekly phase shifts had an average life span of 88.6 weeks, a decrease of 6 percent in the mean life span. One problem with rotating shifts is that they often cause some sleep loss, which soon begins to affect a person's performance.

In a number of studies, Air Force volunteers were tested in a mock-up crew compartment on a sixteen-hour work day, alternating four hours duty and two hours rest. Of eleven men only two maintained high-quality performance for fifteen days. A group of Air Force cadets was subsequently motivated to sustain performance on the same schedule, but even with high motivation certain tasks showed a decline. Cadets performed creditably enough on the schedule unless stressed with further sleep loss, at which point their performance declined notably.

In attempting to see how phase shifts affect efficiency and health, English and American scientists have studied men in the classic rotating watches of the Navy. This is a remnant from medieval times when men did hard physical labor and could not work more than four hours at a stretch. In one study men on a stable schedule of twelve hours work and twelve hours rest were compared with men working an eight-hour rotating shift. The stable twelve-hour work shift was clearly superior, and decision-making improved with stability of schedule.

A variety of studies have been conducted in hope of ascertaining how various factors, such as physical exercise, stress, or simply confinement may affect performance on different schedules, a search prompted in part by the practical questions of manned space exploration. Although phase shifts and non-circadian cycles may not cause gross damage, they create an inner physiological transition that may render a creature more vulnerable to all manner of stresses. The studies of Dr. Franz Halberg, mentioned in later chapters, indicate how such schedules affect rodents.

Dr. Halberg and his associates kept mice on non-circadian schedules and tested their subsequent susceptibility to alcohol. One control group lived in twelve hours of light and twelve hours of darkness, a second group lived on an inversion of this schedule, while a third group lived an eight-hour day (four hours of darkness and four hours of light). After five days of adjustment to the light schedule, groups of mice were injected with alcohol at short intervals around the clock. Mice living on a twenty-four-hour light-dark schedule were most vulnerable at their time of alerting

—the beginning of darkness—as were mice on an inverted cycle. Animals on an eight-hour day were far more susceptible to alcohol generally, and their hours of maximum vulnerability did not seem correlated with the hours of light and dark. It almost appeared that they had a constantly shifting peak of vulnerability that made them more vulnerable as a group at all hours.

The nature of this transitional vulnerability, perhaps arising from a desynchronization of internal rhythms, remains one of the interesting questions of work-rest scheduling. A number of Soviet studies focus upon possible health impairment from work-rest schedules in confinement.

SOVIET STUDIES

Long before manned space flight, Soviet researchers had been studying the physiology of work, correlating pulse, galvanic skin response, and other conveniently measured physiological changes with the performance of workers undergoing the normal stresses of actual labor. They found that the effects of physical exercise could be detected in a person's diurnal test performance, brain-wave response, and general psychological tone. Lack of exercise might cause drowsing and fatigue in people on abnormal cycles of work and rest, or simply in confinement. Many Soviet researchers have expressed a bias that is more conservative than the American outlook. They assume that one could not change the normal circadian activity-sleep cycle without a detrimental effect. The cycle of sleep and waking is considered to be a set of reflexes so deeply conditioned that stability requires perpetuation of the rhythm. Moreover, the fact that the rhythm may be conditioned does not imply that it can be altered. This conservative view of man's rhythms has been reflected in the fact that Soviet cosmonauts have been maintained on their earthly sleep cycles while in orbit. Our astronauts have been exposed to a variety of schedules, including alternations of four hours of sleep with four hours of duty; some of the astronauts have complained vociferously about the lack of rest. Americans tend to expect great flexibility of themselves, so we do not rule out the possibility of living a three-hour or even a forty-eight-hour "day."

In studying possible work-rest schedules for space, Soviet researchers used a wide range of tests of memory, of psychic and mental and muscular efficiency, of balance, pulse pressure, and other cardiovascular functions. They have also looked for signs of pathology, analyzing peripheral blood and urine constituents, and examining clothing for microbes, along with the microbial content of mucus from the nose and mouth, and lysozyme activity of saliva. Oddly enough, men sealed in "hermit chambers" emerged after fifteen days with more skin microbes than they showed before entering, suggesting that isolation may cause changes in immunity.

ISOLATION AND IMMUNITY

Men living in experimental chambers were tested on different schedules, such as an eighteen-hour day, or an alternation of six hours work and six hours rest. They were filmed continuously and recorded for temperature, weight, mental performance, fatigue, physical fitness, and heart functions; meanwhile, blood and urine were analyzed for hormones, ascorbic acid, and other constituents that might reveal something about their state of stress. Tests of nervous and muscular activity indicated that an eighteen-hour day had harmful effects, for it might render a person vulnerable to infection. This was apparent in tests of saliva lysozyme activity, which was high before the experiment but declined most markedly in men on an eighteen-hour day. Lysozymes are the enzymes in tears and saliva and other body fluids that help to destroy certain bacteria. A day after volunteers left the experimental isolation chamber the enzyme activity returned to its normal level.

An eighteen-hour day not only rendered the men potentially vulnerable to certain kinds of infection, but it seemed to leave them somnolent yet restless and

emotionally tense. They performed physical exercises
too fast and with impaired coordination. Physiologically
there were signs of stress, such as an increase of ascorbic acid in urine. Ascorbic acid is used in the production of adrenal hormones; during stress it is used in
much greater quantities. One form of stress may be
adjustment to a non-circadian day, phase shifts, or
simply to isolation. Some people find a change in schedule particularly difficult. Typically, older people cannot
adjust comfortably to a change in schedule. Epileptics
and people with severe anxieties, ulcers, diabetes, and
other ailments have been considered poor risks for any
kind of rotating shift work. Among the millions of people who today drive trucks or work on shifts, some may
adjust reasonably fast as judged by physiological measures, yet studies of body temperature in shift workers
suggest that some people may never adapt.

INDIVIDUAL DIFFERENCES

Eventually, we are bound to recognize individual differences in time structure as we now acknowledge
differences in muscular strength, body build, and height.
Just as some people are not constitutionally fit for living
in high altitudes or hefting cumbersome loads, others
may be incapable of repeated east-west travel by jet or
of a routine involving irregular hours of sleep and
meals. Temporal organization appears to be an important dimension of our being, and one on which we
differ from one another as we do in personality. In each
of the many studies of people on actual shift jobs or in
experimental capsules—studies done over a twenty-year
period in many countries—there have been important
anomalies, individuals who reacted unusually or who
did not adjust.

A number of recent studies have been conducted like
simulated space missions in which people lived in a
highly instrumented capsule where light and darkness
were scheduled from outside, and where they were continuously monitored by automatic devices for performance and physiological change. Drs. Thomas Frazier,

John Rummel, and Harry Lipscomb have found that in such studies some people will react adversely to confinement and isolation, even though continuing to live on a twenty-four-hour schedule. Some people have managed to perform while alternating four hours sleep and four hours wakefulness, although others deteriorate. One study involved a twenty-four-hour day, then a week on a twenty-three-hour day, followed by continuous light. The volunteer showed a whole range of circadian rhythms as well as total disruption.

In German flight studies led by Dr. K. E. Klein, pilots were monitored before, during, and after a flight to the United States and back to Germany. All the while they worked the panel of a simulated supersonic jet that had been programmed with lifelike sudden winds and near-accidents. Some individuals showed much higher amplitude rhythms than others, taking twice as long to adjust a flight instrument at 3 A.M. as at 3 P.M. Individuals varied in the extent to which their performance declined after east-west flight. Although there is some indication that phase shifts may be more distressing to people with greater day-night changes than those with relatively "flat" circadian curves of certain physiological functions and performance, a good deal more evidence is needed before this plausible supposition is borne out.

In attempting to see what qualities make man adaptable to changing schedules, psychiatrists George Curtis and Max Fogel have screened student volunteers for psychological strength. They then exposed them to extremely irregular sleep-waking schedules for two weeks. Some of the young men never received much more than about two hours of sleep at a stretch, in a regimen that resembled the alternation of naps and waking that is seen in very young infants. Although they were initially disrupted, by the end of two weeks on this scrambled schedule they began to show circadian rhythms in physiological functions such as adrenal hormones. Despite the duress of fractured sleep the young men adjusted well. Their adaptation seemed to be correlated with dominance, intellectual efficiency, and good relations with their parents; these qualities were elicited by a personality test.

TEMPORAL VULNERABILITY IN MAN

As more and more of the world becomes industrialized and tends to run continuous round-the-clock operations, night work and rotating shifts, as well as jet travel, will affect huge numbers of people. It may become imperative for people to take tests of temporal and physiological stability before they enter demanding professions or undergo the hardships of medical internship. Just as some doctors bear the sleep loss and odd hours well, others leave their internship addicted to amphetamines and barbiturates, taken in an effort to compensate for continual shifts in schedule. Soviet researchers suggest that vulnerability can be detected by exposing a person to phase shifts, and also to a period of isolation from time cues.

A great deal of information can be obtained from watching a person's activity-rest cycle in isolation—does he live a twenty-five- or twenty-six-hour day? Does he live a shorter cycle of twenty-three hours? The more he departs from the twenty-four-hour rhythm, the more likely that he will experience internal desynchronization. His body temperature may cycle around twenty-four hours, but blood corticosterone and urine electrolytes may fluctuate in a 24.6 hour rhythm. Thus, his sleep and waking will ultimately become out of phase with internal rhythms. The extent of this internal desynchronization may be one indicator of how well an individual will tolerate temporal instability. Another indicator may be the speed with which his physiological rhythms readjust to a twenty-four-hour day, once he has returned to the world of social clocks. Such tests might provide a useful measure of a person's ability to withstand unusual schedules and phase shifts, so it should be possible to screen out people who are temporally vulnerable, preventing them from damaging themselves and others. Such rough-and-ready tests are undoubtedly useful, although a more specific and meaningful diagnosis of temporal vulnerability must await a long series of basic researches. To some extent people can and do gauge their responses to temporal disruption by how they feel when they work at night, change their schedules, and travel by jet. Many people overlook the signals from within, ignoring fatigue and blunted reactions. Travelers do not realize how long it takes for their bodies to resynchronize, even after they feel restored and well.

Soviet researchers, having observed changes in brain waves and glandular functions after the nine-hour flight from Moscow to Khabarovsk, near the Chinese border, encouraged placing all crews on a stable work-rest schedule. After a flight from Paris or Amsterdam to Alaska, Dutch and French medical researchers have seen that the rhythm of urinary elments such as sodium and potassium did not adapt for five or six days. These urinary rhythms took between nine and eleven days to adapt after a flight from Minneapolis to Seoul, Korea, an adaptation rate of about an hour a day.

IS IT EASIER TO FLY WEST?

An FAA study conducted in the early 1960s showed that performance on psychological tasks declined on the first day and then quickly improved after a flight to Rome or Manila. But body temperature took six days to come into phase with the new schedule in Rome, and the rhythm of heart rate took eight days to adapt. Adaptation occurred several days earlier in Manila. Although the men performed well, their heart rate and temperature rhythms had become dissociated from their usual phase relationships. This means that the average tourist may race around sightseeing or that a businessman may be negotiating with a body whose heart rate and urine indicate a state more like sleep than waking. Curiously enough, several experimental crews have shown more rapid adjustment after westward than eastward flights.

To some extent the asymmetry in adjustment may be due to loss of sleep. Night flights to Europe arrive in early morning with crews and passengers who have not slept, who must wait another twelve hours to go to bed, and whose internal rhythms are now six hours out of phase and are likely to keep them awake. On the other hand, daytime flights from Europe to the United States arrive in time for a tired passenger to go to bed. Since the passenger arrives with a body that is in advance of local time, he "feels" it is very late and can fall asleep readily.

There is some scientific debate about the relative difficulties of a phase shift east or west. Dr. Jürgen Aschoff has tried artificial phase shifts on birds and found that they adjusted faster when the day was shortened. Similarly, by turning the lights off early, volunteers in underground compartments were phase-shifted as if traveling eastward. Dr. Halberg and his associates have seen an opposite effect in rodents when their active period was shortened. Since rodents are nocturnal, this meant giving them a six-hour night. The animals' body temperatures remained desynchronized from the laboratory schedule for a longer time than usual.

The fact remains that east-west travel and rotating shifts put a person in a state of internal desynchrony. In some studies, body temperature rhythms have indicated that one person adjusted to a night shift within five days, whereas others did not adjust in twenty-one days. Adjustment is an individual matter, and a feeling of fatigue may be a good guide to adaptation. Some scientists feel that drugs may be used to accelerate adaptation; the Syntex Corporation is investing in research on a way of phase-shifting adrenal hormone rhythms. Hormone therapy may be just around the corner and might make travelers feel better. However, the mechanisms of circadian rhythms are not yet understood, and it seems doubtful that manipulating rhythmic functions within one gland could be successful and safe in advance of more general and basic insight.

RULES FOR TRAVELERS

For the present travelers can follow simple rules of scheduling so that they avoid losing sleep. In traveling east one might prepare by going to bed progressively earlier before the trip to minimize the "loss" of time, doing the opposite before long westerly trips. Moreover, if one calculates his east-west change, one can expect to be alert at certain hours of the day and sluggish at others for about three days after arrival. These high and low points can be estimated by knowing the hours of one's peak performance (and body temperature) and nadir (usually in the last four hours of sleep) at home and calculating the shift.

Dr. Jean Ghata, who studied crew members on a long Europe-Alaska flight, reports that the senior pilots maintain their stability by remaining on their own home time. If it is noon locally when they arrive but midnight in Paris, they draw the curtains and sleep. Abroad, they try to eat the same foods that they would eat at home, minimizing the need for adaptation. The penalties of rapid adaptations are very real. Lowell Thomas, the well-known radio and film commentator, has written vividly about his own terrifying symptoms which included what appeared to be a heart attack after continual and hurried travel around the world.

When a person phase-shifts by traveling or following a new sleep schedule, the millions of peaks of his physiological rhythms go into a new relationship with his activity rhythm and with each other. This means that food and medication may need to be retimed. The reason for all of this readjustment will become apparent in later chapters. However, if one ignores phase shifts, it can result in costly diplomatic and business errors. Many companies now permit a day of rest for their east-west travelers before they engage in company business. The British airlines have extended rest periods for their crews. Timken Roller Bearing Company, Phillips Petroleum, Continental Oil, and others now insist that executives take a twenty-four-hour rest after long east-west flights. An international civil aviation organization with headquarters in Montreal is evolving sane policies for travel schedules.

In general, travelers do not suffer as bad a predicament as do medical interns, truck drivers, or transportation workers on rotating shifts. None of these people would suffer a fraction of their present stress if they were placed on stable shifts. It is better to work and live on a consistent night shift, despite social inconvenience, than to constantly adjust. In one study of medical corpsmen on night duty it became clear that their complaints of insomnia and gastrointestinal distress tapered off when they remained on night duty for more than two weeks. The disadvantages of rotating shifts have been demonstrated so many times that it is particularly shocking to see the inhumane scheduling of duties for medical trainees and hospital personnel. Despite the search for a drug that will instantly phase-shift its taker, it might be advisable to reschedule some of our institutions.

Schedule changes of the same number of hours do not necessarily produce the same effects. For instance, it may be different to travel by jet across electromagnetic lines of force and change one's schedule by three hours than to make the same three-hour phase-shift at home. The period of adjustment and resynchronization may be shorter for the person who delays bedtime, lengthening the day by three hours, than for the person who advances his cycle by shortening his day by the same amount. The effects of a phase shift are further complicated by the fact that each person inherits a time structure that is slightly different than that of the next person. This difference is particularly obvious when people go into isolation; some people have longer spontaneous activity-sleep cycles than others.

ISOLATION IN CAVES

In attempting to determine man's spontaneous rhythm of activity and sleep and of physiological function in isolation, scientists have studied men and women in caves, deep beneath the surface of the earth, or in isolation compartments, soundproofed and insulated against the revealing signs of social rhythms. Researchers above ground have monitored reactions of volunteers through bioelectric measuring devices, carefully preventing any "time of day" cues. While American and German researchers have preferred to construct highly instrumented isolation chambers, French and British scientists have also taken advantage of natural caverns. The subterranean caves tend to be chilly, damp, and dangerous, with dripping walls and loose rock; no sound nor light from above penetrates the dark silence. Within the caves, tents for the volunteers have been made habitable with gas heat, light, books, phonograph equipment, and the accouterments needed for living several months. Each volunteer communicated by one-way telephone to a crew on duty above, but was never contacted by the crew.

Although the caves were dank and hazardous places for research, volunteers seem to have been challenged by the difficulty of survival and were happier underground than in the sterile settings of laboratory capsules or a hospital during base-line studies. One speleologist explained that people in caves feel free, while in a capsule or hospital room they become experimental prisoners. High motivation was needed since the volunteers had to be reliable about phoning base camp before going to sleep, at waking and mealtime, taking pulse, temperature, and psychological tests, and collecting all their urine in numbered bottles, which were set outside the cavern or capsule where they were retrieved unobtrusively by research crews.

THE BASIC QUESTION: ARE RHYTHMS COSMIC?

There are many reasons for studying people in isolation, in caves and shielded capsules. Some motivation has come from a sheer sense of adventure. Some has come from the need to know how man may behave when isolated in capsules over long periods in outer space. But the primary motivation, which would inveigle a scientist into the physical difficulties, the tedious measurements, the frustrating logistics of such studies, is the desire to learn something about the fundamental nature of man's circadian rhythms. What is the origin of a creature's circadian rhythms? Are they genetic, reflecting an innate program that evolved some 180 million years ago as living creatures adapted to this turning earth? Or are these cycles imprinted upon nascent organisms by the external periodicities of the environment and learned from one's parents? There is yet another possibility. We could be exceedingly sensitive, if thoroughly unaware, cosmic receivers, responding not only to the rhythmic changes in light and temperature, but to barometric pressure, ionization, magnetic fields and cosmic rays. Three hypotheses have stimulated a search for the origins of circadian rhythmicity. The first postulates that rhythms are genetically built-in. A second theory suggests that rhythms are acquired as environmental periodicities make their imprint, and a third suggests that the rhythms are geophysical rhythms to which living things merely respond.

In the eighteenth century it was observed that leaves and flowers showed circadian movements, which continued even when plants were isolated from time cues in caves. In the twentieth century Dr. Erwin Bünning indicated that such a rhythm might be inherited. He put plants in a constant environment and found that their rhythm was not precisely twenty-four hours, yet it was never more than about three hours shorter or longer. Each species showed a typical period in isolation. One plant might show a 24.2-hour cycle while another would have a 25.6-hour rhythm. Hybrids had intermediate periods, strongly suggesting that the rhythm had a genetic basis.

As zoologists entered the field, experiments with unicellular organisms, insects, and mammals began to delineate the notion of purely endogenous rhythms. Dr. Colin Pittendrigh has experimented with a variety of organisms, from flagellates and fruit flies to mammals. He concluded that the circadian rhythm must originate in some basic molecular mechanism with a periodicity of twenty-three to twenty-five hours that continues its oscillation in the absence of external synchronizers. Pittendrigh feels that this inheritance is an evolutionary adaptation to a strongly rhythmic planet, in which sun and moon create periodicities of twenty-four to twenty-five hours.

Rhythmicity may have been one of the first forces of natural selection, since organisms that time their activity and life processes in accord with the changing light, temperature, humidity, and other factors of the environment would have had an edge in survival.

In their many experiments with animals, birds, and man, physiologists saw that creatures used natural time cues. The change from light to darkness is an important signal in orienting any creature who lives above the surface of the earth. Light-loving creatures such as human beings, monkeys, and many birds would orient themselves around the hours of light, then becoming active, foraging for food. However, if an animal were starving, or if there were predators around, he would shift his hours to the timetable of available food, or of safety. People are very much tuned to light, yet we are more synchronized by social factors, by the hours of our jobs, the routines of our families. This is one reason why it may be particularly important for us to understand our time properties in making social schedules. Animals and birds are social too, but are far more dependent on the schedule of light and darkness.

One question that has bothered us about ourselves is the limit or expandability of the circadian cycle. Does each creature have a congenital period? Animals have been blinded, and recorded as they fumbled around their cages, ate, drank, and groomed. Similarly, they have been left in constant light or constant darkness. Their rhythms of activity and quiescence have deviated only slightly from twenty-four hours. When rats were trained to control their own lighting, they gave themselves a great deal of darkness (which they prefer for activity) during one part of the day, essentially creating a circadian lighting schedule. In rodents, and rats particularly, the circadian activity rhythm is extremely stubborn, and attempts to induce a different rhythm or to cause an animal to become non-circadian have involved extreme measures, stress with drugs, brain lesions, and physical injury, or freezing. Barring damage in the region of the brain known as the hypothalamus, and severe injury, the animals would always resume their twenty-four-hour activity rhythm the moment they recovered.

COSMIC TIME GIVENS IN PLANTS AND ANIMALS

It seems fair to say that most scientists feel that circadian rhythms are inherited. A roughly twenty-four-hour oscillator within living cells would help creatures survive by causing them to act in tune with the changing environment of earth. Still, a few scientists argue that there is such a continuous inpouring of rhythmic information from geophysical changes that organisms may not need to rely wholly on "clocks." Dr. Frank Brown, a biologist at Northwestern University, has been the most active proponent of the so-called cosmic theory. He has suggested that an independent internal timing system is not necessary, since the environment always generates rhythmic signals, including variations in terrestrial magnetism, electric fields, and background radiation and other signal sources, such as gravitation, from which no creature on earth can be completely isolated. Only experiments in space can isolate life from these cycles.

Using a variety of life forms in which he has ascertained rhythmic changes, Brown has sought geophysical periodicities that might account for them. His point of view is worth expression, for it underscores what we do not yet know about biological rhythms and suggests that man may be a more diversely sensitive creature, subject to the invisible influences of the surrounding universe, than Western science usually considers him to be.

Brown found that metabolism in crabs, and oxygen consumption cycles in shellfish, rats, carrots, and potatoes varied with cosmic ray changes, at a time when cosmic radiation cycles underwent unusual modifications, including cycle inversion. Actually, our atmosphere and its magnetic field protect us from primary cosmic rays. These enter the ionosphere, a protective layer composed of electrically charged particles (ions) of gaseous matter. The ionosphere is held close to earth by the geomagnetic field, shielding us from harmful rays from outer space. However, the ionosphere is not steady. It ebbs at night, drawing away from earth, and increases its density when it draws close to earth by day. This creates an atmospheric rhythm to which organisms may respond.

The uncanny weather detection that is usually considered the exclusive province of animals must depend upon sensing some of these atmospheric rhythms. Animal lore is rich in such stories. Fiddler crabs have been observed to disappear into inland burrows two days before the arrival of a hurricane, and foresters in the Pacific Northwest sometimes predict snow by the behavior of the elk, which begin to gather in the shelter of trees two to three days before a blizzard.

Human beings also feel these atmospheric changes. In an elegant but as yet unpublished study of psychiatric patients in Douglas Hospital, Montreal, Dr. Heinz Lehmann has tried to understand sporadic outbursts of hostile excitement among some patients on the wards. For months continuous observations were kept, and the dates of agitation were recorded. When matched against all possible factors, they did not correlate with staff changes, visitors, menu, medication, barometric pressure, weather, or other environmental alterations. Finally these calendar dates were compared with dates from the U.S. Space Disturbance Forecast Center, in Boulder, Colorado. There was a very decided correlation between solar flares or sunspots and ward excitement. This is not so unlikely as it sounds, for sun flares are bursts of gaseous material, high-energy particles that influence the ionosphere. These changes influence magnetic fields on earth, and sometimes a compass needle will be deflected considerably during a sunstorm. Since the brain is at least as sensitive as a compass, it is likely that we react to large magnetic disturbances.

Frank Brown has demonstrated that worms and mollusks can orient themselves in space according to weak magnetic fields. People also can cultivate a sensitivity to very slight magnetic field changes. This is the trick of the dowser, who senses underground water pools through exceedingly small changes of magnetic field strength. In 1962 a Sorbonne physics professor, Yves Rocard, discovered that by holding the arm very taut, and balancing a long stick, the nerves and muscles in the arm would become sensitive to small changes of magnetic field strength. These changes, from water in the soil, would cause the muscle to relax and the stick to dip. By using a magnetometer, Rocard found that people could sense extremely small gradients (.3-.5 milligauss changes). He planted electric coils underground, approximating natural magnetic gradients, and found that "average" people could learn to detect the tiny magnetic field changes.

Like rats, which are acutely sensitive to X-rays, we also have bioelectric, biomagnetic nervous systems that respond to the geophysical forces our five senses cannot detect. Frank Brown suggests that no place on earth is truly shielded from the rhythmic bursts of particles and magnetic changes. Even in the bowels of earth, waves of neutrinos slip through from outer space. This suggests that cave studies are not truly isolated, and that esoteric rhythmic time cues might still influence man. However, scientists have been satisfied that primary time cues are not available, and have conducted their isolation experiments without worrying about neutrinos or gravity.

EXPERIMENTAL CAVE DWELLERS

The precedent for studying man's rhythms in caves was set by Dr. Nathaniel Kleitman in 1939, in Mammoth Cave, Kentucky. More recent studies received their impetus from a courageous spelunker and geologist, Michel Siffre, who spent two months on a subterranean glacier in the French Alps in 1962. In 1964 a young midwife, Josy Laures, and a cabinetmaker, Tony Senni, lived in separate underground caves for three months; their records of body temperatures, activity, and urinary hormone rhythms were put through a special mathematical analysis, that showed they had lived a "day" that was longer than twenty-four hours. Senni lived a 24.8-hour day (the exact period of a lunar day) and Josy Laures lived a 24.6-hour day.

FREE-RUNNING PEOPLE

In most isolation studies, volunteers have shown a free-running rhythm longer than twenty-four hours. At the Max-Planck Institute near Munich, eighty-five volunteers lived three weeks or longer in luxurious underground efficiency apartments, isolated from obvious time cues. Only one individual spontaneously showed a short period of 23.5 hours. Most individuals have cycled at around 25.05 hours. Judging by psychological tests, these volunteers were more stable than the people whose cycles extended to longer periods (twenty-five to twenty-seven hours). Since gravitational fields and natural electromagnetic fields can penetrate any cave or capsule, these longer rhythms may also reflect other synchronizers; or they may reflect time structure that is compressed throughout life and socially conditioned to twenty-four hours. Perhaps the circadian oscillation that springs from within—the endogenous oscillation—would be somewhat longer than twenty-four hours.

In 1963 Dr. John Mills, a physiologist at the University of Manchester in England, studied a young man who wore a wristwatch throughout his three-month stay in a cave. Although resolved to sustain a twenty-four-hour routine, the man found himself going to bed when tired and rising later each day, a condition known as free-running in which he was out of synchrony with solar day and night.

A similar pattern was observed in a physicist who spent a year doing research in the high polar desert of the Antarctic, where he was remote from the temperate zone alternation of light and darkness, and also from social activity. During his year on the polar plateau he recorded his bedtime and rising time, and gave this calendar to sleep scientists Jay Shurley and Chester Pierce. They found a curious pattern. He had been going to bed fifteen to thirty minutes later each night,

rising that much later in the morning. Soon he was re-
tiring by "day" and awake all "night." The oddest fact
of all was that the drift kept up for only twenty-eight
days. Every twenty-eight days he abruptly shifted back
to his original bedtime, and recommenced his drift,
totally unaware of the pattern. As yet there has been
no explanation of the pattern, although a twenty-eight-
day cycle suggests lunar influence.

FREE-RUNNING IN SOCIETY

The unawareness of drifting sleep patterns may
seem odd to an outside eye, but our own day-by-day
activity usually seems normal to us no matter how
strange it seems to an outside observer. Most college
students get out of phase with society, studying later
and sleeping later until they are sleeping all day and
working all night. Then perhaps on a Saturday and
Sunday they will party around the clock, going to bed
on Sunday night and resynchronizing themselves with
a diurnal schedule.

Occasionally people will free-run in the midst of city
life. Mr. Donald R. Erskine, a pensioned writer in Philadelphia, has been following "body time" for fifteen
years. He has been going to bed about sixty-five to
eighty-five minutes later each night, rising that much
later in the morning. Mr. Erskine feels that for the first
time in his life he really has a sense of well being. Next
to that exhilaration of feeling good, the drawbacks seem
trivial. Because he lives a more-than-twenty-five-hour
day, while the rest of the world lives a twenty-four-hour
cycle, he is out of phase with society. Thus if he wants
to go to a play or make an appointment with a relative,
he consults his calendar in advance to see whether he
will be awake or asleep during that part of the day.
Sleep occupies only a third of each day, so that there
are only a few days each month when his schedule
precludes social activity, although he occasionally finds
himself having breakfast with people who are eating
dinner.

UNSTABLE CYCLES IN ISOLATION

In isolation, free-running rhythms do not necessarily show the kind of stability that Mr. Erskine has reported of himself for fifteen years. During six months of solitary life deep in a cave in the French Alps, Jean-Pierre Mairtet was studied by a team of doctors, led by Dr. Jean Colin. Mairtet showed a stable rectal temperature cycle (twenty-four hours, forty-four minutes), while his activity rhythm oscillated sometimes to thirty or forty-eight hours. Many volunteers, either in caves or comfortable capsules, have shown an initial tendency to oscillate at first, a fact that has encouraged longer and longer studies.

In 1966 Dr. John Mills studied a man who became totally erratic during his first days in a cave. Sometimes he would be active for ten hours and then sleep for nine; at other times he would be awake eighteen hours and then sleep for thirty-five hours. This man slept 60 percent of his time underground, living a totally irregular cycle until the last two months when, like other volunteers in solitude, he settled down and lived a day of about 25.2 hours. Each individual seems to have his own free-running period, but it cannot be determined from just a few cycles. A person may lengthen one day, sleeping less that night and shortening the next activity period. However, in analyzing the over-all time pattern, these transient irregularities are smoothed out.

When living a longer day in isolation, a person's time estimates seem to change. In 1962 Michel Siffre emerged after sixty-three days in Scarasson Cavern, thinking he had been there twenty-five days less. He had imagined that his activity periods were very short when, in fact, he lived a circadian cycle. A later volunteer telephoned base camp to give estimates of his day, and for a while he thought himself living a forty-eight-hour day when his activity rhythm was circadian, yet he would call in to announce a nap and then sleep for ten hours. Several cave dwellers announced naps that lasted over six hours, and most volunteers have vastly underestimated the total time they spent underground.

LIGHT AS A SYNCHRONIZER

Light is an important time-giver for human beings, and Jürgen Aschoff has conjectured that the intensity of illumination might influence the activity and physiological rhythms of man as it certainly influences birds. In a series of studies with human volunteers living in isolation where light levels were varied, the results were suggestive but did not give clear-cut answers. One volunteer lived in an underground apartment for eight days in dim illumination and showed an activity-sleep cycle with a 24.5-hour period, yet his urine excretion followed a cycle with a period of 25.1 hours. When the illumination was made five times brighter, his activity and urine cycles shortened, suggesting that intensity of illumination affects the cycle periods. A woman who lived in a cave in dim light for eighty-eight days led an activity-sleep period of twenty-five hours, but her menstrual cycle shortened from twenty-nine days to twenty-five days. Light, as a later chapter will indicate, may have profound physiological effects.

SOCIAL EFFECTS IN BIRDS AND PEOPLE IN ISOLATION

However, man's most powerful synchronizer is probably social. This has been seen in groups of people studied underground, and also in birds, who oriented their activity around the times of tape-recorded bird songs. Nevertheless, suggestive evidence that social factors cannot alter a person's basic period was seen in four young men living in adjacent suites underground at the Max-Planck Institute. Initially one emerged as a leader of the group because he rose earlier than the others, preparing food and thus initiating activity. In bright light the first week, three of the men showed an average 26.2-hour cycle. In dim illumination the next week they showed a 27.2-hour cycle, but the dominant man showed urine and temperature rhythms that were shorter. He tried to stay in phase with the others, but he had to sacrifice sleep and soon was fatigued. When he gave up trying to lead he became completely desynchronized from the group, rising when they slept and having breakfast as they ate dinner.

This experiment suggested to Dr. Ernst Pöppel, a psychologist who helped run the study, that social situations and motivation might entrain a person's circadian activity cycle only up to a point. Evidently, there are some profound and probably inherent individual differences in timing that may be relevant in selecting groups for compatibility in isolation situations such as polar work or space. One factor that might be very important in choosing people who have to work together in isolation, as in space or submarine missions, is the stability of their physiological functions. In numerous cave studies, scientists have observed that the lengthened activity-sleep cycle is accompanied by changes in the cycle period of physiological rhythms, such as excretion of sodium and chloride. As physiological cycles get out of phase with sleep and activity, a person might have to get up out of sleep to urinate, for instance. Discomfort from dissociation was vague but pervasive, in that the volunteers usually did not feel well.

CYCLES DESYNCHRONIZED IN A HEAVILY SHIELDED CHAMBER

One volunteer observed by Dr. Jürgen Aschoff had an activity-sleep cycle of around twenty-three hours which was accompanied by calcium excretion, but water, sodium, and potassium were excreted in cycles of almost twenty-five hours. About every third or fourth day all these cycles came back into their normal phase relations. Later, the man's diary was compared with the scientist's calendar, and these intermittent days when he was in phase were the days he mentioned feeling well. The internal synchronization of physiological rhythms may be influenced by a number of forces that are still mysterious to us.

The suggestion that our bodies may tune in to geophysical rhythms has been investigated in the experimental underground efficiency apartments at the

Max-Planck laboratory. One of the experimental rooms was heavily shielded with metal plating against magnetic and electric fields, the others were not. Drs. Aschoff, Wever, and Pöppel found that the thirty-three people who lived in the unshielded apartment had an average cycle period of 24.84 hours, while the forty-nine people who lived in the shielded room had an average period of 25.26 hours. (The volunteers had no way of knowing whether their room was shielded or not.) There were also pronounced differences between the individuals in the two apartments. Those in the unshielded room, exposed to natural electromagnetic field changes, showed shorter free-running periods and little internal desynchronization. However, when electromagnetic fields were shielded out, some volunteers showed dissociation; for instance, urinary excretion moved out of its usual phase with the activity cycle, so that the peak no longer occurred in the hours after arising from sleep.

ARTIFICIAL FIELDS AND HUMAN RESPONSE

Soviet and American scientists had already postulated that earth's magnetic changes make it possible for animals to measure time and that they have a pronounced effect upon the brain. Dr. Wever went further by introducing into a shielded apartment a constant electric field about 1,000 times stronger than the corresponding natural field. Volunteers in the shielded room showed an immediate effect, although quite unconsciously; their free-running periods shortened and stabilized at 23.5 hours. Ten subjects showed a tendency toward shorter cycle periods when the field was in operation, and in some, physiological functions were resynchronized if they had been dissociated before. In other experiments alternating electric fields of ten cycles per second were pulsed into the apartment on various schedules. For a few days the subjects seemed to be entrained to the periodicity of the alternating electric fields and showed synchronized sleep-waking cycles, but the entrainment did not last. Thus a periodically changing 10 cps field may have a slight impact as a synchronizer, but the effect is very weak, and natural fields would be 1,000 times weaker.

Probably the signals that continually resynchronize our circadian rhythms are stronger than these. Light is a potent synchronizer, along with social activity. However, if man had to live like moles or worms, one might prophesy that he would soon develop acute senses for gravitational rhythms, or weak changes in geomagnetic fields. Dr. Frank Brown has shown that worms can sense magnetic fields and use this information in orienting themselves. People have also learned to "sense" extremely small changes in magnetic field strength, in a study described at the end of this book. In the hierarchy of synchronizers, these factors do not seem to rank extremely high. Nor could one say that they show us to be dependent upon the environment for our timing.

LIVING A 48-HOUR DAY?

Most isolation studies have suggested that man has an inherent circadian oscillator system that can be entrained to cycles of twenty-three to twenty-eight hours. The rhythm seems to be entrained socially by light, electric fields, and probably other periodicities in the environment. Because of the tendency to longer cycles in isolation, many people have wondered whether we are limited to a circadian cycle or whether we might live a forty-eight-hour cycle. Several scientists have themselves tried a forty-eight-hour cycle above ground, but failed to adapt. In 1966 and 1968, three Frenchmen seemed to have temporarily lived forty-eight-hour cycles, working about thirty-six hours and sleeping twelve to fourteen hours during several months in deep caves. One showed a temperature cycle of twenty-four hours and forty-four minutes, although enacting a much longer day. The newspapers drew considerable attention to these feats, but in 1970 the data had not been fully analyzed, and two volunteers emerged from their sojourn reporting that they had felt drowsy almost all the time, as if in a state resembling hibernation.

The circadian period has not been successfully altered for long in healthy animals, and volunteers in caves on a temporary forty-eight-hour rhythm have not demonstrated the extent of man's temporal flexibility. One can only say that people seem to feel and function best when living on a cycle in which internal functions remain in a certain phase relationship with activity and sleep. In our long evolution on a turning earth we may have acquired an inherent rhythmicity in the range of the solar-lunar day; in addition we are surrounded by visible and invisible forces that rhythmically affect our nervous system and encourage a circadian rhythm. We may try to alter our activity cycle to suit the convenience of social activity, and we may ultimately take drugs in order to live a forty-eight-hour day or apply electric stimulation to our brains to shift phase instantly. All these are possibilities on the scientific workbench.

SPACE EXPLORATION

Time structure in space is another matter. Our successful plunges beyond earth's atmosphere have bolstered confidence that man can survive at least for short periods in nearby space. As people voyage deeper into space, sustaining themselves for months and years, we will need to understand the mechanisms of their time structure, in order to select compatible teams and create conditions allowing internal synchrony and well-being. We do not know what these conditions are.

Everyone speculates on whether man can adapt to space, yet we have not begun to study its effects upon animals. Astronauts on dangerous missions are inappropriate experimental subjects, too busy and too stressed to add to their duties and to wear the kind of equipment that could transmit their many physiological changes to earth. Only in orbit will we learn the extent to which the geophysical properties of earth are needed by earth creatures. Soviet studies have utilized several species of animals in orbit, yet we have done little research on life in orbiting satellites. From earth come the most fundamental synchronizers of our being, that orient us in space and organize us in time—gravity and rhythmic cues such as the alternation of light and darkness. Isolation studies have shown that without environmental time guides there is a tendency for the circadian system to disintegrate and for circadian rhythms to dissociate. We do not yet know whether this breakdown of temporal organization is a stress that leaves permanent damage. There is some evidence of damage in animals maintained in constant light or darkness, and among those exposed to weekly phase shifts. In planning prolonged space missions we may have to create the cycles that can maintain the temporal organization of man—but this temporal structure is not yet known.

We are ready to tamper with our schedules, and people nonchalantly volunteer to go without sleep for days on end, to enter vigilance marathons, or to rotate their schedules. Our casualness may reflect the fact that we do not yet understand time as a firm dimension in our physiological health. Or it may reflect an atavistic view of sleep. Indians and many tribal groups bear with interrupted sleep at night. The Waika Indians of the Venezuelan jungles sleep irregularly. The nights are interrupted for the same reason that the night is interrupted for the tapir or other jungle animals. Night is fraught with both natural and supernatural dangers. However, unlike modern man, the Indian compensates for an interrupted night by spending much of his day in a hammock. How important, how innate is an interrupted night of sleep for modern man? We still do not know.

3 SLEEP, DREAMS, AND THE BIOLOGICAL HOUR

Sleep, rest of things, O pleasing Deity
Peace of the soul, which cares dost crucify,
Weary bodies refresh and mollify.

Ovid

Those who are awake have one world in common: those who are asleep retire every one to a private world of his own.

Heraclitus

It moistens and fattens the body, concocts and helps digestion, (as we see in dormice, and those Alpine mice that sleep all Winter) ... when they are so found sleeping under the snow in the dead of winter, as fat as butter. It expels cares, pacifies the mind, refresheth the weary limbs after long work.

Robert Burton,
THE ANATOMY OF MELANCHOLY

3 Sleep, Dreams, and The Biological Hour

WHY WE SPEND A THIRD OF OUR LIVES ASLEEP, nobody really knows. We sleep around twenty years in a lifetime, a considerable period to lie almost immobile, remote from the waking world, rising and falling in waves of emotional experience that are mostly forgotten. It is astonishing that we can succumb to sleep with so little curiosity. We submit to hours of stillness, passively allowing the motive forces of our personalities and regenerative cycles of our bodies to prepare us for daily rebirth, to fertilize our waking minds and memories with haunting shadows of the people we really are. All of humankind participates in this mysterious rhythm, lying down for about five to nine hours a night.

The daily recurrence of sleep, like the tides of the seas, suggests that it has rhythmic importance to us, but someone is always hoping to find that sleep is expendable. Every year newspapers report that some ancient man or woman, usually in a remote corner of India or Spain, has never slept. When sleep scientists have investigated they have never found the person who never sleeps. It is easier to forego food for several weeks than sleep. After only forty-eight hours without sleep most people experience an inability to sustain attention or to remember what they have just heard, and fragments of images or reverie begin to intrude on their waking activity. Disc jockeys in public wakathons have lapsed into states resembling psychosis after two hundred sleepless hours although well selected and nurtured young men in hospital experiments have shown little impairment from the same sleep loss. Under ordinary circumstances, however, a person feels sleep loss not as a steady increase in exhaustion. Instead, he goes through waves of sleepiness, cycles of alertness and well-being, and cycles of unfocused, vague weariness and distraction. This subjective experience is a hint about the nature of sleep, the rhythmic changes occurring in our nervous systems, our glands, our cells, throughout the night and the day.

People have always felt these rhythmic waves of fatigue, attention, and fantasy, but their pattern began to grow visible only during the last fifteen years, when scientists examined nightlong sleep in the laboratory. In 1953 a graduate student, Eugene Aserinsky, and his physiologist professor, Nathaniel Kleitman, were the adventurers who first began to watch nightlong brain wave tracings of people's sleep. Aserinsky had observed recurrent periods of rapid eye movements in which infants and adults seemed to be tracking something under their closed lids. Brain wave tracings during these rapid eye movements (known as REMs) resembled waking or lightest sleep, and people awakened at this time almost always remembered dreaming, whereas memory was less certain from other states of sleep. Their "handle" for retrieving man's dreams stirred a whole generation of scientists. Today's picture of sleep comes from more than ten thousand volunteers who have slept in laboratory bedrooms, wired up to electroencephalograph machines during a few nights, or as long as fifty nights. Every night, in several dozen hospitals in the United States, sleep volunteers wearing tiny metal electrodes around their scalp, face, and body, fall asleep with wires from their bodies plugged into a cable in the bedroom. The constantly shifting electric potentials in their bodies and brains are transmitted to the EEG polygraph, an amplifier that causes an inked pen to swing up with a change in negative polarity, or down when the shift is positive. As a continuous sheet of graph paper slides forward under rollers, the up-and-down movements of the pens trace out as waves—this is why EEG records are often known as brain waves. Today the EEGs, changes in blood pressure, pulse, temperature, muscle tension, or breathing are also recorded on magnetic tape for computer analysis. As these hundreds of thousands of records indicate, we drift down and up through several distinct levels of consciousness each night, making four or five complete cycles. At particular times in these cycles we release certain hormones, experience degrees of thought, reverie, or dream. By examining the brain wave tracings of a night of sleep, specialists can tell a good deal about a person. They can infer something about the rate of brain maturation in a baby, whether an adult has drunk several shots of alcohol or taken sleeping pills, whether this sleeping individual suffers from extreme anxiety or deep depression, or whether he has just inverted his usual bedtime. Brain wave tracings reveal when a person may be immersed in his most vivid dreaming, when he may sleepwalk, wet the bed, talk, grind his teeth, or utter the muffled shrieks of night terrors. The rhythms of sleep have disclosed information that is practical in treating illnesses, in diagnosing, in improving the use of drugs and the methods of withdrawing people from common drugs.

Civilized people of the future will undoubtedly use and enjoy their slumber differently. Already a huge literature of sleep research offers a map of night for those who wish to train themselves so that they can pick the easiest time to fall asleep, can awaken themselves, can awaken from dreams and thus gain access to that private world in which the mind speaks only to itself. Because sleep is cyclic and regular, a person can begin to learn when he shifts from oblivion into lighter sleep. Problems can be solved during sleep, and westerners, like some Indian tribes, can begin to integrate their daytime selves with their quintessential selves at night by making the effort to know their dream thoughts. Never again can we think of sleep as a blanket of silence occasionally punctuated with dreams or waking.

A brief description of the stages of sleep may indicate the rhythmic orchestra of events that we know as the quality or fabric of a night's slumber.

THE STAGES OF SLEEP

In waking the brain waves resemble a pinched, irregular scrawl, denoting rapid irregular changes in the brain, of low voltage. As a person relaxes in bed, respiration growing regular and pulse even, temperature slowly declines and he may think aimless thoughts, on the border of sleep. Now the scrawl is not quite so pinched, and there are bursts of an even rhythm, nine to thirteen cycles per second—known as the alpha rhythm. The person may be relaxed and serene, drifting in his mind like a raft on water. After a few minutes the alpha rhythm changes, the eyes begin to roll slowly, and with images or vague thoughts, he begins to traverse the gates of consciousness. A sudden spasm —myoclonic jerk—may waken him momentarily: it is a normal sign of transition in brain function from waking to sleep. Even though he might "feel" awake, were the person's eyelids taped open (experimenters have demonstrated this) he would be functionally blind. He is in the first, light state of sleep. At this point the rapid brain waves are growing in voltage or amplitude, and interspersed with bursts resembling wire spindles. With images and fragmentary dreams the person is entering Stage II. Gradually his brain waves grow larger and slower, and he recedes further from the world. About twenty minutes from the time he fell asleep he is showing large slow waves, about one per second—Stage III. These waves are five times the voltage of the alpha waves—some 300 micro-volts. After a few minutes in Stage III, the sleeper sinks into the bottomless oblivion known as Stage IV. Of course the stages of sleep are somewhat arbitrary, based on the classification of the brain waves—but they have proven to be quite distinctive, and different events happen in each state.

STAGE IV AND GROWTH HORMONE

During the slow brain waves of Stage IV sleep a person is exceedingly hard to awaken. Shake him and he may come to the surface momentarily confused.

What he was thinking down there he rarely remembers. He will claim his mind is a blank. It is in Stage IV that children are likely to wet the bed, sleepwalk, or scream with night terrors that they do not recall when awakened. This is the sleep of the weary. If a person goes to bed early most of Stage IV will be spent before midnight—which may explain why Grandma said the best sleep comes before midnight. Children and young people spend much of the early portion of the night in these depths, but it is a depth of sleep that begins to vanish after age thirty. In this deep stage a child may be transported sleeping and stumbling home from a dinner without awakening. Even though a person may not respond to sounds in this state, EEGs show that his brain is reacting to external events—yet the neural mechanisms that convert sound into conscious experience seem not to be working as usual.

Subjectively the obliviousness of this slumber suggests a process of restoration. Only recently have scientists discovered a hormonal component of this sleep which implies an important phase in our metabolism. If a person is totally sleep-deprived he will first make up for Stage IV. If he cuts his sleep to two hours a night he will spend much of that time in Stage IV. At the University of Florida a psychologist-psychiatrist team, Wilse B. Webb, Robert Williams, and Harmon Agnew, prevented sleeping volunteers from entering Stage IV sleep. Webb's team nudged the subjects, without awakening them, into lighter sleep with tiny electric shocks. After a few nights the people complained of malaise, apathy, and depression. In some respects they felt like people with underactive thyroid glands, people who normally have very little Stage IV sleep.

Recently two groups of researchers have found that human growth hormone (HGH) reaches its peak in the blood at the time of Stage IV sleep. One research team in St. Louis was led by Dr. Y. Takahashi, while Dr. J. F. Sassin and his group worked in San Diego. Using a tiny catheter implanted in the arm vein, it was possible to sample blood every twenty minutes without disturbing the sleeping person. They saw that growth hormone increased in the rhythm of slow-wave sleep.

In order to establish that growth hormone levels are more than coincidentally related to Stage IV sleep, the researchers performed a devilish experiment. They let their volunteers go to sleep as usual, but after a couple of hours awakened them and kept them awake for several hours. Finally, after games and conversation, the volunteers were allowed to go back to sleep again. On such nights the volunteers virtually began their night's sleep a second time, and the growth hormone showed two peaks, occurring in each of the separate sleep periods.

It is interesting that high levels of growth hormone are associated with Stage IV sleep, which is far more dominant in the nights of young children than in those of adults. Growth hormone is released by the pituitary gland at the base of the brain. It regulates body growth, height, and weight. It also plays a role in stimulating milk secretion and the activity of sex hormones. By mechanisms that are not well understood, growth hormone speeds healing of bone fractures, lowers blood cholesterol levels, and stimulates tissue growth by influencing the rate of protein synthesis. Although it is not absolutely known how growth hormone behaves in adults, it would seem to have a role in physical restoration. This may be one of the important functions that is fulfilled in the deep, slow-wave oblivion of Stage IV sleep.

There is another stage of sleep in which a person may be hard to awaken, and may feel himself distantly removed, but the apparent depth of sleep is misleading —for in this part of the cycle the individual is in a very different nervous and hormonal state. After falling asleep, he will descend into Stage IV after about fifteen to thirty minutes, spend ten or maybe twenty minutes in the bottom, and then start drifting back up through Stage III and Stage II into light sleep, almost as if he intended to awaken. About seventy to ninety minutes after falling asleep the person will re-enter lightest sleep, yet it would now take a loud noise to perturb him. His eyes dart as if he is looking at something, and he is in rapid eye movement sleep—known as REM sleep.

REM SLEEP AND DREAMING

During the mid-1950s, soon after Aserinsky and Kleitman discovered that people in REM sleep reported dreaming, a young psychiatric student, William C. Dement, stayed awake nights for literally months in order to study the REM dreams of volunteers. He found that REM dreams occurred in everybody. Moreover, they came at regular intervals of 85-110 minutes—90 minutes on the average. There were usually four or five episodes in a night, giving a person a nightly quota of about an hour and a half of REM dreaming. When Dement looked at cat sleep he found a similar pattern of EEG changes, and as subsequent studies demonstrated, it was a universal mammalian rhythm. In man the period of an entire sleep cycle, from one REM period to the next, is about 90 minutes; in the cat it is about 30 minutes, in the rat about 12. Thus cycles of physical and presumably mental change occur in the sleep of all species.

Among animals REM sleep is usually called paradoxical sleep. It is a time when the skeletal muscles "turn off," the body seems flaccid, and a rabbit's ears droop; a cat drops its head upon its paws, yet the whiskers twitch, paws quiver, and inside the nervous system storms of activity surge up from the brain stem into the visual system. If the body seems flaccid, and the creature or human is hard to awaken, nonetheless drive centers in the old brain must be unusually active, for all human males from infancy to advanced old age show penile erections in almost every REM period—regardless of the bland and unsexual content of their dreams. Breath and pulse become irregular at this time, as if the person were afraid, and temperature rises in the brains of "dreaming" animals, suggesting an acceleration in metabolism.

For all the activity within a dreamer's skin, a person who awakened from REM sleep before muscle tone returns would be unable to move, and might think himself paralyzed. Indeed, by putting an electrode on the muscle under the chin, with a switch that signals an

alarm clock, it is possible to awaken a person at the
beginning of REM sleep, for at that moment the chin
muscle goes slack. By adding a delay, it is possible to
awaken the person from the midst of a REM episode,
for the early-night REM periods last between seven
and fifteen minutes, and each individual has his own
special pattern.

DREAM MYTHS DISPELLED
BY AWAKENED VOLUNTEERS

During the last dozen years, thousands of volunteers have been aroused from the midst of a scenario
more engrossing than reality, to report and answer
questions. Many dreams are in color, but people often
forget to mention color unless asked. Moreover, while
some flash dreams may occur in split seconds, experimenters have demonstrated that dreams happen in real
time, too. If a person has been severely deprived of
REM sleep, he may go into episodes lasting as long
as eighty minutes. When deprived of food or drink,
dreamers conjured up images of soft drinks, orange
juice, hot dogs, and cake. Age and circumstances of life
influence dreams, but some people leading monotonous
lives enjoy wild nights, while others leading exhilarating
lives dream mundanely. Some people have dreamed
subjects suggested during hypnotic trance, others solved
problems presented before sleep. During REM periods
volunteers have incorporated sounds and sensations into
dreams; thus a delicate spray of water on the face has
been transfigured into a dream of a waterfall in experiments. Much of our mythology about dreaming may
stem from the evanescence of dream memories. All
people dream all night, but some of us do not remember.

Dreams evaporate in seconds, and a person must be
awakened rapidly and promptly from REM sleep if he
is to recall his experiences. After such awakenings in
the laboratory, a number of volunteers have learned to
recognize the REM state without awakening, to dream
a while and then awaken and record their own dreams.

Others learned to press a buzzer during REM sleep, and some people learned to discriminate between the dream states of Stage II and REM. With training and sufficient motivation, people can learn the progression of their own sleep stages during the night, and awaken at will.

Until recently we conceived of sleep as very discrete from waking, but we do not have pushbutton brains, and many of the functions observed by night also occur by day. Fantasies are not restricted to dreaming, nor do tissues repair and cells divide only at night. It is a matter of degree, of swelling and subsiding cycles. Sleep represents one phase in our circadian cycle.

The quality of sleep changes over the twenty-four hours. In the early night Stages III and IV predominate. REM episodes are short, ten to twenty minutes, and often the content of early dreams is mundane, incorporating the day just past. By morning, however, the person's physiology is changing, and so is the quality of sleep. Sleep is lighter; REM episodes are longer and more bizarre. If awakened from other stages of sleep the person will probably remember dream fragments. If body temperature has been declining into the early morning hours, soon it will begin to climb again. Adrenal hormones have been low, and they will begin to spurt into the bloodstream.

During these wee hours of the morning when REM sleep and dreaming prevail, people with angina sometimes awaken in fear and pain, finding it difficult to breathe normally. During REM sleep people with duodenal ulcers secrete abnormal amounts of gastric acid. This is the period when babies are likely to be born. It is a time when brain temperature rises, oxygen metabolism is faster, and cells in hypothalamic survival centers become more active than at any other time. As Dr. Michel Jouvet and his many colleagues have shown, the REM state is instigated and nourished from primitive regions of the brain stem, the pons, whose signals flood into other parts of the brain in rhythmic cycles.

If an animal is deprived of REM sleep by awakening or drugs, these bursts of brain activity begin to spread into other stages of sleep. What we call REM sleep, or paradoxical sleep, is not a unity, but a conjunction of physiological rhythms and experiences.

REM DEPRIVATION

One of the first techniques for discovering what REM sleep might be was to take it away and watch what happened. Dement, Jouvet, and others found ingenious ways of waking people or animals at REM onset, while allowing them all other sleep. As deprivation continued, people and animals tried more and more frequently to enter REM sleep. When permitted uninterrupted slumber they went into a virtual orgy of REM sleep.

Deprived rats and cats behaved abnormally. Deprived tomcats would, for instance, stalk other cats aggressively, mounting dead or anesthetized animals—an unheard-of breach of normal tomcat conduct. They also showed uncontrolled voracious hunger. Dement and others postulated that REM deprivation might create a state of acute excitement in drive centers in the brain by preventing a normal, cyclic discharge of experience, and biochemical accumulation. Normally rested animals showed characteristic EEG patterns when they heard repeated clicks, but their EEGs after the same clicks were quite altered when they had been deprived of REM sleep. Deprived rats, for example, would fall into convulsions after an electric shock that did not normally cause convulsions.

People deprived of REM sleep, first by Dr. Charles Fisher, Dement, and a succession of others, sometimes became irritable and anxious. Amphetamines, barbiturates, hypnotics, and alcohol all tend to suppress some of a person's REM sleep. If a person suddenly stops taking barbiturates, he is likely to drop rapidly (in four to ten minutes) into REM sleep and to experience unpleasant, even nightmarish dreams. People who are "quitting" the sleeping pill or amphetamine habit are sometimes so disturbed by nightmares that they reach for another pill for sleep—one route to addiction.

Interfering with the normal cycles of REM sleep interrupts a life process, not merely dreaming or specific events. It has been postulated that REM sleep may be a kind of survival rhythm, a rhythmic excitation of body and brain that would enable the sleeping creature to defend himself, if need be, a state close to waking that is not yet awake.

REM sleep—indeed all sleep—is not the same at night as in the morning, for the subrhythms of sleep are modulated by the larger cycle of a day. The habit of nightly sleep acts as a synchronizer in man, maintaining harmony within the body. Hours of sleep and waking normally set the phase for kidney activity, for elimination functions, for increases and decreases in metabolism, body temperature, and many other intermeshed functions. When we shift our hours of sleep these functions also shift. Unfortunately the parts of the body shift at varied speeds, so that heart, kidneys, liver, and adrenal glands may adjust at different rates. During this transition, perhaps during travel, a person may find he awakens from sleep at odd times to urinate, or he feels inappropriately tired at midday, or hungry when all restaurants are closed. Studies of adrenal hormone functions and REM sleep have begun to explain the kinds of feelings a person has after interrupting his usual schedule of sleep.

ADRENAL HORMONES AND REM CYCLES

One of the important determinants in our vitality or fatigue, in our metabolism and resistance to infection, is a class of compounds—hormones known as steroids for their particular carbon ring structure. They are manufactured in the adrenal glands, and released from the outer layer of cells known as the adrenal cortex. They are known as adrenocortical hormones, and a group among them (17-hydroxycorticosteroids) usually abbreviated as 17-OHCS, have been widely studied. These hormones help regulate metabolism and energy supplies, and also influence the transmission of nerve impulses, thus influencing the keenness of our senses.

Every twenty-four hours the levels of adrenal hormones rise and fall. Blood levels decline from midday to midnight and rise before awakening. At one time endocrinologists thought that this was a continuous, smooth change. Then in 1965 a New York neurologist, Elliot Weitzman, managed to take samples of blood from sleeping medical students at short intervals throughout the night. He saw that the hormones did not seep continuously into the blood, in increasing amounts toward morning; instead they increased in sudden spurts, usually around the time of REM periods. Several years later Weitzman and his colleagues took a closer look by sampling blood around the clock, every twenty minutes, from two healthy young men. This study, led by Dr. Leon Hellman at Montefiore Hospital, showed that cortisol enters the blood in spurts like a fountain, and quickly vanishes. Twenty minutes after a spurt there might be no trace of hormone in the blood. Moreover, in a quiet hospital day of reading and television, there were only eight spurts of hormone—and five of them occurred in sleep, in the hours before breakfast. The adrenals were quiet 75 percent of the time.

It seems clear that blood tests to evaluate a sick patient's hormone levels cannot be reliable unless blood is sampled almost continuously for twenty-four hours.

It also seems that a rhythm of activity within the brains and glands of normally peaceable people shows a peak in the late hours of sleep. Cortisol is secreted from the adrenals, only on command from the pituitary gland. The pituitary emits a messenger hormone, ACTH (adrenocorticotropic hormone) which travels through the blood and stimulates the adrenal glands. This ACTH is shortlived, vanishing after about twenty-five minutes. The details are not the issue. The import of this chain of events is that the pituitary gland is actively nudging the adrenals for only a very small time each day. Since the pituitary is, in turn, acting on a command from the hypothalamus, there must be some rhythm within the brain that eventuates in the strange adrenal hormone rhythm that allows us to awaken from sleep with our highest daily concentrations.

A BRAIN RHYTHM THAT MAY
CONTROL HORMONES

Since the 1950s many neurologists and endocrinologists have noticed that sick people with brain tumors or damage to the hypothalamus also had abnormal circadian rhythms of adrenal hormones. A decade later Drs. Dorothy and Howard Krieger saw possible signs of a rhythm in the hypothalamus of cats that could be blocked with drugs at a critical time in the twenty-four hours, and the result would be a blocking of the animal's normal adrenal rhythm.

The chain of command from the hypothalamus in the brain to the adrenals near the kidneys was completed recently. We now know that the hypothalamus does release a substance (corticotropin releasing factor, or CRF) that commands the pituitary to emit ACTH, to command the adrenals to emit steroid hormones.

How does our behavior influence all that endocrine activity? What happens when we change the hours of our sleep?

SLEEP REVERSAL

A reversal of sleep hours is not simple for the body to adjust to, as Dr. Weitzman has shown. Baseline studies were first made of volunteers as they slept by night in the hospital as usual. Then for two weeks they slept by day in the laboratory. Following this inversion of sleep hours, there were gross changes in the normal sleep rhythm. At first the men fell with abnormal rapidity into REM sleep; instead of coming ninety minutes after they fell asleep it appeared within four to five minutes. For two weeks REM sleep was abnormally early. Oddly enough, Stage IV sleep showed no change. It came in the early hours of sleep as usual.

Most people would say that these volunteers enjoyed sufficient sleep, but it was not refreshing and smooth sleep, for they awakened often toward "morning." Their diaries revealed that they felt listless and uncomfortable. Only after two weeks of sleeping by day did they seem to adapt, and by that time their EEGs were beginning to look like their normal sleep patterns.

One factor in their initial listlessness and discomfort may have been low adrenal hormone levels. For some, the sleep reversal seemed to damp the release of adrenal steroids, and excretion levels fell unusually low. Many workers on night shifts claim that they suffer from poor sleep and general discomfort. A part of their trouble may be hormonal.

Because nobody fully adapted to sleep reversal in two weeks, the study was repeated, allowing three weeks of daytime sleep. Now the researchers saw that body temperature didn't show its normal rhythm until the beginning of the third week, although other functions adapted at once. Adrenal hormone levels were abnormal for two weeks. This meant that the volunteers were initially trying to act alive all night with low adrenal levels and body temperature. Significantly, adapting to reversal took over two weeks—but on return to nighttime sleep, adjustment was immediate. Body temperature was "normal" in its rhythm after two to three days.

This instantaneous return to a habitual schedule seemed to imply that habits are deeply programmed into our neuroendocrine systems, and are not easy to change. On the other hand, the slow adaptation to daytime sleep may be somewhat misleading, for the hospital situation does not parallel that of the exhilarated world traveler who seems to adapt to time shifts more rapidly. It is also possible that the traveler's physiology is in a state of transition and quite desynchronized, but he is eager to sightsee in a foreign city, too excited to heed signals from within. Most of us are out of touch with our bodies and tend to ignore distress signals until they become emergencies. This may be the kind of situation that ultimately leads to the symptoms of "jet fatigue."

REM SLEEP AND LEARNING

Along with desynchronization of hormonal and metabolic rhythms, a major change in the normal sleep-waking rhythm may have emotional effects. During the unique REM state of heightened arousal during sleep the cortex, or thinking brain, seems to be working as if the person were concentrating very hard. Quite a number of sleep scientists have concluded that REM sleep is a time when we adapt emotionally. In the stillness of slumber, the busy mind may be pulling out the file drawers of memory, placing the images and feelings of our most recent experiences into the proper slots for future memory. The language of the adapting mind and its symbolic process are unlike the logical language of human communication, and may be the more elusive primary process of dreams. There is indirect, yet compelling, evidence for the idea that REM sleep is a time of adaptation to life experiences. Psychologist Johann Stoyva of Denver persuaded some agile and stalwart medical students to wear distortion goggles during the day. These prism lenses are so confusing that you might find yourself spooning soup over your shoulder, and unable to steer your hand to grasp an object. Volunteers had to be especially careful about crossing streets, until finally their brains adapted and they were functioning normally through the prism lenses. Until they adapted they showed more than the usual amount of REM sleep, but once they adapted to the goggles, REM sleep dropped back to normal. Stoyva did not awaken his volunteers to find out whether their dreams were prismatically twisted, but a similar experiment was conducted in a New York laboratory where the volunteers wore red tinted goggles. Dr. Howard Roffwarg and his associates had wanted to see whether recent experience was reflected in REM dreams. The people wearing red goggles had red-tinted dreams—until they began to adapt to their goggles, and no longer saw a pink world. In Boston, psychiatrists Ramon Greenberg and Chester Pearlman found that aphasic hospital patients showed increases in REM sleep when they were responding to coaching in speech. After accidents or strokes, damage in speech centers of the brain may leave a person able to understand but unable to communicate by speech. People who improved their halting speech after coaching showed increases in the amount of REM sleep, but those who didn't learn showed no difference in sleep. Parallel experiments with animals also suggest that REM sleep may be important in memory storage, in adaptive learning. When deprived of REM sleep laboratory animals failed to learn simple procedures that they had learned perfectly when permitted REM sleep. Along with autonomic excitement, hormone release, and signs of metabolic acceleration, the REM interval may be a time when creatures memorize and adapt to current experiences, and the primal nature of the task may explain the imperturbability of the dreamer.

Hidden within what we consider to be the normal rhythms of nightly sleep are numerous functions that influence our waking lives. A change in the rhythm, a shifting of only one stage of sleep, may have many ramifications.

POOR SLEEP

The charting of sleep rhythms offers a new criteria for evaluating the effects of sleeping pills and tranquilizers, most of which interfere with the rhythm of REM sleep. It also gives us a new means of diagnosing the sundry disorders that are called insomnia or poor sleep.

In the early 1950s psychologist Lawrence J. Monroe, while a graduate student at the University of Chicago, compared well-matched groups of good and poor sleepers in the laboratory. Their sleep cycles differed. Poor sleepers "used up" their Stage IV sleep earlier in the night, and showed higher rectal temperatures before and during sleep than did the good sleepers. They had additional signs that might be interpreted as arousal or stress—higher sleeping pulse rates and constrictions in the blood vessels of their fingers. On psychological tests, they seemed more prone to neuroticism and somatic distresses.

Body temperature curves strongly suggested that the poor sleepers might be people who were out of synchrony with the twenty-four-hour day. The temperatures of good sleepers began to show a marked decline at bedtime, falling steeply to a low point in the early morning. About an hour or two before they awakened in the morning, their temperatures began to climb, and were normal by the time they got up. By contrast, the temperatures of the poor sleepers declined less and were still declining when they arose in the morning. A poor sleeper may be perpetually wishing he could go to bed later and could rise later than is socially convenient, for his body time actually may lag behind clock time (showing a longer period than twenty-four hours).

Free-running rhythms, uncoupled from the twenty-four-hour day, have been observed in isolation. These rhythms have also been observed in men and animals in response to stress, and may explain some of the insomnia experienced by many mentally ill patients. When a person free-runs, he may be doing his waking tasks with a "sleeping" body and subsequently may develop psychosomatic and emotional symptoms as a result of desynchronization. There is little evidence on the way such symptoms start, but it is clear that poor sleepers have reasons for their complaints.

ELECTROSLEEP

In the Soviet Union, Germany, and Israel a number of clinicians treated poor sleepers with electrosleep—a very mild form of electrical brain stimulation. Electrosleep is probably a misnomer since the stimulation may relax a person, without putting him to sleep at the time. Nonetheless, one Israeli psychiatrist has given electrosleep treatments, with extraordinary success, to patients suffering from depression and insomnia. In one instance, an extremely agitated executive of a large computer company had been relying on heavy nightly doses of barbiturates for many years. Then he began spending an hour (the same hour) at a nearby clinic each afternoon for twenty days. He would lie on a bed with electrodes over his eyes (or forehead) and behind his ears. An interfering current—square waves focused upon the back of his head—was now applied for an hour at a strength and frequency adjusted according to his own sensations. Because the eyelids may tingle slightly, many people have placed the electrodes on the forehead. Although this man did not fall asleep, he relaxed and sometimes experienced very pleasant and vivid imagery. However, his nightly sleep was beginning to improve. He stopped taking drugs, began eating more leisurely meals, and for about two years thereafter was able to sleep and work without the incessant use of sedatives and hypnotics.

Russian clinicians have reported similar success with thousands of patients, who suffered such a variety of ailments that the claims used to draw incredulous laughter from skeptical American scientists. The treatments seemed to be effective with depression, insomnia, pregnancy toxemia, hypertension, acne, neuralgia, asthma, and colitis, to mention a few.

To Americans, electrosleep seemed to be a new panacea, a fad applied to every possible symptom. However, many Russian clinicians see a commonality of origin in a variety of ailments that they call neurovegetative, and we call psychosomatic. From their point of view, an electric tranquilizer should be effective for a large range of symptoms that stem from "stress." The precise way in which the electrostimulation may work and the brain regions it may influence have not been mapped. A number of scientists have conjectured that this electric therapy acts as a resynchronizer for dissociated internal rhythms, and realigns the person with his environment.*

Electrosleep techniques are only beginning to be explored scientifically in the United States, a beginning marked by the formation of the Neuroelectric Society, which may usher in a much expanded picture of psychosomatic illness and its treatment. At present, electrosleep therapy remains only an interesting possibility, perhaps a technique that may be used to resynchronize travelers who have become temporarily desynchronized,

* A USSR symposium on electrosleep in 1969 was edited by V. M. Banshchikov, Joint Publications Research Service, Number 50544, May, 1970. This Fourth Symposium on Electrosleep and Electroanesthesia can be obtained from the Clearinghouse for Federal Scientific and Technical Information, Springfield, Virginia 22151.

as well as a great variety of patients and people who call themselves poor sleepers, or insomniacs.

THE DISTURBED RHYTHMS
OF INSOMNIA IN DEPRESSION

By the criteria of rhythmicity, it is now possible to categorize and identify the more serious forms of insomnia. One of the classic tortures is the inability to stay asleep. Many people drop off to sleep readily only to awaken in the dark, cold, predawn hours, lonely and unable to sleep. This early-morning awakening is extremely common in severe depression. Depressed people are more easily awakened by sounds than normal people and may be disturbed by the first sounds of morning.

There are more subtle insomniacs, often accused of prevaricating to win sympathy, for they do sleep but feel they are awake. The quality of their sleep is visible only in EEG records which show that they return to the edge of wakefulness unduly often, hovering on the verge of consciousness. The sleep of a large group of heterogenous people with depression has been studied by psychiatrists at several major hospitals, sometimes for periods as long as a year. Several findings were common to all the studies. The patients lacked a normal sleep rhythm. Some patients had little or no deep Stage IV sleep. Loss of Stage IV sleep has been seen in anxious medical students before examinations, and seemed to be a response to intense stress. Some depressive people had abnormally little or abnormally great amounts of REM sleep, but unlike the predictable REM rhythm of normal people, theirs showed erratic patterns as if oscillating internally.

In 1963 Dr. William Zung, a psychiatrist at Duke University, compared the sleep records of normal and depressed persons, evaluating them by a mathematical method known as a Markov chain analysis. Normal sleep showed a consistent organization, but some depressed patients had EEG records so disorganized that they could hardly be interpreted. They typically shifted from one sleep level to another with undue rapidity, showing cycles shorter than ninety minutes, and often awakening from REM sleep. Whereas the normal person has most of his oblivious Stage IV sleep early in the night, a depressed person might sleep fitfully, lie awake for several hours, and then lapse into Stage IV sleep in the early morning. This is as anomalous in the context of sleep as a person who wants a cigar and brandy for breakfast and orange juice for dinner.

When depressed patients began to improve, so did sleep, and they no longer shifted so rapidly from one EEG state to another. Rhythmicity is part of the organization we call mental health, and some of the drugs that help to lift depression also improve the rhythm of sleep by lengthening the cycles. Zung showed that this was true of the compounds known as tricyclic antidepressants, after their chemical structure. When he tested the drug desipramine on normal young volunteers, he found that it lengthened the cycle from 90 to about 120 minutes, and increased the amount of Stage IV sleep while slightly reducing REM sleep. Other drugs sometimes used to combat depression, such as phenelzine, have an opposite effect and shorten the sleep cycle. Zung's work suggests that one way of predicting how a drug will affect a depressed person is by determining whether or not it lengthens the sleep cycle.

The stillness of sleep has proven to be an excellent time for recording some signs of the person's time organization. Here is one of the symptoms of depression that no person can see in himself, nor can a doctor observe it on the surface for temporal disorganization is revealed in EEGs, in noisy, broken sleep records. Since depression is an illness involving disorganized rhythms, proper instruments should someday reveal signs of disorganization or foreshortening of many other cycles in a sick person's body and behavior during the day as well as by night.

NARCOLEPSY

One relatively uncommon illness, narcolepsy, has fascinated sleep researchers in part because its symptoms reveal the continuation of the rhythm of REM sleep throughout the waking hours. Narcolepsy sometimes takes the form of excessive sleepiness, overmastering a person while he is shopping, driving a car, or making love. In certain cases people even dare not tell jokes or scold their children because normal emotions like hilarity and anger can trigger a seeming fit in which they collapse in a faint. Actually, on EEG examination, this turns out to be an ill-timed seizure of REM sleep in which the suddenly relaxed musculature causes the person to collapse like jelly. A recent study of narcoleptic patients indicates that attacks often occur at two- to three-hour intervals. When observed in darkness around the clock, patients showed incredibly abundant amounts of REM sleep spaced occasionally at intervals of less than an hour. Their rhythm of sleep resembled that of a newborn baby.

THE BIOLOGICAL HOUR

By this point most readers will have the haunting suspicion that the rhythmic undulations observed throughout the nervous system and endocrine system at night, the regular cycles of sleep and dreaming, are not restricted to the dark cover of sleep, but continue throughout the day. Teachers know that schoolchildren show waves of restlessness during the day, and when these waves were plotted in a nursery school, it appeared that the children were restless for about thirty-five minutes, then quiet for thirty-five minutes in a seventy-minute cycle. Most people are aware of a waxing and waning of attention, of concentration, and of daydreaming throughout the day.

Over forty years ago, Dr. Kleitman began systematic observations of change in human behavior and physiology, in temperature, performance, rest, and alertness. Kleitman found hints of regularity and postulated a "basic rest-and-activity cycle." He concluded that such fundamental alternations between activity and repose were inherent in the nervous systems of all homeothermic animals—animals who maintain body temperature within a narrow range whatever the external climate.

As Kleitman saw, the human infant exhibits a sixty-minute basic rest-and-activity cycle, encompassing quiescent and active sleep.

The cycle period varies with the species, the size of the animal, and its age. In adult human sleep, the cycle period is measured from REM stage to REM stage, a ninety- to one-hundred-minute cycle; human babies sleep in cycles of fifty-five to sixty minutes. A newborn cat requires only eight minutes for a cycle, while an adult cat takes half an hour. Like the cardiac or respiratory cycles, the period of the cycle appears to be related to the size of the animal, and is perhaps determined in part by its rate of metabolism, as well as external conditions of security. A small creature like the rat shows cycles of ten to thirteen minutes in sleep, but the elephant has 120-minute cycles.

Since this rhythm has a higher frequency than a "day," it is often called "ultradian." Ultradian refers to cycles such as an hour, with periods shorter than circadian, while "infradian" refers to cycles with periods longer than a day such as a week.

THE TIMING OF NAPS

Ever since the early 1950s, sleep scientists have observed that when they monitored volunteers during daytime naps the sleep did not show the same pattern as night sleep. Webb and Agnew invited volunteers to take three-hour naps in their sleep laboratory in early morning, noon, and early and late afternoons. REM sleep occupied a third of the early morning naps, but scarcely appeared in later afternoon naps. Stage IV sleep did not appear in the morning naps, but appeared in late afternoon. Clearly, as scientists had seen by night, sleep stages and all the distinct functions they imply are modulated by a circadian rhythm. Stage IV comes in late afternoon and early night, while REM sleep normally increases in early morning. This means that the quality of a nap depends upon the time of day, and since it is harder to awaken from Stage IV sleep, this may explain why evening naps leave many people feeling loggy.

In the early 1960s, Gordon Globus, followed by other young psychiatrists, saw evidence in his studies that the roughly ninety-minute cycle of sleep must continue around the clock, modulated by the circadian rhythm to which it seems to be locked. Ekkehard Othmer found a roughly ninety- to one-hundred-minute cycle of drowsing, often with light sleep and REM activity when he took the EEGs of coeds sitting or lying in dim or bright rooms. Daniel F. Kripke detected ninety-minute cycles in physiological functions among people in an isolation tank in which the absence of sound, light, and activity created a perceptual deprivation that was disorienting and terrifying. Subjects found it hard to stay awake as instructed and they napped at roughly ninety-minute intervals.

A number of psychiatrists have speculated that the ninety-minute cycle seen in sleep might involve an accumulation and discharge of basic drives such as sex, hunger, and aggression. The brain mechanisms underlying these behaviors are in the deep, primitive regions known as the limbic system. One needs no special equipment to see the limbic system infusing the sleep behavior of infants. Babies in REM sleep actively suck, grimace, smile, have penile erections, and show many emotional expressions.

A RHYTHM OF EATING IN ISOLATION

Two psychiatrists at Mt. Sinai Hospital in New York, Stanley Friedman and Charles Fisher, suspected that a "drive" rhythm might be found in adults during waking as well as in sleep. They found that people in isolation did indeed show a rhythm of oral behavior. Volunteers were observed through a two-way mirror while they spent eight to nine hours reading and listening to music in a small den where an electric coffeepot and a well-supplied refrigerator offered an ample choice of snacks. Each item was rated; for instance, a cigarette was three points, a carbonated drink nine points. Whatever a person put into his mouth was recorded along with the time. Volunteers showed no random eating and smoking intensity; they had a waxing and waning cycle of eighty-five to one hundred minutes. Like the shortened sleep cycles seen in anxious patients, volunteers showed shortened eating cycles when under stress. One man, observed while studying for an examination, showed a roughly sixty-five-minute oral cycle, whereas his previous cycle had been ninety-five minutes. This may help to explain why people gain weight under stress. They simply eat more often. In this instance the man had increased his oral activity by 14 percent. Psychiatrists have referred to this shortened oral cycle as regressive, for it resembles a return to the shorter cycle of infants.

Perhaps the cycle displayed so distinctly in sleep and observed in waking by Dr. Kleitman and others is a basic unit, a kind of biological hour that seems to reach its adult stability around puberty. In general the sound and fury of social life mask our underlying rhythmicity; moreover, it is difficult to keep continuous records of changes over time, especially when life's demands are exigent. However, many researchers are beginning to notice the traces of a biological hour in their experimental animals.

A BIOLOGICAL HOUR IN CATS

Drs. M. B. Sterman and Dennis McGinty have watched cats who were allowed to feed freely over twenty-four hours. The cats showed bursts of feeding activity every fifteen to thirty minutes in a waking cycle that was continuous with their cycle of REM activity in sleep. Moreover the animals' body temperatures fluctuated in a rhythm of about thirty minutes.

After surgical decerebration the cats functioned out of the brain stem, that primitive lower center at the base of the brain. Drs. Sterman and McGinty saw that there were thirty-minute cycles of muscle relaxation in the neck (reminiscent of REM sleep), corresponding with the rhythmic peaks in temperature. The muscle relaxation engendered in the brain stem seems to be influenced by metabolic rhythms. When the upper brain fails to control that rhythmic relaxation, it may produce symptoms resembling narcolepsy. This metabolic and nervous system rhythm probably has wide-ranging effects upon behavior. Dr. Sterman has postulated that the ultradian rhythm occurs continuously like the cardiac cycle throughout life, and like the cardiac cycle, its consistency is a sign of health.

INDIVIDUAL CYCLES OF ALERTNESS AND SLEEPINESS

Each individual has a somewhat different biological hour, as judged by sleep records, and few individuals have a sense of their own cycle. People who fall asleep rapidly presumably rely upon an internal sense of cyclic sleepiness and alerting. Most people have had an overwhelming soporific feeling at the end of a party, but in the delays of leave-taking, found that they arrived home wide awake and unable to sleep. If the undulations of the sleep cycle indicate waves of alerting and relaxing, one might have to wait about an hour and a half for the next wave of sleepiness. In daytime as well, there are probably rhythms of daydreaming. Athletes and construction workers on high girders seem to undergo recurrent periods when they have to work especially hard to overcome some inner slackening of tension, reflexes, and attention. Sedentary people and students take coffee breaks about every two to three hours. By paying attention to this cycle people should be able to anticipate their peaks of attention and to sense a decline, using it to fall asleep easily and take quick naps. A sense of one's cycle can enable one to awaken from light sleep and from dreams. Mounting evidence does suggest that there is a basic ninety- to one-hundred-minute cycle that ripples on the slower circadian tides throughout our existence. Anxiety, illness, drugs such as sleeping pills and amphetamines, stress, fever, brain damage, and environmental factors can disturb this rhythm.

SLEEP AND WAKING IN ANTARCTICA

Men on polar expeditions often claim to sleep poorly. Psychiatrists Jay Shurley and Chester Pierce have seen one strange alteration in the sleep of men in the Antarctic. Despite heavy physical work, which appears to enhance deep Stage IV sleep, these men showed no Stage IV sleep. One scientist was studied long after his return to the United States, and it was over a year before his Stage IV sleep returned. This raised questions about the possible impact of the electromagnetic environment at the poles.

SPACE

Although sleep has never really been studied in space, American astronauts have not slept as deeply in space as on earth. This is not surprising in view of the danger, excitement, and pressure to accomplish a number of tasks. Weightlessness itself alters sleep rhythms and may reduce the need for sleep. The vestibular system, important in our sense of balance, plays some role in the eye movements of rapid-eye-movement sleep. The vestibular system exerts reflex control over the eyes, permitting us to keep our eyes on an object even when we move our heads. Otherwise the world would appear to rotate each time we turned our heads.

Since man is used to continuous vestibular stimulation from gravity, lack of this stimulation in space might be expected to reduce REM sleep, or disorganize the cycle. Rapid shifts from sleep to waking, bursts of drowsing, and disorganized sleep were observed in one ill-fated macaque monkey sent into orbit in Biosatellite III in 1969. However, this animal deteriorated so rapidly that its trip was aborted after eight days. Rapid shifts of EEGs during waking were also observed in astronaut Frank Borman during Gemini VII. For the first four days of this mission his sleep EEGs were studied. On the first night he alternated between light sleep and arousal, but a more normal rhythm appeared in the second sleep period when he had three cycles that included Stage IV.

If the first Americans in space did not sleep long enough nor soundly, it was partly due to poor scheduling that demanded an alternation of a few hours of sleep with a few hours of duty. Men were expected to sleep during hours when they would normally have been awake, and to do so in a sitting position and in the midst of considerable noise. Soviet cosmonauts, however, maintained their usual earth schedule while in orbit. In 1961 when Gherman Titov spent twenty-five hours in orbit, he easily fell asleep at his usual bedtime, but he awakened earlier than he planned, only to see his arms dangling weightlessly and his hands floating in midair. Titov reported:

> The sight was incredible. I pulled my arms down and folded them across my chest. Everything was fine— until I relaxed. My arms floated away from me again as quickly as the conscious pressure of my muscles relaxed and I passed into sleep. Two or three attempts at sleep in this manner proved fruitless. Finally, I tucked my arms beneath a belt. In seconds I was soundly asleep.
>
> Once you have your arms and legs arranged properly, space sleep is fine. There is no need to turn over from time to time as a man normally does in his own bed. Because of the condition of weightlessness there is no pressure on the body; nothing goes numb. It is marvelous; the body is astoundingly light and buoyant. . . . I slept like a baby.

When permitted to sleep on their usual earth schedule, some American astronauts are reported to have rested comfortably.

VOLUNTARY CONTROL OVER SLEEP CYCLES: IN CATS

It appears that people can learn to change the phase or even the period of the sleep cycle to some extent. The mind is the computer that controls the

body. Cats have been trained to lengthen their sleep
epochs and man may also learn to improve his sleep.
Sterman and McGinty have placed cats in special cages
where they could move freely while brain waves were
being recorded. Whenever a cat's brain waves showed
a particular rhythm resembling a spindle, an automatic
switch would be activated, giving the cat a reward of
milk. Thus the cat's brain controlled the switch that
gave the reward. In this feedback situation cats soon
learned to produce the rewarded spindle rhythm which
they often did by standing very still, at "attention." The
rhythm seemed to occur when the animals suppressed a
certain kind of motor activity. During sleep the training
showed its impact, for the spindling activity was increased. Their sleep had actually improved, in the sense
that they showed fewer bursts of the muscle twitches
that often interrupt sleep. These trained cats had longer
stretches of deep quiescent sleep than untrained control
animals. Moreover, the benefits lasted and the cats still
showed more quiescent sleep than controls two months
later.

It is clear from sleep researches that mental activity
and mental habits leave an indelible impression on sleep
rhythms. Mind and brain, brain and body are not separate. It is no wonder that worriers have a hard time
falling asleep and need training in new bedtime mental
habits and in muscle relaxation. Sleep researchers recognize the traces of anxiety in EEG records. When
volunteers come to a laboratory for study, the first night
or two is discounted since the strain and novelty of the
laboratory distort the person's normal rhythms. Just as
stress and emotional misery may distort a person's sleep
rhythms involuntarily, a person can voluntarily change
his sleep. In the sleep laboratory some people have
learned to discriminate, while sleeping, between the
dream experiences of Stage II and REM. The levels of
sleep "feel" different. Evidence is beginning to appear
that people also can learn to shift the preponderance of
their REM sleep from the end of the night, when it
normally occurs, to the beginning.

People may also learn how to counteract the dis-
organizing influence of stress by lengthening their bio-

logical hour. Doubtless, future generations will look back upon us with disbelief. Now modified EEG machines are becoming instruments of teaching, and educated people in the future will know how and when to fall asleep, how to intensify their rest, how to awaken from an interesting thought or dream, or to awaken at an hour of their choosing without an alarm clock. By repeatedly being informed when one is emitting certain brain-wave patterns one may begin to learn the feelings of these elusive states. Cultivated people in the future will be in touch with themselves, waking or sleeping, in a manner that few people today enjoy. Unlike their primitive ancestors, the generations just ahead will have a useful sense of their own rhythmicity.

Current researchers in sleep are hastening this future, for they offer us a way of understanding how rhythms change from infancy to old age. An understanding of these fundamental cycles is essential in caring for babies and children, in preventing sleep problems, in coping with the hardships of the aged. In the course of rearing children, it should be possible to impart some of this new knowledge, but at the least it should ease the conflicts and expectations between parents and their young.

RHYTHMS OF INFANTS

When a newborn infant first arrives home, he seems exasperatingly unpredictable. His hungers and needs, moments of mirth or squalling, and hours of sleep all are out of step with the rhythm of family life. Only around the sixteenth week does the baby begin to conform to the patterns of night-long sleep and daytime waking that adults take for granted and consider "natural." As exhausted parents understand, a new baby cannot be coaxed to be hungry at a certain hour nor forced to do his sleeping at night and his crying by day. His wetting and excretion are "irregular" as well, and he shifts toward "regularity" at a pace dictated by the speed of brain development.

INFANT SLEEP

Thirty years ago, Nathaniel Kleitman and T. G. Engelmann began recording systematic observations of newborn infants around the clock. These babies were raised on a self-demand schedule, in which the cry of the baby, rather than some fixed clock hour, dictated feeding and diapering. Contrary to the popular belief that newborns sleep twenty-one to twenty-three hours, Kleitman and Engelmann saw that on the average they spent about eight hours awake, but much of their wakefulness occurred at night when normally nobody would be noticing. As these pioneer researchers reported, babies spontaneously alternated between naps and waking in cycles of about fifty to sixty minutes. Arthur C. Parmelee and his co-workers have since refined EEGs and other recording instruments to observe infants during the first days of life. They found signs of individuality at birth; some babies slept nearly twenty-one hours a day at first, but others spent only ten to sixteen hours asleep, in what may be a clue to lifelong differences in sleep needs.

At birth, infant sleep shows roughly a forty- to fifty-minute cycle, according to the EEG records of Parmelee and associates. The infant spends about twenty-one minutes in active, REM-like sleep in which he kicks, sucks, grimaces and may even seem awake. Then he drifts into deep, quiet, slow-wave sleep for eighteen minutes, then up into another activated phase. Every three to four hours the baby awakens. Judging from very sensitive recordings made on premature babies, infants must begin alternating between a REM-like phase and a quiescent phase long before they are born. At birth, however, 50 percent of an infant's sleep time is spent in REM sleep (85 percent if he is very premature). Probably infants are not dreaming in our sense of the word during this time in the womb and just after birth. Still, miraculously, at birth a baby knows how to cry and suck. Perhaps it is during his prenatal state of REM-like arousal that he was stimulated to practice survival behavior such as kicking and thumb-sucking. Swedish photographs taken within the womb have shown the unborn sucking their thumbs, kicking, grimacing, and making neuromuscular preparations for survival after birth.

REM AND LEARNING IN INFANTS

We accept the aptitudes of the newborn infant without much thought, yet the brain grows by action, and behavior repertoires must be built from rudiments, the firing of brain cells, contraction of muscles, and ultimately the smooth movement of the hand toward the mouth. We grow as we react to stimulation, but there is relatively little stimulation in the womb. Floating tilted in the dark amniotic fluids, the infant may feel the rhythm of his mother's heart beat, may feel some loud sounds outside her body, and her movements. Rhythmically alterted, perhaps from the mother's hormonal cycles, the brain stem may trigger the limbic and visual system, stimulating drive centers and movement in the beginnings of an activity rhythm. The first movements may be signs of the first laying down of neuromuscular programs. In the first months after birth, as well, the baby spends considerable time in what seem to be random gestures and grimaces of REM sleep. If the signs of REM sleep do in any way reflect the amount of learning that must be stored, it should surprise no one that normal infants spend fifty percent of their sleeping time in this state. Infants with genetic defects such as mongolism, or phenylketonuria, and other retarded infants show less REM activity, and their brainwave tracings differ noticeably from those of normal infants during quiet sleep. Sleep appears to be related to the central nervous system processes that permit learning, processes often called cognitive, for the acquired ability to use the mind for solving certain kinds of problems. The newborn infant is continuously learning. In computer language one might say that the bugs have to be gotten out of the system, for nothing works quite right. The baby must "learn" to swallow without choking, to cough without drowning himself, to sneeze, excrete, turn over, and respond to the overwhelming flood of new sensations, voices, the feeling of being held, changes in temperature. Although he has been preparing himself to some extent in the womb, and there is a continuity between prenatal and natal life, the first weeks after birth are an almost incessant learning experience. As time goes on the welter of signals from outside begins to gain meaning of a new sort, for the identification of language sounds begins. The less primitive region of the brain, the cortex, begins to show rapid development.

When an infant is eight months old, he will be spending twice as long in quiescent sleep as in REM sleep. His sleep cycles will approximate the ninety-minute cycles of adults. The increase of quiet, slow-wave sleep suggests brain maturation since the slow-wave activity is dependent on the cerebral cortex. In many ways the EEGs of sleep, and the timing of infant activity, give indications of normal or abnormal maturation. Normal full-term infants show more regular sleep stages than do premature babies. The regularity of sleep cycles is one early indication of central nervous system maturation. The foreshadowings of a basic activity and rest cycle begin long before birth.

FETAL RHYTHMS

Cycles of rapid eye movements have been recorded in unborn animals, along with corresponding changes in pulse rate and blood pressure. Basic cycles of activity have been recorded by Sterman in fetuses twenty-two weeks old up to birth. He studied eight pregnant women who were willing to sleep wearing EEG leads and an electrode on their abdomens in his sleep laboratory. Dr. Sterman found that there were two fetal rhythms. One was an intrinsic activity rhythm of about thirty to fifty minutes, the other was an eighty- to one-hundred-minute rhythm related to the mother's REM cycle. In later stages of pregnancy, the women occasionally had to interrupt their sleep to get up and urinate, so their sleep cycles were broken. Yet the fetal activity rhythms remained a stable ninety to one hundred minutes. The stable REM cycles in the fetus during the waking of the mother suggested that some manifestations of the REM cycle were being transmitted, perhaps hormonally, during waking. At birth the ninety-minute cycle disappeared. The infants now showed a forty-minute cycle of respiration, EEGs, body movement, and eye movement. The REM cycle in infants runs about forty to forty-seven minutes, and lengthens to about ninety minutes when the baby is about eight months old, persisting throughout life. The infant also shows roughly a 180-minute cycle of hunger and feeding.

DEVELOPMENT OF CIRCADIAN RHYTHMS IN INFANCY

The newborn infant seems to sleep more than he actually does. By ten months an infant may sleep only three hours less than he did at birth, but now his waking hours cluster in daytime when his parents can observe him. He also eats and wets by day. Although newborn babies may seem to disregard day and night, if fed according to demand they will be more insistent about daytime feedings than night feedings. The circadian activity rhythm appears in infants around sixteen to twenty weeks. However, not all of the baby's physiological functions show rhythms in phase with those of adults.

Different systems in the body show circadian rhythms at different ages. It is not clear how to interpret the staggered acquisition of circadian rhythmicity in the body, but it may reflect the fact that various body systems, such as the heart, kidneys, and adrenal glands mature at different rates. It does mean that the routinized and harmonious functioning of an adult cannot be expected of a child. The advent of circadian rhythms has been charted for only a few functions, but in the not-too-distant future, the parent's guide for infant care will contain a table of many important physiological functions—and the parent will be able to find out when his infant can be expected to show a circadian rhythm in taste sensitivity, in adrenal corticosteroids and fatigue, and many other body functions.

In testing 300 infants for various bodily functions, Drs. T. Hellbrügge and J. Rutenfranz found only one rhythm that they could identify as circadian in the first week of life. This was electric skin resistance. Resistance was high in the morning and low at night. The conductivity of the skin may be related to changes in the chemistry and moisture of the skin that result from nervous stimulation. Thus, skin conductivity has been interpreted as an indicator of activity in the autonomic nervous system which regulates survival functions. However, potassium and sodium levels in urine also may reflect aspects of nervous and cortico-adrenal activity, and they did not show day-night differences. As Hellbrügge found, a newborn infant had a pattern of sleep and waking, of eye activity, of body temperature, pulse, and excretion levels of potassium, calcium, and sodium that were not in synchrony with the twenty-four-hour period of the world around him. This discrepancy in timing may cause one of the first stresses of life, since there may be long delays in attention when a crying infant is wet, hungry, or uncomfortable, but his parents are asleep.

Studies have indicated that in the second and third weeks of life, the rate of urine flow exhibited a rhythm which became greater by day than by night. However, this rhythm did not seem to depend on the baby's habits of fluid intake, for the infant drank nearly as much at night as by day.

An adult's temperature varies a degree or two in the course of a twenty-four-hour period. This pronounced circadian rhythm of body temperature does not emerge early. Between five and nine months of age the higher daytime temperatures are easily detectable. It is about this time that there is a detectable periodicity in the infant's levels of blood sugar, in the constituents of the urine, and in the urine flow. Between four and twenty weeks, the infant is beginning to give signs of a circadian rhythm in heart rate. Only much later, as a child of one-and-a-half years or almost two, does he show a

strong circadian rhythm in the excretion of chloride and
creatinine, a urinary by-product of muscular activity.
He develops a rhythmic excretion of ions (charged
elements)—phosphate, sodium, and potassium—that
are presumably active in nerve-cell firing. Some of these
developmental patterns also have been seen in animal
studies. Newborn infants do not show the circadian
rhythm of adrenal hormones that is so prominent in
adults. Dr. Robert Franks has found that blood levels
of the 17-OHCS did not show a consistent adult circadian rhythm in children under two years. However,
children between age three and thirteen years did show
rhythmic change comparable to adults, suggesting that
the development of the adrenal tides may occur some-
where around age three.

As the next chapter will indicate, the levels of adrenal hormones modulate sense perception and fatigue.
Because adults are rhythmic, they can predict these
subtle changes in themselves, but the child under three
is presumably not very predictable. The rate at which
a child develops circadian adrenal rhythms may be
partly enhanced by his environment.

STIMULATION IN INFANCY

Animal researches in the laboratories of Drs.
Curt P. Richter, Seymour Levine, and Robert Ader
have shown that the rate of growth of the adrenal system in rats can be influenced by manipulating the mother
before delivery or by stimulating and handling the infant after birth. Initially, a newborn rat shows no daily
rhythm in his blood levels of the adrenal steroid corticosterone. Adrenal secretion becomes rhythmic only
after the animal is twenty-one to twenty-five days old.
Animals that are shocked and handled right after birth
mature earlier. They show an adrenal hormone rhythm
at sixteen days, five to ten days earlier than animals not
handled. Apparently early experience speeds maturation and speeds the appearance of an adrenal hormone
rhythm.

Ironically, Seymour Levine and Geoffrey Harris had expected to produce neurosis and psychosomatic disease in their rats. They had conjectured that rough handling in infancy might be the root of neurosis, and they shook infant rats, shocked them, and exposed them to what is known as the open field test—in which a small creature is observed in a very large cage, or on a floor that is vast and exposed relative to the rodent. The stressed animals were not the ones who cowered and defecated. On the contrary, it was the protected animal, brought up in isolation and carefully left untouched, who showed the signs of exaggerated fear and undue adrenal hormone responses. When the scientists compared the animals physiologically, it was clear that the protected, isolated animals had less mature adrenal systems than the creatures who had been "stressed." It appeared that some early demands, experiences, or stresses actually benefited the animal and helped his adrenal system calibrate its output and the speed of its response to the demands of living. Experience, rather than a vacuum-like protection, seems to be necessary for the development of human infants, too.

Studies of human infants indicate that adrenal hormone levels rise when babies are crying. Moreover, the circadian rhythm of sleep and waking seems to mature faster among babies in what would seem to be the slightly stressful environment of a lying-in nursery. This finding was made by a team of psychiatrists led by Dr. Louis W. Sander, in an effort to see how early experience and caretaking affects later adaptation.

PARENT-BABY COMPATIBILITY

One of the definitions of parent-child compatibility must be the degree of synchrony of timing between them. Dr. Sander and his associates studied the amount of crying and the sleep-waking patterns of a number of babies during their first month; some of them remained in a nursery after birth where they were tended every four hours, others were continuously cared for by a surrogate or real mother. It was clear that the nursery infant had a rhythm of activity and crying that was out of synchrony with the nursery schedule, and in the first ten days these infants tended to cry increasingly at night while babies with rooming-in nurses cried increasingly by day. Crying records also indicated that the surrogate mothers differed very much in the sensitivity and timing of their responses. However, it was the infants who spent their first ten days in the nursery who developed a circadian rhythm of waking and sleep more rapidly than infants who had a single caretaker. The infants in the nursery presumably underwent more stress, since their activity periods did not correspond with the times when they were fed. This stress may influence the baby, making him conform more nearly to a twenty-four-hour day, thus adapting to the rhythm of his caretakers.

Dr. Sander and his associates in Boston remarked that the nursery infant spent his first ten days out of synchrony with his environment, not a very pleasant or soothing state. However, because he had to conform to the environmental routine the nursery infant developed a precocious circadian rhythm in which he spent prolonged periods awake by day, and distributed more of his sleep to the night. The medical researchers did not interpret this accelerated maturation as an advantage, for they thought these infants might fatigue themselves with prolonged waking and be less able to adapt to novelty than the babies who had been tended by a single person. On the other hand, adult timing might make a child more flexible, and allow him to be cared for by more than one individual.

Timing is certainly a most important element in the first interactions of mother and child, and it is beginning to be studied.

MOTHER-INFANT SYNCHRONY

One curious instance of synchronization was observed in a sleep laboratory at the University of Oklahoma by Dr. Boyd Lester. As mothers and infants were recorded simultaneously throughout the night in the medical school sleep laboratory, some pairs of mothers and babies seemed to slip into REM sleep simultaneously—a synchrony that may have begun before birth, when fetal activity cycles coincided with the mother's REM cycles. Occasionally the mother-infant synchrony of sleep cycles was disrupted when the mother had come to the laboratory after emotional upset, such as a fight with her husband. On that night and subsequent nights, she and her child would not exhibit synchronous sleep rhythms. This is not surprising since novelty and stress alter the rhythms of sleep.

RHYTHMS FOR ORIENTATION

Infants and children respond to joy and stress by rhythmic, repetitive action. From the head-banging and rocking of young babies to the spoon-banging and marching of children, there is evidence that rhythm is rewarding in itself. Perhaps rhythm is actually one of the earliest and most inherent ways of orienting oneself. Floating in the darkness of the uterine waters, the fetus experiences vibrations of his mother's heartbeat and the pulsing of blood vessels. Judging from the pulse rates of animal fetuses, the unborn do respond to sounds outside. Then, at birth, there are no longer the familiar beats, but new noises, movements, tactile changes that may seem chaotic and unpredictable. Perhaps the rocking and patting a mother gives her newborn child helps him bridge the transition from a world of simple beats into the chaos of living. As she holds the baby, their respiration may approximate a synchrony. She may partly recreate the stimuli of breathing and pulse that oriented the baby before birth.

RHYTHMS *IN VITRO?*

In the future, and probably not far enough in the future for the mental comfort of most people, genetic engineers predict that embryos will be nurtured *in vitro*. Women will no longer have to carry children, and the infants themselves may be grown for especially desirable traits such as intelligence and sweetness of disposition. These embryos, allowed to go through gestation in a chemically rich and nourishing environment in a laboratory bottle, will need more than a good temperature and proper food mixture to nourish their growing nervous systems. What would an infant be like if grown in quiet, without the movements of the mother, the rhythmic infusion of hormones, sounds, heartbeat? Would such babies develop rhythms so that they would function smoothly? How, indeed, does the rhythm of the prenatal world affect the growing infant?

In that first, intimate symbiosis of mother and child, one often witnesses a rapport as the mother makes rhythmic sounds, and helps the infant learn the rhythm of sucking. In later childhood there is almost no act of coordination, no game or movement the child can make that is not improved by rhythm. It is our word, in fact, for all smooth, harmonious movement, and there is no sport, no physical action that is not improved by rhythmicity. Early in infancy there are discernible individual differences in the rhythmicity of children, some of which seem to predict their later development.

"RHYTHMIC" AND "ARRHYTHMIC" CHILDREN

A New York research group, Dr. Alexander Thomas, Stella Chess, and Herbert G. Birch, have studied 141 children (in eighty-five families) closely from birth to about age ten, and have found that one important clue to temperament and later adjustment is the regularity or irregularity of feeding, sleeping, and other habits. The infants differed at birth, and the researchers found three general kinds of temperamental configurations. Their description in *Scientific American* is worth quoting.

One type is characterized by positiveness in mood, regularity in body function, a low or moderate intensity of approach to, rather than withdrawal from new situations. In infancy these children quickly establish regular sleeping and feeding schedules, are generally cheerful and adapt quickly to new routines and new people.

In contrast, we found another constellation of characteristics that described "difficult" children. These children are irregular in bodily functions, are usually intense in their reactions, tend to withdraw in the face of new stimuli, are slow to adapt to changes in the environment and are generally negative in mood. As infants they are often irregular in feeding and sleeping, are slow to accept new foods, take a long time to adjust to new routines or activities and tend to cry a great deal.

These were the children who tended to throw tantrums when frustrated, and whose parents were required to be consistent and tolerant to an unusual degree. Forty percent of the children were "easy" adapters, 10 percent were difficult, while another 15 percent seemed to be slow to respond.

They typically have a low activity level, tend to withdraw on their first exposure to new stimuli, are slow to adapt, are somewhat negative in mood, and respond to situations with a low intensity of reaction.

About 35 percent of the children did not fit these categories.

It is no surprise that 70 percent of the "difficult" children developed behavior problems, by contrast with 18 percent of the "easy" children. Many factors mysteriously combine in the evolution of a personality, and the child-parent interaction is usually most shaping. However, the temperament of the infant strongly influences all those early childhood relationships. The element of timing seems to be extremely important. Perhaps, indeed, the difficult child is always responding to his own irregularities while the regular child fits in with his environment effortlessly. A profile of rhythmicity, in the New York study, showed that the regular infants were on four-hour feeding schedules from birth. They had regular bowel movements and were falling asleep by a certain hour at six months, and napping after lunch at age one year. Perhaps the hours of feeding and care helped to synchronize these babies and, like the nursery infants in the Boston study, circadian rhythmicity was accelerated. At age five these "rhythmic" children would fall asleep when put to bed, and had regular bowel movements, and at age ten, they were sleeping the same amount each night and eating only at mealtimes. The irregular child was awaking at a different hour every day at age two months, varying in food intake and amount of napping at six months, showing irregular bowel movements, and taking over an hour to fall asleep at age two years, and even at five years. At age ten the irregular child's food intake would vary, and he would fall asleep at a different time each night.

A child whose own body is unpredictable, and who cannot foresee what it will do next, is bound to have a more difficult time learning the simplest kind of self-control. This child is almost doomed to have trouble at school. Indeed, from the infants' profiles of rhythmicity, it is possible to foresee the poor sleep, the insomnia, and the psychosomatic ailments of later years. Smoothness of function requires a harmony of circadian cycles, and these infants begin life at a disadvantage that may account for some of their negative moods, tantrums, and withdrawal. Could they be helped by regular feeding and handling schedules from birth on? Certainly in the future all infants could be diagnosed for rhythmicity at birth. Perhaps they could be entrained by scheduled feeding, lighting, and stimulation. However, it is not clear whether these irregular children have physiological defects too small to be detected (like the very common subclinical epilepsy discovered by Dr. Milton Tobias in many Los Angeles schoolchildren) which interfere with the timing mechanisms of the nervous system. It is not clear why these infants are irregular, but that seems an important question for research. We do not yet know how much of our circadian rhythmicity is learned, entrained by outside routine, by light and darkness. To what extent is our rhythmicity inherited? For a sizable and troubled percentage of the population these are urgent questions, whose answers might prevent lifelong suffering.

Clearly, the early schedule of the nursery does help shape the infant's rhythms. Still rhythmicity must be partly inherited, for a human infant is not likely to evolve a day length of nineteen hours or of fifty-four hours even in isolation. He would seem to be pre-set, capable of oscillating to an external rhythm around twenty-four hours.

NON-CIRCADIAN CYCLES IN RATS

It would be inhumane to test the elasticity of the circadian activity cycle in human babies, but a number of distinguished scientists have raised generations of animals in isolation from time-cues, hoping to see whether they would develop non-circadian cycles. In some instances, rat pups were placed with a foster mother, who had been kept on a different light cycle than their natural mothers, and therefore had a different activity rhythm. It was discovered that rodents do most of their mothering and nurturing during the hours of light. By erecting a divider in a carefully balanced cage, and leaving the litter on one side and the mother on the other, it was possible to record the time when the mother would jump the barrier to be with her litter, to nurse and clean her pups. When rat mothers had been raised on six hours of light and six hours of darkness, they nonetheless reverted to a circadian cycle of mothering, and did most of their nursing during one period of illumination each twenty-four hours. Researchers tried to confuse the animals, by inverting the light schedule on the nursing rat. Although she would shift the phase of her mothering rhythm she continued to exhibit a circadian cycle. Dr. Robert Ader and his co-workers at the University of Rochester Medical School have performed many permutations of the light-dark schedule with their animals. When subjected to certain schedules (such as eight hours light, and eight hours darkness) the animals did not develop a sixteen-hour activity rhythm, but reverted to a circadian cycle. Many seemed disorganized and became inactive. It would seem that mammals have inherited potential oscillations close to twenty-four hours, a rhythm that can be entrained by light, darkness, and social cues. So far the laboratory evidence does not make it seem likely that future generations will live cycles that are noncircadian, unless they are multiples or fractions of the twenty-four-hour day that will permit an underlying circadian rhythm.

AGE AND SLEEP

At one end of the spectrum, infants sleep and wake in a rhythm of naps, and at the other end of life old people tend to return toward this polyphasic alternation between naps and waking. Sleep tracings of the young are clearly distinguished from those of elderly people. The deep slumber of Stage IV does not appear in the EEGs of the elderly. Youngsters between three and seven typically spend the first hours of the night mostly in this state of profound oblivion. Often young children are picked up by their parents and carted home after a dinner party and put to bed, all with no more wakeful cooperation than a grunt or two. Set on his feet in this stage of sleep, a two- to three-year-old may collapse or behave like a sleepwalker; it is in these first hours of deep sleep that parents should expect sleepwalking incidents, sleep-talking, bed-wetting, and night terrors. An eight-year-old spends over three hours in this state, while an adolescent will spend two and a half hours. This phase of sleep is not observed in elderly people, for one of the trends of age seems to be a general decrease in the EEG amplitude.

Every older person knows the subjective sign of this change, for he no longer sleeps so deeply. The imperturbable sleep of childhood vanishes by middle age. On the other hand, the proportion of REM in the sleep cycle remains the same throughout life, unless a person has suffered brain damage from cardiovascular or other diseases. Some changes in sleep rhythms are an indication of illness within the maturing and aging brain, but others may only mean that the restrictions of society have loosened their hold on the individual who no longer needs to meet daily schedules of job and family. A retired person is free to nap if he wishes. Elderly patients who complain about insomnia frequently nap by day. An older person's naps may begin to be spaced like the polycyclic sleep pattern of the infant, but studies of blood levels of 17-OHCS in old people in a hospital and in nursing homes showed no abnormal rhythms. These people were, however, forced to live a normal day-night schedule by the institution.

CIRCADIAN RHYTHMS IN OLD AND YOUNG PEOPLE

One preliminary study has compared circadian rhythms in a group of young and a group of older men. Drs. Harold A. Cahn, Edgar Folk, Jr., and Paul E. Huston undertook the difficult job of making measurements at short intervals around the clock. They collected samples every hour over a thirty-three-hour period.

As the next chapter will emphasize, not all body systems reach their daily peak of activity at the same time, but they are coordinated. In this instance the researchers chose indices that would give clues about the coordination of metabolism, kidney activity, and heart function. They carefully selected functions with peaks that are normally close together. Since the peaks of body temperature, urine flow, heart rate, and potassium excretion usually occur within the same four-hour span, it would be possible to see discordance if one or more of these peaks moved out of the usual phase. Three groups of volunteers were studied: young men in their twenties and thirties, a group of healthy older men in their late fifties and sixties, and a depressed group of men from the psychiatric clinic in their late forties to late sixties. Each volunteer was studied individually in a controlled experimental chamber where light was scheduled, food and water measured, and all external disturbances screened out.

Of eleven young men, all but two showed perfect internal synchrony, and two showed a slight dissociation of one rhythm. Of six elderly men, three exhibited dissociation, which is to say there was no neat parallel between the peaks and troughs of their four measured functions. Peak urine flow, for instance, might occur during the afternoon, yet the peak potassium excretion would be way out of phase, occurring at night when urine flow was low. Four out of five depressed patients showed dissociation.

Since potassium may influence the function of the nervous system, the movement of peak excretion out of phase with other functions might be symptomatic of illness. The authors wondered whether this discordance might be one indicator of an early change in timing that could lead to depression. Thus, this study may be a first indication of a tendency toward dissociated rhythms in older people, particularly among depressed older people. A dissociation of physiological rhythms might emanate from many origins—organic illnesses, lack of social pressures and schedules, irregular habits, virus, fever, shock, and emotional stress. All of these may contribute to the increasing load of mental and physical disease that a person suffers as he grows older.

Rhythms and social schedule may be very important in treating geriatric disease. It is possible that internal discordance evolves when a person's activity and rest schedule are not strong enough to force him to follow an unvarying routine of sleep and wakefulness. The typical insomnia of older people grows worse when there is no routine and they nap all afternoon. A greater knowledge of their physiological rhythms might make it easier to time meals and ministrations, to treat them at the pace they need.

RHYTHMS AND CHILD-REARING

Throughout life an individual maintains a pace of work and recreation, of rest and accomplishment in a tempo that is very much influenced by his culture. Children learn this time sense early, pacing themselves in the example of their culture but in a way that is haphazard rather than intentional.

Like adults, some children awaken slowly from sleep and do not begin to function efficiently until midday. Presumably the so-called owls and larks will be discovered to have physiological curves of metabolism and hormone levels that are different in slope and phase like the different temperature curves of good and poor sleepers. Today, anyone who is not an early rising lark is likely to be castigated for his nature. Children have no choice of going to school early or late in the day, and many youngsters who are not alert in early classes are believed to be stupid or inattentive. Restlessness and reverie are punished, although attention spans might instead dictate the length of classes. Just as the findings of psychology have relieved millions of people from the guilt and misery of thinking their problems unique, the study of time structure will alleviate the self-blame of children and adults who doggedly try to conform to the steady pace, steady attentiveness, and steady activity that is "required," despite the regular undulations of their bodies.

Little is known about developing rhythms but already enough has been published to suggest a new view of the many conflicts between parents and young children. The toddler under three does not yet have a circadian rhythm of adrenal hormones, meaning that his time of fatigue, or his most sensitive moments of taste, smell, hearing do not come predictably at the end of the day as they do in the adult. As the studies of Dr. Thomas and his co-workers strongly indicate, the arrhythmic child, the child with irregular sleep hours, food intake, bowel movements is very hard for parents to train. It is obvious why the proverbial struggles of toilet training are worsened in a child who, at age five, has irregular bowel movements.

RHYTHMICITY OF THE INDIVIDUAL TEMPERAMENT

A convergence of studies points to an unavoidable conclusion. The temporal organization—the internal harmony—of the newly arrived infant is a critical dimension in his later adjustment in life. It will dictate the synchrony or asynchrony, the peaceableness or abrasiveness, the tractableness or intractable quality of his relationship with his parents or caretakers. It will dictate how much of his psychological energy must be expended on controlling his unpredictable self. By improving temporal harmony, resynchronizing a child with the twenty-four-hour world around him, it may be possible to transform the lives of people who, until this point in history, were treated wearily or exasperatedly as children with difficult temperaments, paradoxes on earth whose existence was a torture to parents. If an important attribute of this difficult temperament is timing, research on the cause of irregularity should be a high-priority goal. If timing is a crucial element in a miserable childhood, then temperament may not be an axiomatic predisposition that has to be accepted as given. Mistiming may be considered an abnormality like the failure of the body to produce sufficient insulin, and like a car with an improperly tuned motor, a child who is out of kilter with the world cannot be expected to move smoothly. The fact is so obvious that it is almost a tautology. However, it does give parents a new way of evaluating young children and their own style of coping with their children. As further studies of "chrono-pediatrics" begin to appear, it is likely that the pendulum of child rearing will swing away from feeding infants on self-demand, toward providing a routine that will help entrain body cycles, to enhance a baby's ability to be synchronized with the home and school in which he lives.

SCHEDULE OF LIVING IN THE OLD AND YOUNG

The framework of time, the schedule of daily living may be important in training the very young, and equally important in maintaining the very elderly on a circadian schedule. Older people tend to drift away from the hurly-burly of the world, napping intermittently, eating irregularly, and facing long lonely nights

on which they cannot sleep. Yet when they follow a
routine, as in nursing homes, they do not have such
insomnia. Older people tend to revert to the biological
hour, sleeping and waking around the clock. Although
this span of alerting and relaxing may be roughly 90-
120 minutes in the adult, the span of attention and
restlessness is shorter in childhood. Lessons designed
for young children probably should not exceed the
thirty-five-minute span of alerting. Because the clocks
and calendars of schools and most of society are designed for convenience (or economics), it is important
for each individual to learn to detect his own cycles and
schedule his life so as to protect his own health.

TEACHING CHILDREN ABOUT TIME SENSE

Children acquire what is called a sense of time
and they learn to pace themselves in the example of
their own culture, but generally this learning comes
about haphazardly rather than by intention. From an
early age children sense the cycles of change in their
environment. For a while they live almost totally in the
cycle of a day. Each day is its own year. Within each
fraction of the day the attention of the small child is
focussed upon basic biological functions, eating, wetting,
being changed, bathed, allowed to walk on the floor.
Adults rarely help children to anticipate cyclic changes
within themselves. They could be taught to anticipate
excretion and hunger, how to enjoy rather than fear the
changes of falling asleep. Instead of resisting this nightly
process, they might learn to relish the sea of images and
sensations, the convulsive jerks and sudden falling sensation, which can now be anticipated and explained as
the normal neuronal changes that everyone experiences
on the threshold of sleep. The unknown abyss of night
is beginning to be charted, threaded with scientific
guidelines. A child's night can be charted for him ahead
of time. He can learn when to expect dreaming, just as
his parents can know that sleepwalking and talking are
not rare, but often the phenomena of Stage IV sleep.
Indeed, parents often can unwittingly induce an episode

of sleepwalking as they lift an enuretic child to his feet in the early hours of deep sleep, to take him to the bathroom. The predictability of bizarre behaviors, dreams, illusions, whose time course is beginning to be charted, means that the rhythmic events of sleep can be drawn from the terrors of the unknown to the mutuality of human experience. And it is time to share this new knowledge with children.

KNOWING ONE'S OWN RHYTHMS

A child who is taught to listen to his inner rhythmicity receives tools of self-mastery. He can learn to fall asleep easily, to awaken when he wishes, and to experience the fluctuations of his abilities and moods without anxiety. If he knows that he has penile erections with REM sleep, and during the day goes through cycles of attention, and that he may change slightly over days and weeks, these changes will not alarm him. Unfortunately, at the most basic level youngsters are often taught to ignore rather than attend their rhythms. They are taught to eat when they are not hungry, to ignore the signals of colon or bladder that might interfere with convenience. A child who could hear his own drum beat need not be desynchronized from the world around him, but would be able to anticipate his hours of efficiency or sleepiness. He would not expect a machine-like stability of himself, and would not be quick to blame his inner changes upon the world around him.

The child of the future will know a great deal more about himself than his parents and his life will be more integrated. Just as we have seen a kind of continuity between the prenatal development and rhythms after birth, sleep research has repeatedly hinted to us that there is a continuity between waking and sleep, which we simply fail to recognize and use. The sharp discontinuities we have imposed upon ourselves hinder scientific thought, and prevent human beings from maturing with a full sense of their biological and psychological nature. Rhythmicity is a good example. Most people do not know how regular they are, in basic functions such as the amount of food intake, time of sleep, excretion, mood, thirst, and fatigue. Most people do not realize that they dream at regular intervals each night, and that they might allow these inner voices to inform their waking consciousness. They may learn to awaken and recall the pageantry of their dreams, since these evanescent scenarios are relevant to the way we act by day.

DREAM AND SLEEP LEARNING

The Senoi Indians of Malaya are said to have developed an extraordinary transaction between waking and sleeping life. Because they felt that dreams represented a person's struggle to mature and adapt to life, they considered dreams relevant to waking behavior, and important to share. Families would discuss dreams in the morning. If a child recalled hitting his best friend in his dream, his father might give him a present to take to his friend before the potential hostility could damage the friendship. Conversely, the Senoi were said to use hypnotic trances for suggesting and influencing the content of dreams, for they felt that a child who could overcome his fear of a monster in a nightmare might awaken with a greater sense of mastery. Because they shared dreams, the Senoi were able to share inner experience to a degree that would be inconceivable for most Americans. But a greater understanding of each other is bound to occur as we begin to make more contact with ourselves.

From sleep research we have learned that we can be awakened from rapid-eye-movement periods, each ninety minutes or so, and remember dreams. We can alter the content of our dreams by suggestion in waking. Although the current data on sleep learning from recorded lessons is unimpressive it needs to be re-evaluated, for experienced yogins can remember what is said to them in deep slow-wave states of sleep, and many surgeons have been chagrined to discover that patients in deep anesthesia have recalled conversations over their bodies on the operating table. Learning in sleep has been demonstrated only in a minimal way, but problem-solving takes place in sleep all of the time. To greater or lesser extent we all solve problems in sleep, and some people, indeed, have experienced momentous creative discoveries. One of the famous examples is that of Nobelist Otto Loewi, who discovered that nerve impulses were transmitted by means of chemical substances. The idea had been brewing in his mind, and yet he had actually found no way to test his theory.

> The night before Easter Sunday of that year (1920) I awoke, turned on the light, and jotted down a few notes on a tiny slip of thin paper. Then I fell asleep again. It occurred to me at six o'clock in the morning that during the night I had written down something most important, but I was unable to decipher the scrawl. The next night, at three o'clock the idea returned. It was the design of an experiment to determine whether or not the hypothesis of chemical transmission that I had uttered seventeen years ago was correct. I got up immediately, went to the laboratory, and performed a simple experiment on a frog heart ...

The results were unequivocal, and of the utmost importance to all physiology and medicine since. Nerves do not directly influence the heart, but they liberate from their terminals chemical transmitters that cause muscle to contract. When a person's daytime thoughts are focussed on interesting problems, his nights may become a time of fermentation and creativity. Although dreams cannot manufacture genius, everybody can solve problems in sleep, and people are likely to use their sleep more deliberately for problem-solving in the future.

CONTROL OVER WAKING—TIME SENSE

Clearly, sleep is not a unitary state, discrete from the rest of consciousness, but a confluence of rhythms taking us through many levels of altered consciousness. In the future people will sense the rhythmicity of their sleep as a sign of health, perhaps using more care in taking drugs that shift the phase of adrenal rhythms and leave a hangover by day. Like the skilled surfboarder, people will learn the cycles of their inner waves, sensing when to wait, when to ride the crest, when they can fall asleep rapidly, and when they can emerge at the end of a cycle from light sleep, awake. The roughly ninety-minute cycle of rest and activity, of REM and quiet sleep, are like hands of an internal clock. Some people seem to be in touch with these time-givers, perhaps acutely sensitive to very delicate patterns of sensation, for they can awaken from sleep without an alarm clock, and consult their heads to know the hour.

Only recently, Dr. Charles Tart tested ten college students who attempted to awaken from normal sleep, at preassigned times that were randomly distributed throughout the night. Three of the most accurate awakeners were then studied, in the sleep laboratory at the Davis branch of the University of California. Sometimes they awakened with uncanny precision, on target. One subject, who seemed to have misunderstood his instruction, was heard to mumble in his sleep, "Wake at 2:23," and awakened at 2:22 A.M. He had been told to awaken an hour earlier, so this night was not counted as valid for analysis. Nonetheless, it was clear that some people are able to awaken from sleep at preset times, with great accuracy. Yet the stage of sleep did not predict the awakening, and people awakened off target from lightest sleep as well as from other stages. However, as Dr. Tart observed, these people seemed to be relying on a more refined and reliable clock in their brains than the currently known rhythms of sleep would permit. Strangely enough, the faculty for self-awakening has not been studied very extensively, although it should help us to understand the complexities of sleep consciousness, of time estimation, and of the subjective view one entertains regarding the quality of sleep and the amount of time one slept.

A sense of inner time is bound to become more accurate as we pay more attention to internal cycles. Our rhythmicity is a crucial organizing principle of behavior and health, and one sees a relationship between regularity and easy adjustment even in very young babies.

Our habits are part of our health, for we "set" our entire body by the time we go to sleep at night. Regular habits help to keep us together—quite literally. Regular hours of sleep keep us in tune with ourselves, and the hour we select for bedtime calibrates our day with the twenty-four-hour world of society. This unit of twenty-four hours is only one of the periods expressed in our behavior, but it is our most important social time unit. As the hours go around each day, we change visibly. Our mental acuity, the keenness of our senses, our vulnerability to stress or infection, even subtle displays of vitality and idiosyncrasy all show circadian rhythms. If we take a nap in the morning we are likely to have some REM sleep, but in the late afternoon we are more likely to sleep in Stage IV. As the wheel of consciousness shifts from day into night, from waking into deep sleep, we can see how much we change every twenty-four hours. Alert in the afternoon, the telephone call in the middle of sleep can find us groggy and imbecilic, incapable of remembering what is said or answering with better than a *non sequitur*. The contrast between our most alert moments and most feathered obliviousness is only one indication of the rhythmic change taking place in our physiology each twenty-four hours.

4 DAILY CHANGES

That period of twenty-four hours, formed by the regular revolution of our earth, in which all its inhabitants partake, is particularly distinguished in the physical economy of man. . . . It is, as it were, the unity of our natural chronology.

C. W. Hufeland,
THE ART OF PROLONGING LIFE

Time tells me what I am. I change and I am the same.

Mark Strand

4 Daily Changes

EACH DAY OUR FEELINGS AND BEHAVIOR, OUR senses and physiology show a pattern of changes, almost as if they were following a musical score that repeated every twenty-four hours. One's body moves rapidly from day to day in a pronounced rhythm of sleeping, eating, working. If one could peer inside that body, one would see a repeated pattern. Some cells would become more active in sleep, others in waking; some hormones would be more visible in morning, others would appear in the early night. In this complex pattern one could see the normal phase relations of internal body rhythms. The familiar pattern would repeat itself more or less the same until one caught a virus, or suddenly changed one's hours of sleep and waking. Then, like an orchestra out of tempo, there would be a few days of disorder as it readjusted to the beat, restoring its former pattern.

By our own habits and actions—as the sleep reversal studies show—we can maintain the usual phase and harmony of internal rhythms, or disrupt them in a manner that could ultimately damage our health. Although one doubts it in youth, life patterns have an insidious way of reverberating in middle age. At present only the individual himself can listen to his daily changes, attending the regularity and harmony of his activity and physiology as a whole. The effects of ignoring an inner call for rest or stability are not acute. Nobody dies from skipping sleep or leading an erratic life. The effects seem to be cumulative, and may hit later when the person is not expecting them. How and why this happens is the story of the next three chapters.

121

It begins with the unit of a day. This is our primary social unit, and extremely influential in our physiology. Round-the-clock researches on normal people have begun to yield compelling evidence that there is a kind of circadian time map in the body. What we have at present are only the first fragments of a vast jigsaw puzzle. Some data are imperfect and others simply have to be accepted because they cannot yet be explained. Still, these initial fragments suggest the outlines of a time-structure inside us. Ordinarily, for instance, our daily excretion of salt, potassium, and the metabolites of hormones follows an order; this orderly progression in the peak excretion of waste products implies an order in the peak activity of the glandular systems that produced them. Perhaps the sensation of "being all together" that we enjoy when we are feeling our best stems from the fact that our multitudinous functions do not all reach peak activity at once, nor simultaneously subside. They are not random or irregular, but rather they all maintain specific phase relations to each other like players in an orchestra.

A look inside the circadian cycles of our bodies offers a physiological basis for the daily changes we experience in vitality, fatigue, mood, and hunger, and it indicates how our own actions may reverberate in our bodies.

BODY TEMPERATURE

Everyone seems to know that the body temperature drops at night, falling a degree or two during the night, and rising in the morning to a plateau, where it remains until evening. The circadian low temperature point at night is a time often known as the dead spot, a time when people perform badly by most criteria, and would rather be asleep. Although the change of a degree might seem small on a thermometer marking off 108 degrees, it is actually a sizable change, and probably represents a considerable decrease in metabolism. Man, after all, survives within a narrow temperature range. At 94, one is likely to feel stuporous, as a person freezing to death, and at 104–106 an adult is likely to be delirious and in danger of dying. In health we live between 96 and 99, a range of only three degrees. Body cells must burn a lot of oxygen to raise the temperature half a degree in the morning.

One might suspect that body temperature and metabolism decline because we lie still and sleep at night, but this simply isn't so. Sleep or not, the rhythm continues. It cannot be explained by the heat of muscular activity, which dwindles to almost nothing when we sleep, nor can it be explained by the timing of meals. Physiologists have tested these conjectures, varying the meal times of their volunteers, running them on treadmills in some instances, forbidding all exercise in others. They have kept people in bed isolated from time cues, and in each case the body temperature rhythm persisted. Only people who are very sick with encephalitis, cancer, or fevers will show distortions of the rhythm.

Even when volunteers have lived for weeks or months in the isolation of deep caves, stretching their day so that they would be awake twenty-four hours and asleep for twelve (a thirty-six-hour day), records of body temperature continued to show a cycle approximating twenty-four hours. Metabolic processes underlie the temperature maintenance, but it is also controlled by the hypothalamus. This important structure, deep in the primitive regions of the lower brain, plays an important role in regulating body temperature, and when this brain region is damaged the person may suffer from sudden, sharp, recurring fevers. Still, it is not at all clear that the clocking of the circadian temperature rhythm takes place in the hypothalamus, or indeed, in any single location. The body temperature rhythm is extremely reliable, and so easy to measure by rectal or oral thermometer that it has become a most convenient indicator of "time inside the body."

URINE

Next to the rhythms of temperature and nightly sleep, our daily pattern of urination follows the most tangible circadian rhythm. Most people do not realize urine flow is rhythmic unless they occasionally have to get up out of sleep and then they are annoyed. Oddly enough, most of us sleep through each night although we drink as much in the evening as at other times of day. Although children have to be taught to empty their bladders before going to bed, they seem to do it naturally and without being told in the morning. In 1890 a German researcher named Lahr experimented on himself by staying in bed and taking fluids around the clock. He reported that his urine flow remained rhythmic, declining to a nadir during the eight hours when he would ordinarily have been asleep.

The English physiologist Dr. John Mills was among the first to point out that great changes occurred in kidney function around the clock. He and his associates tried to see what influences the rhythm of urine flow and its chemical constituents. They studied fasting people and those who ate meals that were evenly spaced around the clock. They kept people in bed and studied workers on unusual work-rest shifts. By analyzing the contents of the urine obtained at different hours of day and night they could see that the kidney itself functions differently at different hours, showing a circadian rhythm.

The kidneys are huge bean-shaped organs on either side of our spinal column stretching up from the lumbar, or bottom region of the spine, into the central thoracic cavity. They are detoxifying organs, a kind of filtering and secreting system. One measure of kidney function is the rate at which it filters the metabolites and unwanted wastes from the blood and expels them from the body in urine. What we eat and drink is metabolized and converted into energy or tissue or placed in storage. Many remaining by-products are eliminated in water as urine, thus the urine is a "diary" of many body functions. Creatinine, found in urine, is a by-product formed in the breakdown of creatine compounds which supply energy for muscle contractions. It is a final leftover from muscular activity.

In ancient Greece and in medieval times, urine was considered a valuable source of information about the body. In the fifteenth and sixteenth centuries, indeed up until recently, a good physician would carefully sniff the urine of his patient to smell the cause of trouble. Most of the by-products in the urine are not strongly aromatic, although almost anyone could detect by its ammonia-like fragrance whether a person had eaten asparagus. Today, instead of trained noses, we have a huge battery of chemical assays. At each phase of day and night the urine looks different on these tests.

Urine contains ascorbic acid which may be excreted in very large amounts by the adrenals during stress and after drug-taking. Among the most commonly measured elements in urine are electrolytes—sodium, potassium, calcium, and magnesium. These elements can bear electric charge, and are then known as ions, which influence activity in the nervous system. Sodium, potassium, and calcium are believed to be exceedingly important in biasing the properties of membranes of nerve cells, thus influencing the cells' excitability and the manner in which the nerve cells fire. Other cells also require sodium and chloride for retaining water.

The kidney normally clears the metabolic by-products of our many systems of tissue growth, protein utilization, and hormonal output; it also clears the biochemical wastes that indirectly result from our emotions. Since one can sample urine without hurting a person or limiting his freedom, urine analysis has become a means of indirectly observing activity in the nervous system. Many scientists interested in the consequences of stress, but unwilling to disturb their volunteers by taking blood, have examined urine samples, sometimes at four-hour intervals, although usually just once a day.

HORMONES IN URINE

Urine contains traces of activity from a complicated group of glands including the pituitary, the thyroid, the gonads, and the adrenal medulla and cortex. There are more than forty substances secreted by the adrenals alone. Some are considered hormones. Others are precursors, the building blocks of hormones or the metabolites that are the breakdown products of hormonal activity.

A quick rundown of some of these hormones will

indicate what diverse roles they play. Adrenalin is released by the medulla, or core of the adrenals, in moments of fear or danger. A sudden explosive noise, a near fall, or sudden horrifying thought may cause a sensation of fear and energy, the heart pounding faster, the breathing faster, with the aid of adrenalin.

In stress, particularly continued stress, energy for sustained tension is contributed by hormones from the outer layer of the adrenals, the cortex. A message from the pituitary gland causes the cortex to accelerate the production and release of such hormones as cortisone, cortisol, and hydrocortisone. They mobilize body and brain, influencing nerve transmission and releasing extra blood sugar.

Some hormones (such as aldosterone) regulate the amount of salt and of water retained in body tissue. Still other steroid hormones (17-ketosteroids) include the male hormones testosterone and androsterone, also secreted in the testes. Because the signals to secrete and release these many hormones originate in the brain, their waste products are considered very indirect traces of emotions.

RHYTHM OF URINE VOLUME

We do not excrete urine at a constant rate, but in a circadian rhythm, more in morning and midday than at night.

Parents of young children may have difficulty believing that such a rhythm exists, for infants soak their diapers night and day, and some youngsters continue to wet their beds for five or six years. There seem to be many reasons for enuresis, real problems in bladder volume and control, psychological resistances, and even a reluctance to forego certain of the special pleasures of extreme youth. As one seven-year-old was overheard exclaiming to his well-trained brother of five, "How come you don't like it? It feels so nice and warm!" Neither children nor older people appreciate being awakened by their bladders, but the volume at night is nevertheless smaller. The larger amount of urine in daytime and overall circadian cycle may be the result of several other rhythms.

The many constituents of urine each rise and fall in concentration rhythmically, but they reach their peaks at different hours. Generally, a person who retired at 11 P.M. and rose at 7 A.M. would excrete most of his day's potassium between 10:30 and 2:30. Potassium is particularly easy to study because its concentration changes so markedly. Moreover, when a person travels or shifts his schedule of sleep and waking, potassium quickly adjusts. If some of the studies of sodium and potassium rhythms seem to conflict, it is because the people were not on standardized diets and routines. In general, however, sodium and potassium are excreted mostly around midday and afternoon.

These substances can indicate how a person is adjusting to phase shifts, and to living on non-circadian schedules. In the 1950s Dr. Mary Lobban and her associates took a group of volunteers to Spitsbergen, Norway, to live in the continuous light of summer in isolated camps in uninhabited country, with no way of judging time of day. By giving the volunteers "cheating" wristwatches, they were encouraged to live a twenty-one- or twenty-seven-hour day. Adjustment was judged by the phase relationships between body temperature, and certain urine constituents. At the end of six weeks, although some functions seemed to adapt, potassium excretion stubbornly held to a twenty-four-hour rhythm —indicating that there was now a disruption internally. Nobody could conjecture what this might mean in the overall sense of well-being and health. The dissociation of potassium may simply be a clue that some important aspect of the person's physiology had not adjusted to the new "day," and perhaps there would be later ramifications.

We may be unaware of the changing chemistry of our urine, yet it indicates a history of changing emotions and glandular responses to the day's events. These are biochemical traces of feelings superimposed upon the cycle of changes that occur in the body.

BLOOD AND HORMONES

A person changes around the clock from the bone marrow that produces blood cells to the blood itself. Whole blood is composed of many varieties of cells that we divide into white and red. Their relative numbers, the populations of certain kinds of white cells relative to red cells, may give an index of liver or adrenal function and of health or infection. By separating blood samples into their components and counting different kinds of cells under the microscope, it has been possible for researchers to estimate the proportions of different cells that constitute the blood of a normal person at different times of the day. The numbers of blood cells can indirectly indicate what is happening in the cortex of the adrenal glands. Before it became possible to specifically measure the adrenal hormones, patients suspected of adrenal disease were given blood tests, and the white cells known as the eosinophils were counted before and after injections of cortisone. When the white cell count was high it was found that blood cortisol and cortisone would be low, and vice versa.

BLOOD HORMONE RHYTHMS IN ANIMALS

In the early 1950s Dr. Franz Halberg at the University of Minnesota began to show why these diagnostic tests were often in error. He showed that the blood eosinophils rose and fell in a circadian rhythm that nobody had suspected because they believed the human body kept a steady state. Halberg did hundreds of experiments on rats and mice. He demonstrated that light and darkness were exceedingly influential in synchronizing the internal rhythms of the animals, so his colonies were kept on rigid lighting schedules in carefully controlled environments. These became the standard protocols for studying rhythms in animals. In rats one could construct an unvarying cycle of twelve hours light and twelve hours darkness, and observe hormone rhythms with a regularity that is not seen in man. Relative to activity, the rodent's adrenal rhythm is much like ours. However, rats are nocturnal and adrenocortical hormones would reach their circadian peak just at the onset of darkness, before the resting rat began his period of activity. The rhythm was so regular, under controlled conditions, that it could be used as a pointer. By knowing where an animal was on his hormone cycle, it was possible to predict how he would respond to many kinds of stimulation, to stress, cortisone, and drugs. If the schedule of light and darkness were shifted by a few hours, the animal's adrenal rhythm would follow, taking about four days to adjust. Like human beings after sleep reversal, rodents took nine days for their hormone rhythm to return to its usual phase after they went through an inversion of light and darkness.

RHYTHMS IN BLOOD CONSTITUENTS: ANIMALS

Studies by Drs. John Pauly and Lawrence Scheving and their various associates make a very strong point that our blood is not at all the same at different hours of day and night. In 1966 their animal studies showed that the properties of blood went through huge cyclic changes. The animals were living under carefully controlled conditions. One of their findings is likely to interest not only hematologists and physicians, but also teachers, mothers, and all of us. They found that the blood coagulates faster at one time of day than another. Rats showed the shortest clotting time at the end of their activity period, around the time that the lights went on. Lights were turned on at 6 A.M., and the shortest clotting time was at 7:30 A.M. In the middle of the activity period, at 1:30 A.M., blood took 50 percent longer to clot. If this can be translated to man, one would expect the longest clotting time to occur at midday, the shortest clotting time to fall at night.

Some blood rhythms affect immunity to infection. Blood that has been separated into components, or fractionated, contains a number of proteins. Gamma globulin is the fraction of blood serum containing most of the immune antibodies to viruses, bacteria, and other foreign proteins. Scheving and his associates have found that levels of mucoproteins change by as much as 41 percent and gamma globulin by as much as 28 percent each day. In rats the rhythm of gamma globulin showed a peak during the last hours of darkness and a nadir during the first hours of darkness. The animals seem to have the highest levels of gamma globulin during the last six hours of their circadian activity period. If the same kind of pattern is true of human beings, we should find that we are more immune to infections at the end of the day than in the wee hours, or even early morning.

When we stay up late at parties or invert our sleep schedule by east-west travel, we are exposing ourselves to viruses and infection during the very phase when gamma globulin and resistance are lowest. This may account for some of the complaints of colds and infections made by travelers, by students studying for exams and people on rotating work shifts.

ENERGY AND THE LIVER

The changing components of the blood are very much influenced by rhythms in that major organ, the liver. Aristotle thought the liver was the seat of the emotions. Its indirect effects upon behavior can be so dramatic that it is possible to see how the idea arose. The liver detoxifies the metabolites of many foods and drugs. Through its role in the metabolism of carbohydrates and proteins the liver is able to affect the brain. People who have cirrhosis, for example, sometimes act erratic and strange. When the liver is severely damaged, nitrogen from meats and other proteins may form ammonia, and along with other changes, this may interfere with brain metabolism causing sleepiness, coma, or even transient psychotic behavior.

BLOOD SUGAR AND THE LIVER

A more familiar change related to metabolism is the irritability of low blood sugar—hypoglycemia. Married couples sometimes notice a rhythm of quarreling: fights begin around the hour of a delayed dinner, or in the wee hours of morning, both times when blood sugar is low. Some psychiatrists have suspected a relationship between energy metabolism and mental illness, and there are anecdotal reports of sudden changes in the eating behavior of intermittently psychotic patients. Just before they lapse from a period of normal living into acute psychosis, they become restless, anxious, and abandon their normal diet of meat and vegetables for candy, ice-cream, potatoes, sugars, and carbohydrates. Hypoglycemia is sometimes discovered in depressed people, but the symptoms are only worsened by the instinctive attempt to satiate their craving with sweets and starches and poor nutrition. Since we do not eat around the clock, glucose has to be supplied from storage.

Most of our cells synthesize glycogen, a basic substance that is converted into glucose, but only the liver contains stores of glycogen. Therefore it is the liver that regulates blood sugar supplies around the clock. We need glucose at all times. When a person is starving the glycogen is supplied by the liver, and transformed into usable energy for the brain. The storage source is particularly important at night when glucose is not available from food.

Our glycogen levels begin to decline in the late afternoon. The circadian rhythms, first traced in animals, have since been recorded in man. By early morning (3 A.M. and 6 A.M.) a person's liver has used up much of its glycogen. The importance of knowing and anticipating this rhythm is clear in the case of diabetics. These people take insulin, a hormone that enhances the disposal of blood sugar. If they were to take insulin and speed glycogen disposal at a time when there was little reserve in the liver, they might go into shock. When the blood sugar is reduced too suddenly, a person will begin to sweat and feel anxious or dizzy, finally go into a state of convulsions and collapse as the nervous system begins to run out of the huge supply of constant energy that it requires to keep running.

Although the glycogen rhythm has some strong implications for metabolism in body and brain, it is not clear what invisible timer causes the circadian rhythm. Halberg and his associates have pursued the circadian glycogen rhythm to the point of death in animals. They found that the glycogen rhythm of the liver did not depend on food or drink, but persisted in the livers of birds even to the point where they died of starvation and thirst. The absolute level of glycogen dropped, of course, but it continued to fluctuate in a circadian rhythm.

METABOLISM AND HUNGER

When a person fasts for a day or two he becomes aware of this circadian rhythm and of subrhythms of hunger pangs that come every four to six hours. The economy of our metabolism, which may be related to our waxing and waning attention, is revealed in hunger periods. The shortest is about two-to-three hours. Although we tend to speak of hunger in the stomach, studies of appetite and obesity indicate that hunger has little to do with the gut and much to do with the brain. Extremely fat people are sometimes people who are "out of touch" with their own sensations of hunger. By asking groups of normal and obese people to swallow a small instrument that would signal stomach contractions, Dr. Albert J. Stunkard and his co-workers at the University of Pennsylvania found that normal people responded to their periodic contractions, but obese people did not. The rhythmic signals from their bodies no longer serve as guides for eating.

The hypothalamus generates signals felt as appetite, causing us to eat or to stop eating. Animals with damage in the hypothalamus may overeat without cease, becoming hyperphagic and grotesquely fat or they may stop eating altogether if the damage is in a slightly different location. The sugar content of the blood normally provides a signal to the brain indicating whether we need to eat more. The hypothalamus responds directly to the level of blood glucose (from blood circulating in the brain). Because we depend upon liver glycogen as a reservoir of energy, when blood glucose is low, the rhythm of the liver may indirectly influence our desire to eat.

GLUCOSE AND ATP

The daily rhythm of glucose utilization is an important aspect of our smooth functioning. Energy, in the form used by the body, is hard to measure. However, animal studies have indicated that there is a rhythm in the production and breakdown of the body's most fundamental energy unit. This is ATP—adenosine triphosphate. Glucose is the raw material of ATP, and when it is broken apart it releases energy that is trapped to form ATP. Available energy is the *sine qua non* of our existence, determining the rate at which our minds operate, the weight we can lift, our endurance and mood. When a cell requires energy its enzymes break up the bonds holding the huge molecule of ATP together, forming water in a process known as hydrolysis. In the course of hydrolysis one of the phosphates is stripped away, forming ADP (adenosine diphosphate) and releasing energy.

Biologist Dr. Colin Pittendrigh and his associates studied this process of energy release in hamsters, which are nocturnal animals. They found that ATP was being transformed to release energy 25 percent more rapidly when the animals were active than during the day when they rested. This is not surprising. However, it does not mean that with a steady supply of food an animal could use energy at that rate continuously, without resting.

As one looks at different aspects of the body's energy metabolism, it seems evident that the smooth regulation of energy and food supplies is accomplished by a kind of rhythmic intermeshing of functions, and that sleep provides one important part of this rhythm, a time when energy expenditures may decrease. The timing of meals is another part of the over-all daily energy system, for foods are not utilized in the same way at all hours of day and night.

PROTEIN METABOLISM IN HUMANS—TYROSINE

Dieters are frequently urged to make breakfast their heaviest meal, and perhaps weight-watchers should seriously consider the timing of their meals. Recent studies are a first step in the direction of a time-table of food utilization, indicating when proteins and carbohydrates will be most efficiently used. Even at this very early stage in research, the implications are that breakfast may be the most efficiently utilized meal.

Amino acids are the molecules that make up the building blocks of proteins. Beginning in the 1960s, a number of biologists and endocrinologists began to find that the blood levels of such amino acids as tryptophan were fluctuating in a twenty-four-hour rhythm. It happened in chicks, it happened in mice, and the same rhythm occurred in human adults. Tyrosine, one of many amino acids found in the liver, is utilized to make proteins and hormones. Tyrosine is essential in producing melanin, a substance that determines skin color. It is also a component of thyroxine, the thyroid hormone that helps to control body metabolism. Tyrosine may be used in the process of transforming fats or proteins into sugars for body energy.

Endocrinologist Richard Wurtman observed the rhythm of tyrosine levels in six healthy MIT students. Blood samples were taken at three- to five-hour intervals around the clock, and analysis showed that tyrosine concentrations reached their high point at about 10 A.M. and their lowest point from 2 A.M. to 4 A.M. In order to evaluate the effects of exercise, two subjects walked a treadmill from 4 to 4:45 P.M.; their tyrosine levels went up 8 percent. Although the absolute amount of tyrosine in the blood seems to depend upon the amount of protein one eats, the rhythmic fluctuation does not. When eight men were put on a very low protein diet for two weeks, their tyrosine levels fell extremely low, but the rhythmic rise and fall seemed to persist. The greatest rise in amino acid levels occurred when the men were asleep.

The crude proteins in the food we eat are broken down into amino acids in the intestines. Then they are delivered to the liver to be transformed into useful body compounds and distributed to tissue. One way of studying how proteins are utilized, and to understand the timing, is to examine the activity of an enzyme that alters a specific amino acid. Enzymes in the liver show rhythms of activity.

TYROSINE TRANSAMINASE IN RATS

Wurtman became interested in a liver enzyme that works on tyrosine—tyrosine transaminase. Early in his career he had worked with Dr. Julius Axelrod at NIMH. There, in studies of rats, they had discovered that the enzyme was four times more active after nightfall than in morning. The speed with which amino acids are incorporated into cells can be enhanced by adrenocortical hormones. It is probably no coincidence that amino acids are lowest in blood in the hours when these hormones are at their daily peak. Tyrosine transaminase in the liver became far more active when animals were given adrenal hormones. However, its daily rhythm persisted even when the animals were adrenalectomized. The enzyme was not active unless the animal had eaten some proteins.

Wurtman found that he could accelerate the peak of the enzyme activity, merely by cutting the role of the intestines out of the metabolic process—by giving animals amino acids directly instead of proteins. In a long chain of experiments Wurtman was exploring the connected processes that culminate in the daily rhythm in which tyrosine is removed from the blood and converted to its many uses.

The factor of timing in the utilization of protein is likely to complicate research on nutrition or on metabolic diseases. For instance, a researcher may observe that an enzyme quadruples its activity and think he has produced the effect, not realizing that an identical increase occurred in an untreated animal at that hour of day. As Wurtman has written:

> ... time-dependent changes in enzyme activities suggest the existence of parallel alterations in the fates of their substrates. Such alterations may, in turn, explain why drugs are often more potent or toxic at certain times of day than at other hours; they may help us to select the optimal times that food should be consumed

to insure the utilization of the greatest proportion of its protein content for the synthesis of body protein.

TIMING MEALS

Amino acid levels are not significant in themselves. They do not tell us about carbohydrate metabolism. Nor are they related to metabolism in the manner of body temperature. They are only a marker, a signpost, indicating that the intestines have broken protein down into usable subunits, or perhaps that stored fat has been catabolized. Amino acid levels have nonetheless offered a neat way of looking at the relationship between the timing of meals, sleep, and metabolism.

Dr. Ralph D. Feigin and his co-workers measured amino acid levels in six healthy men who stayed in a metabolic ward of an Army research hospital where diet, sleep, and activity were carefully controlled. They saw that the amino acid, methionine, showed a 100 percent increase in the evening. Methionine is found in eggs and other proteins, and helps in the process that prevents an excessive accumulation of cholesterol. All of the eighteen amino acids measured showed circadian rhythm. During one phase of the study, three men consumed very heavy protein test meals at different times of day. Blood samples were taken before the test meal and again repeatedly throughout the next six hours.

Five hundred grams of liver eaten at 8 A.M. led to a very swift rise of amino acid levels, yet the same protein meal at 8 P.M. did not raise blood levels of amino acids above the fasting value! In fact, there was a decrease. Eating a heavy evening protein meal did not prevent the usual nightly drop of blood amino acid levels. Manipulations of diet showed that it did not matter whether a person reduced protein intake to 10 percent of his normal level or doubled it. The blood rhythm of amino acids in each subject remained about the same. A single day of starvation also had no detectable effect on the amino acid concentration nor on the periodicity.

Normally the volunteers slept at night and peak levels

of amino acid were found in the blood between noon and 8 P.M. When they reversed their hours of sleep, the amino acid rhythm rapidly adapted to the phase shift. Some men, however, took six days before their body temperatures shifted into normal phase with their activity rhythm—yet their amino acid rhythm adapted at once. This suggested that the underlying metabolic mechanisms for the body temperature rhythm and the amino acid rhythm may be different.

In attempting to ascertain the source of the amino acid rhythm, the volunteers were put on low protein diets, and were exercised, but there was no detectable change in the rhythmic rise and fall of blood amino acid levels. However, it was clear that to increase the blood levels, it was not the amount of protein that mattered, but the time it was eaten.

In examining the possible blood constituents that might account for the amino acid rhythm, the researchers postulated that thyroid and growth hormone may play a role. Growth hormone is released into the blood from the pituitary during the early part of the night's sleep—in deep Stage IV sleep. Perhaps a lack of this hormone during sleep deprivation may help to explain why people seem to need more protein if they lose sleep.

SLEEP LOSS AND PROTEIN NEEDS

In 1965, Dr. N. S. Scrimshaw studied protein requirement in nineteen MIT students, as they underwent sleep reversal and sleep loss. Protein utilization was measured by the amount of nitrogen excreted in urine. The diet of the students was portioned out so they ate equal amounts four times a day. After forty-eight hours of sleeplessness the nitrogen excretion corresponded to a 12 percent increase in their need for protein. Some students showed a 20 percent increase in nitrogen excretion. Sleep reversal also enhanced nitrogen loss.

The efficiency with which a person utilizes food seems to be related to the regularity of sleep and waking. Since protein is not utilized evenly around the clock, some people need to compensate more than others. People on rotating shifts may require more protein, and many people complain that they overeat when they work at night and then tend to gain weight. Many sleep researchers have remarked on this penalty of night-long vigils in the laboratory. They probably would not gain weight on protein, but their customary foods are not available at night and they tend to eat what is at hand—candy and carbohydrates. There seem to be hours at which almost anything tastes good.

CIRCADIAN RHYTHMS IN TASTE, SMELL, AND HEARING

While it may be efficient to eat a big breakfast, people throughout the world seem to prefer a large midday or evening meal as the social and culinary event of the day. This may have something to do with levels of adrenal hormones that create a rhythm of taste and smell acuity each day. It may be no accident that dinner smells so good, or children's play seems a little louder at night when people cannot tolerate as much noise as in the morning, or that lights may feel irritatingly bright; sensitivity varies during the day.

Our sensory keenness probably fluctuates in a circadian rhythm, judging from the work of a group of endocrinologists, led by Dr. Robert I. Henkin at the National Heart Institute. The work was originally oriented around the peculiarities of patients suffering from insufficient output of adrenal cortical hormones, either because of Addison's disease or other pituitary problems. Such people often suffer from extreme fatigue and sometimes crave salt. This is curious in the light of some earlier research. Physiologist Curt P. Richter had found that rats without adrenals would avoid a salt solution that normal rats would drink. They did not dislike salt, he discovered, but they had become so sensitive that a tiny amount of salt was too much for them. Thus it seemed that a lack of adrenal hormones might heighten taste sensitivity.

In 1962 Henkin and his associates compared taste acuity in normal people and in patients with Addison's disease. The first thing in the morning, after the person rinsed out his mouth, drops of distilled water were placed on his tongue. The water contained tiny but increasing amounts of salty, bitter, sweet, or sour substances. How many increments of the taste substance had to be added to the water before the person detected that it was different from plain distilled water? There was no ambiguity in the results. Without medication the patients with adrenal insufficiency were at least 150 times more sensitive than the normal people. If they were given a control hormone (DOCA), it had no effect on the acuity of taste, but after treatment with cortisone their taste sensitivity dropped to normal.

Not only does the person with Addison's disease taste and smell more sensitively than a normal person, he also hears sounds inaudible to the normal person. An "average" person can hear low tones of about fifty cycles per second, a rumble, and tones as high as 15,000 cps, just lower than a dog whistle. As a person grows older this frequency range shrinks, and most older people cannot hear much over 10,000 cps. However, people with Addison's disease detect sounds softer than can be heard by a normal person of the same age, and older patients hear much higher frequencies than normal people of their age. In short, the person with low adrenal cortical steroid output seems to be unduly sensitive to all sensory stimuli. Addisonian patients are easily disturbed by noises and feel uncomfortable in a normally noisy room. However, their range of hearing and detection of soft sounds diminished to normal after they took carbohydrate-active steroids such as cortisone.

There was a strange discrepancy between the acuity of the Addisonian patient and his inability to discriminate. When asked to rate the loudness of different sounds or repeat lists of words spoken through a distortion filter, these patients did surprisingly badly. They could not reliably repeat word lists, recognize filtered speech, judge loudness, nor discriminate between a steady and a warbling tone as well as normal people. Deficiency of adrenal hormones rendered them more acute in detecting sounds, but they lacked an auditory sense of direction, and could not accurately localize sounds. Their entire performance became normal after they were treated with carbohydrate-active steroids. These steroids seemed to influence the nervous system in a way that affected the integration of sensory stimuli.

Dr. Henkin and his co-workers soon found that these adrenal steroids existed in brain tissue and in the spinal cord in concentrations that could permit an impact upon nervous activity. When they removed the adrenals from cats, the brain levels of the steroids fell. Did the adrenal hormones affect the speed of nerve conduction? Cats, normal humans, and patients with adrenal insufficiency were given a slight shock to the ulnar nerve at the elbow, and muscle contraction in the hand was timed. Surprisingly, adrenalectomized animals and patients reacted much faster than their normal counterparts, but after treatment with carbohydrate-active steroids, Addisonian patients responded like their normal counterparts.

Once again it was clear that a dearth of adrenal corticosteroids seemed to accelerate nerve transmission. The moment Addisonian patients were brought up to normal levels of adrenal hormones, the ulnar nerve slowed down. At first this finding seemed to be a paradox, or perhaps an error.

Further studies corroborated that conduction was faster in the axons or nerve fibers of adrenalectomized cats than in intact creatures. However, conduction across the synapses, the tiny gaps between the contacts of one nerve cell and another, was slower. Microscopic electrodes on both sides of the synapse began to reveal how adrenal hormones might mediate the speed of nerve transmission. In a normal cat, the nerve impulse was conducted at the right speed for the message to be integrated. When the cat's adrenals were removed, the axon conducted more rapidly and the synapse more slowly than normal, so that signals were no longer processed at proper speeds for cell-to-cell communication. This might explain why Addisonian patients are overly sensitive to taste, smell, and other sensory stimulation, yet have difficulty judging, discriminating, and integrating this sensory information. To a very minor degree this is what happens every day to a normal person as his adrenal hormones rise and fall in circadian rhythm.

Every four hours and around the clock for three days, the NIH team tested taste, smell, hearing, and nerve conduction velocity in normal volunteers. Sensory keenness reached its peak around 3 A.M. (the time of lowest cortisol levels) in people who were going to sleep at 11 P.M. After 3 A.M., depending upon the person's sleep routine, sensory acuity took a sudden drop as steroid levels began to rise, and hormones spurt into the blood around the time of rapid-eye-movement sleep. During the day the steroid levels decline. Around 5-7 P.M. acuity increases and discrimination declines. Food may taste better, but the decline in hormones is also felt as fatigue. Overstatements of the nervous system seem to send loud music or the screech of children's voices directly into the brain at evening, so along with sensory keenness may come irritability. In the daily waxing and waning of these interior substances that bias emotional responses, one may glimpse the way in which an unseen time-structure of the body begins to set patterns of behavior and habit.

Evening fatigue and changing abilities do not all originate in the availability of adrenal hormones. Many rhythmic changes occur in the nervous system during the day.

CIRCADIAN RHYTHMS IN THE BRAIN: EEGs

Some of these other changes have been observed in continuous brain wave tracings. Certain brain wave patterns recur in waking and sleep as if they were "background states" of consciousness. Very slowly changing, high-amplitude waves resembling Himalayan peaks are typical of deep sleep but also appear occasionally in waking. They occur mainly toward late afternoon and in the early part of the night in a circadian cycle. Continuous recordings from rhesus monkeys have been analyzed by Dr. Halberg, who found distinct circadian rhythms in their EEGs. Human tracings have been difficult to obtain outside of the hospital EEG laboratory because of a lack of miniature equipment that could transmit brain waves to a receiver recorder while a person moved around.

In 1965 Soviet scientists published a biotelemetry study led by Dr. D. Ivanov. EEGs were continuously recorded from volunteers as they went about their usual business of work and recreation. Upon analysis the researchers found a circadian modulation of the frequency and amplitude (the bioelectric intensity) of the brain-wave rhythms. Although alpha rhythms (nine to thirteen cycles per second) occur around the clock, they are not distributed evenly, nor are they exactly the same in frequency. By absolute count there were more alpha rhythms during sleep than in waking, and the Soviet study concluded that the rhythm was faster around 5 P.M. than in early morning. While some scientists have surveyed the brain-wave patterns, or the activity of single nerve cells in the brain, others have sought insight into our timing through clocking the slowly shifting chemistries of different brain regions. They have concentrated on certain substances that have broad effects on behavior and emotion.

BRAIN CHEMISTRY

Norepinephrine (also known as noradrenaline), serotonin, dopamine, and histamine are often referred to as biogenic amines, that is, biologically potent molecules of the amine family, which are nitrogen compounds structurally related to ammonia and to the more complex molecules that form protein. Serotonin appears to be among a number of amines that help to induce sleep. Norepinephrine, which is thought to be produced throughout the nervous system, is related to adrenaline. Histamine, which causes reddened tissue in allergies, has an as yet unknown role in the brain, possibly helping to promote wakefulness. Norepinephrine is ubiquitous, acting like a messenger in the tiny synapse between one nerve cell and another. Nerve cells fire a chemical molecule from their many branches to cross the synaptic gaps to other cell receivers thus interacting with receptor nerve endings. After its brief errand, the chemical transmitter quickly vanishes.

There are about ten billion neurons in the central nervous system of an adult human being. Each cell has about a hundred receiving synapses and a hundred projections that terminate on other cells. This astronomical network is the key to all we experience as life, our survival functions, and our feelings. It is not known whether neurotransmitters merely grease the path for a bioelectric code of impulses, or whether they modulate the frequency and extent of nerve firing. However they perform their roles they have a pervasive effect throughout the brain and in the peripheral nervous system.

In the mid-1960s a number of researchers began to see that the levels of important brain amines were fluctuating in a predictable way. Drs. Alexander Friedman and Charles A. Walker sampled brain tissue from rodents around the clock and found evidence of circadian rhythmicity. In an area known as the midbrain they found that norepinephrine and histamine reached peaks during the animal's waking period, a time when serotonin levels were at their lowest. Serotonin was at its peak during the animal's rest, suggesting that these substances might play different roles in stimulating states of consciousness. The complexity of chemical roles in regulating consciousness has become apparent as a number of scientists have contributed to a time map of brain chemistry. A remarkable survey of twenty-five regions of the brain and spinal cord of cats was accomplished by a New York group led by Dr. Donald Reis. They found that each region was very specific. Some regions had circadian rhythms, but other regions had twelve-hour rhythms. Moreover, a substance might be at its peak in one region and its trough in another. Usually either norepinephrine or serotonin showed a cycle in a given location but not both; in a few cases where both amines fluctuated they were out of phase. This reciprocal rhythm was visible in regions of the hypothalamus that control body temperature regulation and may offer one clue to our daily temperature rhythm.

CIRCADIAN SYSTEM OF THE RAT
TIMING: EXTERNAL ACROPHASE (ϕ)

SITE	VARIABLE
ADRENAL GLAND	Corticosterone
	Pantothenate
BRAIN	5-Hydroxytryptamine
	Norepinephrine
LIVER	Glycogen
	Tyrosine Transaminase
PINEAL	5-Hdroxytryptamine
URINE	Chloride Excretion
	Potassium
	Sodium
	Urea
	Histamine
	Volume
SERUM	Alkaline Phosphatase
	Cholesterol
	Corticosterone
	Phosphate
	Urea
	Uric Acid
BLOOD	Neutrophils
	Eosinophils
	Lymphocytes
MOUTH	Mitosis (retromolar mucosa)
WHOLE BODY	Temperature, i.p.
	Motor Activity
	Feeding
	Susceptibility to pentobarbital

95% Confidence Interval

BY PERMISSION OF FRANZ HALBERG   12-hr. L Span   12-hr. D Span

Various biochemicals and physiological functions reach their daily peaks (represented by dots) at different times. This diagram shows the distribution in a laboratory rat living on a schedule of twelve hours of light (represented by the unshaded section) and twelve hours of darkness (represented by the shaded section). Since the rat is nocturnally active, and man is diurnal, one would generally expect to see that man's distribution of peaks is reversed with respect to daylight and darkness.

The specific regional rhythms of these substances suggested that the rhythms of brain areas may be regulated independently, and may influence rhythmic fluctuations in the activity of cells and the amount of nervous discharge.

What organization integrates these many rhythmic changes into the harmony that we experience as a steady sense of being? It is not yet known. Nonetheless, some magnificent and subtle system allows us to change gradually each day without sudden jolts into sleep or hyperactivity. Along with alternations of activity and sleep, a continuum of vital functions is intermeshed, leaving their gradually changing signs in the blood and urine, in our levels of hormones, and in the utilization of food. Adrenal steroids and growth hormone, cycles of enzyme activity of energy metabolism, cell division, and tissue repair wax and wane in a manner that is integrated with sleep and waking, and with essential rhythms of psychological function such as the bizarre and flamboyant cycles of nightly dreaming that seem to be important in memory storage and our ability to cope. A masterful organization intermeshes these many functions with our schedule of activity, increasing body temperature, brain metabolism, and energy by day, yet preventing the shocking confusion that we would feel if mistimed dream periods were to break through our waking consciousness. This is the delicate balance we know as sanity or normal health.

IMPLICATIONS FOR DAILY LIVING

Normal health depends upon a harmony in the networks of body and brain. This chapter has touched on a few of the circadian rhythms that may influence the way we feel and behave. The daily rhythm of adrenal hormones is probably very central, modulating our ability to respond to stress, and our sensory perception. The social custom of eating late in the day may be related to heightened taste sensitivity at a time of declining steroid levels. However, this is not the best time for a person to make fine discriminations, for his ability to integrate his perceptions is diminishing with steroid levels. A sizable literature indicates that job performance is best during the time of day when temperature is high. Most people sense this. But some people have been befuddled into thinking they should be the same smiling, efficient functionaries at all hours. We are not the same at all hours.

The relationship between sleep habits, stress, and nutritional needs is of interest to most Americans. The little data at hand suggest that sleep loss, stress, and phase shifting may cause a person to need more pro-

tein—although that is not what most people eat when
they are keeping late hours. Moreover, it appears that
food is utilized more efficiently early in the day, yet
Americans eat almost 80 percent of their food after
6 P.M. Food is also metabolized more readily when in-
gested in small amounts, yet most of us eat large meals,
the largest of them all at night. Amino acid levels, as
we have seen, respond not to how much protein a person eats, but his timing. At a point when Americans
are considering the types of foods they eat and their
role in such diseases as atherosclerosis, it may be op-
portune to reconsider the distribution of foods in the
course of the day.

We do not need to wait until there has been enough
research to construct a time map of the body, for each
person with a little introspection can begin to sense his
own inner timing—hunger contractions, the chill of
dropping temperature, the quality of fresh vigor, emotional ebullience or anxiety and irritation. An hour-by-
hour evaluation of mood, alertness, and sensations will
begin to give each person the shape of his daily changes.
One can sense rhythms in digestive enzymes, glands,
waste-disposal, and responsiveness of one's senses, and
begin to see how the most innocuous habits of eating
and sleep affect this vast physiological maze within the
skin. Many people have been taught to feel no kinship
with the remarkable physiological service organization
that pulsates within, and many people are frightened
by the sight of blood or internal organs. Still, one can
listen to one's own daily round of changes without
opening up the body to look.

In health we are being transformed by circadian
cycles. Our reaction to drugs and to stress, the intensity
of pain in illness, and symptoms of allergy or disease
also occur rhythmically, determined in part by the normal cycles within our physiology. The circadian rhythmicity of the body sheds new light on metabolic diseases
such as diabetes, and on cancer. What does it tell us
about allergy, drugs, or the manner in which mental
and physical illnesses evolve? The next three chapters
discuss the way timing enters into the development,
symptoms, diagnosis, and treatment of illnesses.

5 RHYTHMS OF SYMPTOMS AND CELLS

Not chaos-like, together crushed and bruised,
But, as the world harmoniously confused:
Where order in variety we see,
And where, though all things differ, all agree.
Alexander Pope

So in one place the blood stops, in another it
passes sluggishly, in another more quickly. The
progress of the blood through the body proving
irregular, all kinds of irregularities occur.
Hippocrates

5 Rhythms of Symptoms and Cells

IF YOU HAVE A PEPTIC ULCER AND YOU FORGET to eat or drink something to coat your stomach, you can expect to feel pains at about the same time each day. Few ulcer patients who have had this experience realize that the regularity of the pain is a favorable sign. A Swedish doctor, M. Arborelius, noticed that patients with ulcers or stomach cancer complained of hungerlike pains that were suppressed by eating a meal. However, the pain seemed to come at a regular hour in ulcer patients, while it occurred capriciously and irregularly in patients with stomach cancer. In a study of some 200 patients, Arborelius found that almost all of the cancer patients and none of the ulcer patients showed irregular rhythms of sodium chloride excretion. Irregularity seemed a possible clue to cancer. No doctor relying on X-ray diagnoses would have been as accurate in separating these patients as a doctor who merely listened to their complaints of pain and made a note of the hours, since the pain of ulcer patients was regular, while that of cancer patients was unpredictable.

Sometimes the symptoms of an illness may reflect exaggeration or change of a normal rhythm. There seems to be good reason why people with peripheral artery disease may be awakened from sleep with acute pain. As Dr. V. Bartoli has found, blood circulation in their arms and legs shows a pronounced circadian rhythm, with a low point between midnight and 4 A.M. At this time their tissues are starved for oxygen, which inevitably causes pain.

Great clinicians from Hippocrates' time to our own have made note of the regularity or irregularity of symptoms. Dr. Werner Menzel of Hamburg was probably one of the first modern physicians to keep time charts of his patients' symptoms. He would jot down the peaks and troughs of body temperature, urine constituents, and complaints. As he observed, many sicknesses involved disordered timing. Instead of showing a twenty-four-hour rhythm, a child with lymph disease had a twelve-hour body temperature rhythm. People with liver diseases often showed their peaks of urination and temperature at night instead of morning. One very depressed patient with asthma had body temperature peaks at 6 A.M. and noon, and urinary components peaked in the opposite of the normal rhythm. Dr. Menzel, well ahead of his time and well ahead of medical technology, began to suspect that a desynchronization among circadian systems in the body could eventually explain the recurrent symptoms.

STRESS ILLNESSES

A great many common illnesses—ulcers, hypertension, atherosclerosis, asthma, depression, and even arthritis—are sometimes referred to as "stress" diseases. And these are only a handful in a long roster of stress illnesses. The concept was originated in the early 1950s by Hans Selye, who showed that the body of a mammal would respond to stress by mobilizing a defensive system involving the pituitary and adrenal glands. The adrenal hormones suppress inflammation and prevent tissue damage, enhance metabolism and make extra energy available to the body. Activation of the adrenal glands can be caused by burns, temperature extremes, disease, and drugs, but also by a gamut of emotional situations, by fear, anxiety, crowding, loud noises, or simply exposure to a new situation. The animal in a new cage, the child in a new school, the stranger at a party all show the same quiet, intense orienting to their surroundings, with signs of tension. Messages from hypothalamus to pituitary and from pituitary to adrenals stimulate the synthesis and release of glucocorticoids. Ultimately, when the hormone levels in the blood are sufficient, the hypothalamus responds by signaling the pituitary to stop its messages to the adrenals. This adaptive reaction, a feedback device, turns on whenever one worries, when a child is ill, or when one contemplates changing jobs. The stress need not be unpleasant. It may be the thrill of an exciting movie, anticipation, hilarity. At some point, however, in a life of continual changes and continual exposure to crowds or to new experiences, this adaptive system may begin to deteriorate. What follows is an illness, with tissue damage and perhaps emotional breakdown, too. How does the healthy adaptive response begin to erode? One possibility is that desynchronization occurs among body rhythms and that one or more move out of phase with the activity cycle of the patient. Timing may deteriorate, losing some of its precision, like an undisciplined orchestra.

Night-long studies have recently shown that the abnormal gastric secretions of ulcer patients are exceedingly badly timed: they come when the stomach is empty. They occur at the times of increasing levels of adrenal corticosteroids. Adrenal cortical hormone levels spurt up in the blood of sleeping people in a rhythm that is almost in phase with REM sleep.

Anthony Kales and his associates found this periodicity of gastric secretion in patients with duodenal ulcers. The fifteen- to thirty-minute collections of gastric secretion, taken from stomach tubes, indicated that ulcer patients secreted three to twenty times as much as normal people. Moreover, their abnormal secretions were preponderantly in phase with REM sleep, while normal secretions had no perceptible rhythm. REM sleep may represent a rhythm of excitation within the hypothalamus, a portion of the brain governing many survival functions. It is interesting to note that a few other night-time symptoms such as migraine headaches also seem to cluster around REM sleep. In attempting to understand illnesses that may arise after emotional stress, many researchers have explored the adrenal hormone system.

Until the late 1940s most endocrinologists believed the body was homeostatic and normally in a state of true constancy—an assumption that still influences the norms of diagnosis, treatment, and considerable laboratory research. Throughout the 1950s Halberg's laboratory had made it amply clear that a healthy man on a regular sleep schedule, or an animal on controlled lighting and feeding schedule, showed an unmistakable circadian rhythm in adrenal hormone levels. Moreover, their ambitious studies displayed the phase relationships among many internal rhythms. For instance, there is about a ninety-minute lag between the daily peak of body temperature in a person, and the early morning peak of adrenal hormones (17-hydroxycorticosteroids) in the blood. If the individual showed his peak temperature at the usual time of morning, but his adrenal peak came two hours later, one might say that the two rhythms were out of phase—that he was internally desynchronized. In a very rough way, people who are depressed may be suffering from such a desynchronization.

DEPRESSION

There are many kinds of depression, which, put together, compose one of mankind's most dreary and pitiable miseries, particularly common among middle-aged and older people. During any year there are 90–125,000 Americans in hospitals, so severe is their illness, while another 200,000 are being treated in clinics and at home. For these very ill people life is a hopeless prison sentence, and they themselves feel worthless and unloved. Whether they act agitated and anxious or inert and apathetic, a great many attempt suicide.

In 1967 the Public Health Service published a survey of a large population of normal adults: about a third of the men and half of the women said they felt depressed. Indeed, most adults in our culture have been depressed by frustrations at work, financial catastrophe, or the illness of someone very much beloved. Culture is important in this group, for the same symptoms do not occur in supportive African tribes. Nonetheless some individuals react intensely and sink into a limbo in which they cannot concentrate or enjoy life. They are said to suffer from reactive depression, while many people show a distress that is thought to begin with an inner biochemical flaw. Clinicians have conjectured that these people may react to internalized stress, resulting in an unusual output of adrenal hormones.

Psychiatric literature contains many studies but little clarity on the relation of adrenal hormones to depression. Unwilling to intensify the anguish of sick people, doctors could not take frequent blood samples, so in the past urine was often collected instead of blood. Chemical analyses have so developed in the last year that it is now possible to assay a drop of blood, blood samples from a tiny catheter can be taken every fifteen minutes around the clock without the patient noticing. Using such methods, Dr. Edward Sachar and his colleagues at Montefiore Hospital in New York have been obtaining a new view of depression. The blood levels of adrenal hormones may reflect emotional arousal—and elevated levels are seen in some agitated patients, in normal people who are anxious, but not in apathetic depressed patients. In many instances high levels of steroids have indicated the intensity of a person's panic and misery, giving warning of intended suicide. There is a mood rhythm among depressed patients that also parallels adrenal steroid levels. Typically they feel most abysmal in morning. When they first awaken their gloom is impenetrable, their mental processes are blunted and slow, and if they have body pains, these too will be more intense.

In round-the-clock blood analyses of two normal people and three very anxious patients, there were blatant hormonal differences. The normal person showed a quick spurt of cortisol into the blood, which rapidly vanished, leaving no hormone detectable. The patients never showed a "zero" level; there was always some adrenal hormone in their blood. Moreover, they secreted more. The normal person secretes most of his cortisol during the last hours of sleep; the patients secreted during the day and evening. Depressed patients usually suffer from terrible insomnia. In the terminology of sleep research this insomnia consists of abnormal sleep cycles, irregular REM, loss of Stage IV sleep, and frequent awakenings. It is during these awakenings that cortisol may shoot into the blood.

The recent blood studies have shown that some depressed patients have no detectable circadian rhythm of hormones. Others have perplexing rhythms: one man showed his highest levels at 11 P.M., when a normal person would be approaching his lowest levels. The psychiatrists working together at Montefiore have been nonplussed by their evidence. Even after shock treatment when a patient was recovered and feeling well again, the levels of blood cortisol were abnormal. Studied after discharge from the hospital, when subjectively the people felt good, the hormone levels were still abnormal. It appears that the endocrine system takes several months to recover.

Because the glucocorticoids are so important in metabolism and nerve transmission, it is possible to imagine that an abnormality in the circadian rhythm, not to mention sustained abnormal levels, would affect every aspect of a person's functioning, blunting his senses, disturbing the rhythms of food absorption, energy distribution, tissue repair, and memory, reverberating throughout the individual like a state of dissonance.

Without further studies, one can only infer that these patients must have been desynchronized internally. Is a disturbance of the internal time structure the start of such an illness?

A POSSIBLE CAUSE OF DEPRESSION

The harmony of internal phase relations can only be inferred if round-the-clock samples are taken from different body systems, or measures of changing function in organs such as the heart or kidney. Most researchers have not done this, and as the following study shows, there are many difficulties in doing time-series studies with people. If the reader begins to notice that the peak excretion of potassium, for instance, seems to occur early in the day in one study, later in afternoon in another, and at night in yet another, he is noticing the knots and snarls of a science that has not yet established a methodology. The following study points up some of these inconsistencies, and one must remember that the people studied were living on different schedules beforehand, without undergoing uniform scheduling, and that they were sedentary and isolated. Nonetheless, this was one of the first attempts to compare inner cycles for possible signposts of inner harmony or of rhythms moving out of phase with one another.

The work was done at the University of Iowa, by Paul Huston, Edgar Folk Jr., and Harold A. Cahn. They compared a group of healthy young men in their twenties with healthy older men and a group of older depressed men. Each person was acclimated to an isolation chamber, then studied intensively for thirty-three hours. His heart rate was telemetered by a small radio capsule in his undershirt, and he received food and water at regular intervals. The circadian rhythms of heart rate, urine flow, potassium excretion, and body temperature were recorded.

Ordinarily the adrenal corticosteroids will come to their peak in the blood before temperature rises, which precedes the peak urine and potassium excretion. Here the peaks of temperature, heart rate, and potassium excretion typically occurred between 5 P.M. and 9 P.M., and urine flow reached a peak slightly later. Some people showed peaks in late afternoon, while others showed peaks between 7 P.M. and midnight. Since they had all been living different schedules before they came to the laboratory, the subjects were in different phases. However, the normal individuals were remarkably consistent. Some of them were again studied after a day, a week, a month, and in one case, a year. They did not change. The phase relationships were remarkably stable in the healthy individuals. However, the depressed patients seemed to show potassium excretion that was out of phase with urine volume, perhaps a hint that dissociation of timing rather than some absolute biochemical level might be important in depression.

What is cause and what is effect in this ailment of

melancholy, that seems to leave so many people in a state of unhappy frenzy, or in suspended animation, unable to be fully engaged in their lives?

ADRENAL HORMONES AND HEART DISEASE

Ironically, it is the computer that may finally allow psychiatrists to glimpse the answer by seeing how all the factors of biochemistry and mood fit together. Depression is only one of many stress illnesses in which there are signs of abnormal adrenal hormone rhythms. Many of the researchers who seek to understand ulcers, colitis, and hypertension have studied adrenal rhythms. However, there are other groups of adrenal hormones than the ones that influence carbohydrate metabolism.

Aldosterone is a steroid hormone that causes the body to excrete potassium and retain sodium, thus enhancing water retention. Excessive aldosterone is sometimes found in people with high blood pressure or hypertension. Dr. Frederick Bartter and Catherine S. Delea have studied a number of patients with ailments we think of as heart or circulatory disease. Patients who suffered from aldosteronism differed from normal people in relatively subtle ways. Most clinics would not have detected that their urinary excretion of aldosterone was out of phase with the excretion rhythm of normal people. In collaboration with Halberg, Bartter and Delea analyzed the data by special methods, revealing a temporal disturbance that may be imperceptible to most clinical observation. They have indicated that new methods of clinical diagnosis are essential, and this often means round-the-clock measurements. A single reading of blood pressure, for instance, may allow a hypertensive person to appear normal. They found patients who had normal blood pressure at 8 A.M., but by 6 P.M., the time when normal blood pressure reaches its daily peak, these patients had high blood pressure. Any insurance examiner who judged a person from a single blood pressure reading around 10 A.M. could easily misjudge him.

Circadian rhythms may be an important sign of body

integrity. Perhaps there beats within us a vestige from our dim beginnings on this rotating planet, a rhythm that meant survival to early plants and creatures. Whatever their origins, circadian rhythms provide a yardstick of harmony within the body's functions, from the relatively gross fluctuation of blood pressure down to the microscopic convolutions of cells.

RHYTHMS OF CELL DIVISION

For many decades it has been observed that the cells of the body do not divide at an even rate at all times of the day, nor is the rate the same in all seasons of the year. In 1917 a Dutch physiologist saw that cells in the cornea of a two-day-old kitten divided most rapidly around 10:30 P.M. and least rapidly at 10:30 A.M. Later it was noticed that cells from the human prepuce skin divided in a circadian rhythm. In the 1950s in a study that has become a prototype for laboratories elsewhere, Halberg and his associates began tracking circadian rhythms of cell division in the ear skin and mouth tissues of mice and hamsters under controlled conditions.

The most pronounced circadian rhythms occur in cells known as renewal populations, surface tissue such as skin, ears, mouth, tongue, eyes, and hair that are in constant contact with the outer world. Eroded and damaged each day, they must be replaced at a rapid rate. In adult humans, for instance, skin cells divide mostly between midnight and 4 A.M. when a person normally is asleep. This might be one of the important functions of sleep with its immobility and the changes in metabolism and hormones. The rate at which new cells are produced roughly equals the rate of loss. It can be observed by watching mitosis, or by counting radioactively labeled cells after a radioactive substance known to be used in cell replication is injected into tissue.

Drs. Lawrence E. Scheving and J. E. Pauly used radio autographs to track circadian rhythm in the division of cells of the corneas of rats. The peak of labeling and therefore of mitosis occurred around noon at the midpoint of the animals' rest period. However, when animals were kept in constant light for over two weeks, the mitosis rhythm disappeared and there was significant harm, such as the disappearance of the rods from the retina.

Biological and physiological rhythms seem to be calibrated to rhythms in the natural environment, and the biological potency of light is such that no creature can be considered a closed system.

TIME STRUCTURE OF THE LIVER

Halberg and his associates have attempted to discover how the rhythms of cell division are organized into organic function. Many of their studies of cell division rhythms used liver tissue because the liver is a large and influential organ that regenerates very swiftly after surgery. A twenty-four-hour rhythm of glycogen in the liver had been known for some years. By injecting a radioactive phosphate, a substance used by dividing cells, the researchers could watch the relative uptake of this phosphate and thus track the rate of cell mitosis. Bit by bit they began to uncover the microscopic production line that underlay the circadian rhythms of glycogen and other liver substances.

DNA AND RNA SYNTHESIS

Halberg and his associates looked at different components of liver tissue, down to the tiny microsomes and events in the nucleus of each cell. There in the most fundamental level, they found a twenty-four-hour rhythm in the rate at which cells were synthesizing DNA and RNA. DNA (deoxyribonucleic acid, a huge, twisted strand of a molecule) is believed to be the fundamental unit that bears the pattern of chromosomes, transmitting hereditary characteristics from one generation to the next and giving each cell in the body its distinctive pattern. RNA (ribonucleic acid, another large molecule found in the nucleus and also in the cytoplasm around the nucleus) among other things appears to regulate the rate at which each kind of protein is produced in tissue.

The Halberg laboratory found the RNA and DNA rhythms were not precisely in phase. One might expect that RNA and DNA would be most active at times when many cells were preparing to divide. Moreover, one would not expect to find RNA and DNA at their maximum synthesis simultaneously. Judging by phosphorus uptake, the DNA activity arrived at its peak just as RNA activity was dropping to its nadir. Since the work in the Minnesota laboratory, many scientists have added complementary information about rhythms of mitosis in nucleic acids.

CELL DIVISION

The Minnesota laboratory began to map the phases of DNA and RNA synthesis in relation to the phase of cell division. In turn, these mitosis rhythms could be related to rhythmic increases and decreases in the levels of substances such as fats and sugars in the liver. Cell activity in the livers of young animals showed a cycle. For about eight hours there was a stage when most of the dividing cells were completing their final step; in this eight-hour interval RNA and phospholipids were at their peak. Next came another eight-hour stage with peak DNA synthesis. Following this period was the eight-hour period of peak cell division. In the first four hours of this span, glycogen levels reached their daily high point. Thus, the various stages of cell metabolism and mitosis in the liver follow a reproducible sequence that can be timed by reference to a lighting cycle and reliably detected.

In this mapping of rhythms one sees a biological mechanism that permits smoothness and continuity in the functioning of an organism through an overlap of one process after another. Populations of cells do not all begin DNA synthesis at once; mitoses are not begun in unison. Instead, there is a trend provided by rhythmic change in which numbers of cells are behaving the same way at roughly the same time. Gradual rhythmic shifts allow the body to change without suffering the great disadavantage of discontinuity.

As the Minnesota team extended its analysis to the cells of the kidney, adrenal cortex, skin, pancreas, small intestine, and to the pituitary, hypothalamus, and other portions of the brain, they inevitably found circadian rhythmicity. There were specific sequences of phase relationships among cellular rhythms within an organ, but not all organs showed the same pattern. In some tissues, such as liver or skin, maximum cell division took place during the animal's sleep, while in other tissues, the adrenal gland, for example, peak cell division occurred during the period of high-motor activity.

BIOPSY

This is relevant for medical laboratory work. If tissue is taken from the body at one hour of the day, the fixative and stain (the chemical that is used to make it visible under the microscope) will not act in the same way that it acts if that tissue is taken from the same individual at a different hour. Tissue changes so considerably around the clock that histochemical substances will interact with the tissue unevenly, depending upon the biological time of day the sample was taken. Thus at one testing a patient may seem to have signs of a particular illness, but further blood or tissue samples taken at another time give a different picture of the likely reason for his ill health.

DIABETES

Most of us know someone with diabetes mellitus with vague symptoms such as variation in weight and lack of energy. The diabetic person can suffer from hunger even when well fed, for he does not produce enough insulin at the right time nor does he utilize the sugars in a normal diet.

Even in sleep the brain consumes 25 percent of the oxygen used by the body. Unlike the rest of the body, the brain has little in the way of carbohydrate reserves and depends upon constant nourishment from glucose in the blood. A decline in the glucose supply means a drop in the brain's main source of energy. Glycogen is the form in which sugar is often stored, and for this reason liver glycogen levels are of interest in several illnesses. In the diabetic person the hormonal balance required to metabolize and store sugars in useful form has been disrupted, and his brain may lack sugar at the very time he is excreting unused sugar in urine.

At the Karolinska Institute in Stockholm, Drs. Jacob Möllerstrom and Arne Sollberger found abnormal rhythms of acidity in the blood and urine of diabetic patients, who would show excessive acidity in their blood, with peaks around 4 P.M. and 4 A.M., often accompanied by nausea and headache. By studying rhythmic changes in other constituents of blood and urine these researchers discovered a disruption of intermeshed rhythms which might result in a transient acid-base imbalance.

Until recently, diabetics have been given insulin on the assumption that the body needed the same amount at all times. However, studies of healthy people have shown a circadian rhythm in blood insulin and blood glucose. This means that therapy for diabetics ought to restore the normal insulin rhythm. There are other reasons why rhythmic hormone replacement might be better than a steady dose, for insulin affects other hormones. Recently, Dr. M. Serio and his co-workers studied diabetic patients before and during insulin treatment. During insulin treatment, they no longer showed their usual circadian rhythm of adrenal cortical hormones, but when insulin treatment was stopped, the adrenal rhythm reappeared. In the delicate balance of carbohydrate metabolism, levels of insulin must be timed to match and counterbalance the action of a hormone from the pituitary gland. This means that therapy may need to reproduce the correct phase of rising and falling insulin levels instead of merely increasing deficient levels.

GLUCOSE TOLERANCE TEST AND FATTY ACIDS

If a person suffers symptoms that might be caused by diabetes, he is likely to be given a glucose tolerance test in which he receives an intravenous dose of glucose after a night's fast. Then he continues to fast while his blood is sampled, preferably over the four or five hours following injection. The purpose is to see how fast the glucose is dispersed from the blood and presumably converted into other useful forms of energy. In normal people there is an abrupt increase in blood insulin, reaching a maximum about five minutes after the glucose injection, followed by rapid decline. A study by endocrinologist Robert Abrams of New York Downstate Medical Center has shown that there is not much variation in the normal person's insulin response to glucose at different hours of the day. This suggests that the rate of glucose disposal is not directly tied to the blood insulin level, which does show a circadian rhythm. Instead, glucose disposal appeared to be related to levels of fatty acids known as triglycerides. Abrams and his co-workers were surprised at the high fatty-acid content of the blood, especially since the levels were measured after more than five hours of fasting. They then found that the triglyceride levels were not related to meals but appeared to rise and fall in a circadian rhythm with a high peak at about 6 A.M., the time when adrenal cortical hormones are high.

It has long been known that adrenal hormones must influence the use of glucose. An oral dose of the adrenal hormone, hydrocortisone, produces an excess of blood sugar some three to six hours later. Abrams found a sharp increase of cortisol in the blood about 6 A.M., and six hours later a very sharp drop in the glucose disposal rate, which fell to its trough about noon.

The lag time between the peaks of these various rhythms—the adrenal hormones, triglycerides, and glucose disposal rate—may be clues in attempting to find out how diabetes mellitus begins. Abrams has thought that the diabetes that arises in people from ages thirty to forty-five might be related to erratic schedules, since the desynchronizing effects of stress or trauma may mean an aberration in the rhythmic utilization of carbohydrates. Ultimately, a metabolic illness such as diabetes involves the intermeshing of many biochemical gears. No one knows whether metabolic rhythms that were out of normal phase would set off a concatenation of disorders. However, it seems possible that stress and irregular schedules may play such a role in generating illness.

CANCER

During the late 1950s a British biologist, Janet Harker, published some very provocative experimental results. She had joined together cockroaches with activity rhythms that were 180 degrees out of phase, and had subsequently seen tumors forming. Dr. Harker had been looking for the brain region that might govern the creature's activity rhythm. She zeroed in on a hind region in the cockroach brain, a kind of secondary, neurosecretory brain that secreted hormones, which in turn seemed to be related to the rhythm. When she removed this section of brain from a creature, it became erratic, arrhythmic. When she grafted onto an arrhythmic animal a brain segment from another roach, it began to show the donor's rhythm. Dr. Harker summarized a number of her experiments in her monograph, *The Physiology of Diurnal Rhythms,* and a succinct excerpt will give an idea of the delicacy of the work.

The method of producing the dual cycle is fairly simple. In Periplaneta the time of secretion from the neurosecretory cells is determined, in a light:darkness cycle, by the time of the beginning of darkness: the phase, once determined, is stable. Therefore when two groups of cockroaches are kept in light:darkness cycles which are 12h (hours) out of phase with each other, and the suboesophageal ganglia from one group are implanted into the cockroaches of the other group, the implanted animals will contain two ganglia secreting

12h out of phase with each other. If the implants are renewed every day for at least four days, the recipient cockroaches begin to show signs of serious pathological disorder, and by sixteen days from the beginning of the experiment malignant tumours are found in practically all animals.

In these experiments, the high hormone concentrations produced as a result of the presence of two ganglia, rather than any rhythmical phenomenon, could be the critical factor in tumour production. A high concentration of hormone, however, does not have any effect when it is produced by implantation of even a large number of ganglia, providing that these are secreting in phase with the animal's own ganglion.

Subsequent attempts to replicate these experiments have not come up with the same results, nor indeed with the identical conclusions about the neurosecretory brain as a "clock." Nonetheless, Dr. Harker's experiments leave a haunting reverberation, like a truth only partly revealed. Might large amounts of certain hormones, at the wrong phase of the circadian cycle, influence the rhythms of dividing cells? Might emotional trauma, stress, or virus infection disrupt the circadian harmony of the body in a manner critical to cell multiplication?

HEART TRANSPLANT

What may this mean for the success of transplanting kidneys and hearts? Clinicians are beginning to wonder. For over a decade biologists have demonstrated that tissue would continue to exhibit its circadian rhythm for some time after it was removed from the body. If the heart were removed from the body and sustained in nutriment, its rate of contraction would continue to show a circadian rhythm, just as *in vitro* adrenal glands or thyroid would continue to secrete hormones in circadian rhythm. Recently a group at Baylor University analyzed seventy-two hours of electrocardiograms and electrotachograms in a man who had received a heart transplant a month earlier. His heart now showed two rhythms, for there was a detectable circadian rhythm in his own remnant of heart tissue, and also in the grafted heart. The grafted heart was leading the recipient, by 135 minutes. This is a small phase difference, and Dr. Irvin Kraft and his co-workers have not speculated on the implications of a phase difference in the success of the transplant. However, it seems likely that the amount of phase difference between donor and recipient might bias the outcome of major organ transplants and other tissue grafts. Would some diphasic tissues become malignant?

CANCER RHYTHMS IN RODENTS

Researchers and clinicians are beginning to ask whether there are forms of cancer that are the consequence of altered time structure. The cancer cells that ravage parts of the body show a rampant growth that differs in tempo from the surrounding tissue. These rhythms of mitosis indicate an abnormal rate of multiplication that often seems to be apart from the circadian period of mitosis rhythms in normal surrounding tissue. In their extensive studies of cell division rhythms, Franz Halberg and his associates found that normal cell populations showed the peak division during particular intervals in the twenty-four hours. Mitosis in the skin of hamsters and mice fell to its lowest point during the time of darkness when the animal was active, and rose to a peak during the illumination period when the animal was at rest. But cancer cells did not show this circadian rise and fall in mitosis.

Halberg's studies suggest that mistiming may be one of the earliest indicators of cancer. His laboratory associates implanted tumor tissue or carcinogenic chemicals in rodents, and long before mammary tumors occurred, they found arrhythmic cell mitoses in the skin of the animals' ears. The traces of abnormal cell division rhythms preceded any gross physical signs, suggesting that arrhythmic cell behavior at the surface of the body might be an early clue to developing cancers. Records taken from two human cancer patients, living in the controlled regimen of a hospital, also showed surface irregularity. This irregularity has been documented in a startling manner by Dr. Halberg with a group of rectal temperature charts on cancer patients. The temperatures were taken every six hours over many days and were so erratic that they resembled those of no other patient in the hospital.

HUMAN CANCER

Working with Dr. Mauricio Garcia-Sainz, at the Oncological Hospital in Mexico City, Halberg has analyzed cell mitoses in tissue from humans as well as animals. In one instance tissue samples were taken at two-hour intervals around the clock from cancer patients before they went into X-ray treatment. A second set of samples was collected in the same manner from these patients after treatment. By a strict count of dividing cells and objective method of data analysis, it was clear that the cell proliferation was not circadian before X-ray treatment. However fast the cells may divide, many more should be dividing in normal tissue at a certain phase of the twenty-four hours than at any other time. Before X-ray treatment the cancer cells divided in non-circadian rhythms; some followed a twenty-four and others followed an eight-hour rhythm. Their lack of circadian rhythmicity suggests some defect in the time integration of these cells in the overall rhythm of the body, creating temporal anarchy as well as a visible disorder in tissue. Thus cancer cell activity seems to fall outside the temporal harmony of body functions which are integrated around the unit of a day.

X-RAY TREATMENT

X-radiation interferes with the process of cell division and synthesis, particularly in cells such as those of cancer that are proliferating rapidly. After X-ray treatment the picture changes, for the mitoses in cancer tissue showed a more nearly circadian rhythmicity and fewer signs of fast mitotic cycles. Unfortunately X-ray treatments also cause many rapidly dividing cells to slough off, and the patient may become nauseous, suffer diarrhea, and show other unpleasant side effects. It now seems possible that the side effects can be reduced by strategically timing the X-ray treatments.

In 1963 Dr. Donald Pizzarello and his co-workers found that the dose of X-irradiation that made rodents sick during the day would kill them at night. Soviet researchers Dr. Y. G. Grigoryev and his co-workers have suggested that this vulnerability and death may result from damage to the tissues in which blood cells are formed. Perhaps the rhythm of radiosensitivity may be traced to cycles of activity in the bone marrow and spleen where blood is formed. Presumably, although the Soviet research was performed on mice, the same cyclical change occurs in the blood-forming tissues of human beings.

SEX HORMONES

Radiation treatment seems likely to be influenced by circadian rhythms, and so does the use of sex hormones. In 1967 two groups of medical researchers, led by Dr. Fernand Dray in Paris and Dr. Louis A. Southren in New York, independently discovered that men show a pronounced circadian rhythm of testosterone, which rises to a peak around 8 to 9 A.M. and sharply declines around noon. Since sex hormones are often used to treat cancers of the uterus, breast, and prostrate, a knowledge of secretion and dispersion rates would seem useful for treatment and critical for diagnostic procedures. In most hospitals testosterone concentrations are measured in morning blood samples, a procedure similar to measuring the average depth of water when the tide is high, for early morning testosterone concentrations are 35 to 40 percent higher than the minimum around midnight.

ANTIMETABOLITES

Today many forms of cancer are treated with antimetabolites, drugs that slow down the process of protein synthesis. Each day as DNA synthesis increases and drops, there is a ten-to-one difference between the amount of synthesis at the peak and at the trough. Tumor cells are generally out of phase with normal cells, and it may be possible to hit tumors during their peak hours of cell division while minimizing damage to normal cells. Recently, Dr. Garcia-Sainz found that patients respond to X-ray treatment in a circadian rhythm. This differential response may mean that treatments can be calculated to attack the cancer at its vulnerable mitotic phase, yet minimize the side effects felt by the patient.

While research on cell rhythms may offer the possibility of early diagnosis and strategic timing for cancer treatment, other researchers have suggested that cancer may be a disease with a genetic propensity. Some of these studies involve the rhythmicity of extremely simple organisms, and some researchers have suggested that there might be a circadian oscillator, a nearly twenty-four-hour clock of sorts, within each cell.

LABORATORY TESTS AND MEDICAL DIAGNOSIS

A great deal of modern diagnosis rests upon the laboratory, and here, too, biological time of day exerts a profound influence. The proteins from blood, a "Pap" smear, or any other tissue sample from the body will bind differently according to the time of day they were taken. Thus, even the histologist needs time-of-day information in making plates. Cell division reaches its peak in certain tissues and organs at various times of day or night. Thus, in biopsy it is necessary to know the phase of the cycle from which the tissue was taken. If a person suspects that he has cancer, repeated tissue samples become an agony, and indeterminacy, which is often prolonged, becomes wrenching to his family and his physician. Time-tagging tissue samples might help to reduce some of this suspense and emotional drain and to detect malignancies much earlier. Similarly, it is necessary to measure levels of proteins or sugars in urine or blood to diagnose metabolic diseases, or sometimes to measure a patient's response to an injection of ACTH, or a hormone, or hormone blocker. Once again, methods for ascertaining time of day within the patient at the hour of the test might help to minimize the number of ambiguous readings and repeated medical tests that are worrisome and expensive to patient, doctor, and laboratory.

At present, a clinician with a baffling patient, who suspects a temporal disorder, faces a difficult and in many cases impractical prospect. In order to get biological time-of-day data, there is currently no choice but to place the patient on a rigid schedule of sleep and waking and meals. Moreover, physiological measures must be made at reasonably short intervals around the clock, preferably for several days in a hospital. Since no measure of physical function or test of performance is complete without accounting for biological time of day, one might expect this to be a high-priority area of research in medicine. The technology that can place men on the moon can assuredly develop a miniature device to clock changes in several functions in a freely moving person.

For almost a decade people have been discussing the importance of a miniature biotelemetry instrument, like those developed for manned space flight. In their epidemiological surveys to trace the origins of bronchial disease and cardiac ailments in large populations of Londoners, the British have used miniature instruments that can be worn like a wristwatch. Halberg's laboratory has designed a seven-day thermometer. Engineers and scientists are collaborating in many laboratories, at the Franklin Institute in Philadelphia, at the Institute of Living in Hartford, Connecticut, at the Brain Research Institute of UCLA, but these projects have lacked adequate financial support. The evolution of such instruments ought to be a boon to hospitals, making it possible to schedule X-rays, surgery, and drugs

for the time when the patient is most likely to be benefited with the least stress or side effects.

Engineering such devices is subtle and difficult. In
the usual turbulence of a day's activity the sensors on
a person's body would absorb a lot of noise, perhaps
drowning out the small signals of rhythms. In principle,
however, a body clock might simply keep track of such
fluctuations as blood pressure, pulse, temperature, and
perhaps skin conductance. More to the point than
engineering difficulties is the lack of knowledge and
research on human timing.

Even for the purpose of making medical diagnosis
more precise, it will be essential to know a great deal
more about the variety and range in human circadian
rhythms, the shape of the daily curve for important
body functions, the stability of phase relations, and
what ordinary influences from everyday life may affect
them. Each person has his own time print, just as he
has a fingerprint. A physician who knew his patient's
time print, the shape of his temperature and activity-
rest cycle, and who knew where his patient was on this
daily roller coaster, might have much less trouble inter-
preting the results of clinic tests.

Once it is possible to learn about a person's circadian
(and other) time structure, it may be possible for doctors to practice prophetic medicine. Just as high cholesterol levels in newborn infants suggest that these individuals may need to take precautions not to clog
their arteries with fat in later life, time prints may allow
physicians to predict which infants may be vulnerable
to temporal disruption, who may need strict schedules
simply to maintain health. The idea that there could be
such a thing as temporal vulnerability, equivalent to lifelong tendencies to upper respiratory infections or to
gastrointestinal problems, may sound wildly speculative
only because we have not yet adjusted to the fact that
we must be constructed out of time.

6 HOURS OF VULNERABILITY AND RESISTANCE TO DRUGS AND ILLNESS

Time is a brisk wind, for each hour it brings something new . . . but who can understand and measure its sharp breath, its mystery and its design? Therefore the physician must not think himself too important; for over him there is a master—time—which plays with him as a cat with a mouse.

Paracelsus,
HOHENHEIM'S GERMAN COMMENTARY ON
THE APHORISMS OF HIPPOCRATES

In letting of blood, three main circumstances are to be considered, who, how much, when?
Robert Burton,
THE ANATOMY OF MELANCHOLY

6 Hours of Vulnerability and Resistance to Drugs and Illness

IN THE EPIC POEMS OF HOMER, THE TERM "pharmakon" connoted a charm or drug that might be used for good or evil purposes, but its action for good or evil did not depend solely upon the natural qualities of the substance. Even modern Greek denotes both drug and poison in the word "pharmaki"—and so they are. Pharmacologists and doctors who prescribe drugs are just beginning to discover an invisible factor which may cause a drug to be therapeutic on one occasion and poisonous on another—time of day within the patient. We know a good deal more about the rhythms of specific vulnerabilities in rats and mice than in humans, and the figures are striking. For instance, a dose of amphetamine can kell 77.6 percent or 6 percent of a group of animals, depending solely on the hour the dose was administered. If one's response to drugs, surgery, or infection depends upon the time of day within the body, the timing of drugs and vaccines must be, in some cases, as pertinent as the dosage and the drug itself.

CHANGING TOXICITY

Toxicity is, of course, a major worry of the manufacturer. One of the standard toxicity tests is the famous LD 50, which establishes the dosage at which a drug kills half of a group of test animals. If the same dose will kill 77.6 percent at one hour and 6 percent at another hour, the LD 50 is quite meaningless unless it is accompanied by the biological time of day that the drug was administered. No doubt many so-called "unexpected" drug reactions now may be explained: what is a safe dose at one phase of the circadian rhythm may not be safe at another time. Today, when millions of Americans are ingesting billions of dollars in drugs each year, the impact of rhythms research on commercial pharmacology might prevent untoward side effects and considerable misery. Most drug companies are likely to resist the expense and difficulty of time series studies. If, as some manufacturers have claimed, it costs over a million dollars to test a new drug, it will cost more when the same manipulation must be repeated at intervals around the clock. One can anticipate many rationalizations for not adopting such methods—on the part of commercial pharmacologists—while many academic pharmacologists incorporate time series studies into their own work. Ironically, scientists in the Department of Agriculture have been more interested in the implications of circadian rhythms for conserving insecticides by advantageous timing, than have medical researchers in the Food and Drug Administration. Twenty years ago there were not sufficient data to inspire any great consternation about timing. Now the data are accumulating, and their significance is clear; timing may tip the balance between survival and death.

RHYTHMS OF SUSCEPTIBILITY IN RODENTS

The history of these researches goes back twenty years to the vision of Franz Halberg, whose laboratory undertook the Herculean task of assembling—from scratch—a time map of vulnerability rhythms. One of their earliest studies involved injecting inbred mice with the bacteria, *Brucella,* that cause undulant fever. Standardized doses were injected around the clock. The bacteria proved to be least harmful to the animals by day (when they are inactive) whereas they were almost uniformly lethal by darkness, during the waking hours of the rodents. This is not to imply that all bacteria are most fatal during the activity span.

Indeed, when mice were exposed to intestinal bacteria (*Escherichia coli*) only a few recipients died if they received it during their waking and active hours. However, the same dose was lethal to animals at the end of their rest span. A graph of mortality rates against hour of injection reveals some of these differences.

RHYTHMS OF IMMUNITY

Someday we will undoubtedly understand why specific bacteria and viruses have their maximum impact at a certain phase of the daily cycle, for we will know more about rhythmic changes in immunity factors and target organs as well as in the pests themselves. As we read in Chapter 4, Lawrence E. Scheving and John Pauly found that gamma globulin, the blood fraction with many antibodies against bacteria and viruses, reaches a circadian peak in rats during the last six hours of darkness. In another laboratory when mice were exposed to *pneumococci*, the ones who survived best were those who had been injected at 4 A.M. during the hours of peak gamma globulin levels. The latter study was performed by Dr. Ralph Feigin, who suspected that if vulnerability to pneumonia were rhythmic, responses to vaccination ought to show a circadian rhythm, too.

Feigin and his associates had previously found circadian rhythms in certain amino acid levels in humans. Blood levels were lowest around 4 A.M. and maximum around 8 P.M. Now they upset the amino acid rhythm with injections of a vaccine for a virus disease known as Venezuelan equine encephalomyelitis. Men immunized at 8 A.M. showed less disturbance of amino acid concentrations than men who received vaccine at 8 P.M. Because this vaccine contained a live virus, the scientists inferred that time of day and the amino acid rhythm probably influenced the body's response to infection.

As this frontier in preventive medicine develops, we are likely to become particular about the hour of vaccination, calculating the biological time at which a vaccine will offer the most immunity. Similar calculations may help in treating several of mankind's worst diseases, the parasite diseases that afflict Africans and many millions of Asians.

PARASITES: ELEPHANTIASIS AND MALARIA

In some diseases a circadian rhythm is visible when a parasite population makes a cyclical migration from one part of the body to another. The microfilaria known as *Wuchereria bancrofti,* tiny worms responsible for elephantiasis, infest millions of people in Asia and Africa. Adult worms live in the lymph vessels, but the larvae inhabit the bloodstream. By day the larvae vanish, appearing by the millions each night. Dr. Frank Hawking and his associates found that in monkeys the microfilaria actually accumulate in the lungs during the day and their migrations can be influenced by oxygen. They also discovered that malarial pests are influenced by temperature.

In malaria, parasite reproduction cycles are reflected in regularly occurring attacks that often come every other day in the tertian variety or every four days in the quartan variety. Usually around noon, or at the midpoint of the victim's activity span, he may begin to shiver and have headaches and back pains that intensify by evening when fever and sweating become pronounced. Then the fever abates and the symptoms vanish, leaving the person exhausted but normal the next day, until noon the following day when the chills begin again. The life cycle of a malaria parasite is completed within a multiple of twenty-four hours and reaches infectious form at night, the time when most mosquitoes usually bite. The symptoms may be a result of the wastes the parasites leave in the blood.

Malarial pests multiply and ripen in tune with the victim's temperature rhythm. In other illnesses, the rhythmic symptoms may stem from a circadian change in other aspects of the person's physiology. In some cases, however, the waxing and waning of discomfort may be expressions of the person's changing subjective

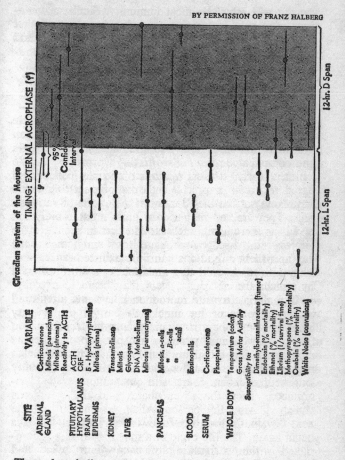

These data indicate the phase relationships of a number of circadian functions in the mouse, relative to the hours of light and darkness. The dots represent the peak, or maximum of the function. In addition, it is possible to see the hours of maximum vulnerability to a tumor-producing chemical, to loud noise, and to various poisons and medications.

perceptions. Pain tolerance, for instance, may rise and fall in a circadian rhythm.

PAIN TOLERANCE

Pain is extremely mysterious. It comes and goes. The schoolboy, in a fight, feels no pain until the fight has ended. During World War II, men in the Normandy invasion were able to fight with broken backs, while others with serious wounds did not go into shock, were clear-headed, and needed no morphine—perhaps in the knowledge that their wounds would soon send them home. The emotional aspects of pain have made the study and testing of analgesics exceedingly complicated.

In the early 1960s, Weitzman and his colleagues wanted to create a precise measure of pain tolerance in monkeys so that they could test the effects of various drugs. They trained monkeys to press a bar rapidly to prevent an incremental increase of electric shock. However, over the twenty-four hours they saw indications that the monkeys had a rhythm of pain tolerance, accepting more "pain" at some hours, less at others. Changes in the nervous system may begin to explain why sick people request more pain-killers and attention at certain hours of the night and early morning. In illness there may be a rhythmic change in the tolerance of pain, as well as rhythms in the parasite or organic function causing the pain. Our responses to analgesic drugs or sedatives also fluctuate in a circadian rhythm along with circadian changes in our nervous system.

TIME ESTIMATION FOR TIMING TREATMENT

In the near future physicians will doubtless begin to experiment with the scheduling of drug administration to anticipate the hours of most intense pain. Since a patient may be desynchronized, whether at home or in a hospital, the physician has no immediate method for knowing what "time of day" it is inside the patient's nervous system. Alertness, motivation, and other aspects of nervous system excitability appear to change in a rhythmic manner, waxing and waning in 90–120 minute periods, in periods of three to four hours, and most obviously, in the course of the day. Perhaps a first rough guess about time of day in the nervous system might be gotten by asking the patient to estimate a two-minute interval (and count to 120 in two minutes) at intervals throughout his waking period.

A circadian rhythm in time estimation was demonstrated by Dr. Gwen Stephens, in a careful round-the-clock study on herself. For thirty-six days, she recorded her temperature and her pulse, and estimated a two-minute span—at intervals, seven times each day and night. She found that she counted two minutes most rapidly at the time when her pulse rate was at its peak. Other tests such as the rate at which flashing lights began to look like a steady beam (critical flicker fusion), may begin to suggest what phase it is within the nervous system of the patient. Just as brain biochemicals have been shown to rise and fall, in various regions, this chemical rhythmicity must influence the person's reaction to a wide variety of analgesics, tranquilizers, sedatives, hypnotics, stimulants, and other psychoactive drugs.

EPILEPSY AND AUDIOGENIC SEIZURES

Circadian rhythms in the excitability of the nervous system may begin to explain why certain epileptics have seizures at particular hours of the day. In attempting to understand changes in brain excitability of possible relevance to epilepsy, some researchers have studied what are known as audiogenic seizures. Certain inbred mice and rats have a remarkable reaction to bursts of high-pitched noise and will dash around uncontrollably, finally falling into convulsions and sometimes dying. Noise does not invariably produce this sequence. At certain times the animals react by crouching as if offended or by walking around, but not running. In 1955 Halberg and co-workers tested mice with electric bells, producing a noise roughly as loud as a jet engine. By day the animals seemed impervious, but at night they fell into convulsions and died. Their peak sensitivity seemed to coincide with their daily peak in temperature. However, when their lighting schedule was inverted, causing a phase shift, the mice became highly susceptible during the light hours of their former activity span as well as during the dark span.

If an underlying circadian change influences proneness to epileptic seizures, it is quite possible that epileptics would be extremely sensitive to the phase shifts of east-west travel. If they usually had their seizures at a particular time of day, they might become more seizure-prone at all hours after a phase shift. Dr. Halberg and his associates studied a number of epileptic patients in a state hospital, and found that seizures clustered toward morning. By recording EEGs around the clock, they saw that brain-wave abnormalities occurred at the time of day an epileptic patient usually suffered his seizure even if he had no attack on that day. Moreover, when three of the patients were studied again ten years later, their brain-wave tracings showed spikes and paroxysms around that same time of day. This suggests that anticonvulsant drugs might be timed for maximum effectiveness at the hours of usual attacks.

ANESTHETICS, ALCOHOL, AND STIMULANTS

Underlying rhythms of the nervous system must alter our responses to tranquilizers, stimulants, sleeping pills, anesthetics, and alcohol. These common drugs, which Americans take in an increasing volume, amount to several hundred million dollars in sales each year. They affect the nervous system differently at different phases of the daily cycle. Judging from rodent experiments, the barbiturate dose that is safe in evening may have exaggerated effects by early morning. So, too, the effects of our most common drugs such as alcohol are not the same at all hours of the day.

Unlikely as it might seem, the rodent is not a bad test animal in evaluating drugs for man, since it more nearly resembles man in metabolism than any other experimental animal except monkeys. Using controlled lighting schedules so that all the test animals were positioned at known phases of their cycle, studies of circadian drug reactions all follow roughly the same procedure. Out of a large pool, sometimes containing hundreds of inbred animals, a subgroup is injected or tested at a specific hour, and subsequent groups are tested at two- or four-hour intervals around the clock for one or two days.

Halberg's group found that when mice were injected with a large amount of alcohol, akin to a person drinking a quart of vodka, it was lethal at the end of their rest span. Sixty percent died if given alcohol at their usual time of awakening, but only 12 percent died at the onset of illumination and rest. Social drinking customs seem to reflect this rhythm. Most people do their drinking at the end of the day, rather than the beginning, with the exception of alcoholics. One of the distinctions between heavy drinkers and alcoholics has been the time of day a person begins drinking. Alcoholics will drink before breakfast, if they eat any, a time at which alcohol should be very toxic, judging by the experimental studies of animals.

SURGERY AND ANESTHETICS

Similar questions have not been asked about the timing of surgery. In most city hospitals, the schedule for the operating theaters resembles the arrival-departure boards at busy airports. In addition to the logistics involved in assembling all of the necessary participants, anesthetists, aides, nurses and surgeons, the hospital must cope with unpredicted emergencies. A serious surgical procedure, a long grueling open-heart operation, or a delicate operation on the retina are likely to be scheduled for the time of day at which the surgeon functions best. In some cases this is early, 6–8 A.M. But what about the patient's best time, giving him the best chance for survival and a quick recovery? The patient is changing. His adrenal rhythm may influence his resistance to infection. The phase of his nervous system, changing with the hours, will likely react to the trauma of incisions and drugs differently at different hours. Responses to surgery are likely to be biased by the biological time of day.

Since a major factor in surgery is the influence of the anesthetic, these depressants may have pronounced cycles of maximum impact. Reported ill effects from the anesthetic halothane prompted Halberg's group to conduct a time-series study in mice. A ten-minute exposure to a standard dose killed 5 percent of the animals or 76 percent, depending upon biological time of day. Maximum sensitivity seemed to occur at the middle of the active time when the animal was least sensitive to many other toxins. Anesthesiologists have noticed that patients may change in their sensitivity to anesthesia even during a long operation, but no time-of-day response curves have yet been obtained from human beings. Neither do we have any measure of man's circadian response to stimulants and sleeping pills.

STIMULANTS AND SLEEPING PILLS

Scheving and Pauly have looked into the rhythmic response of rats to depressants and stimulants. For instance, the amount of time a rat sleeps after an injection of the barbiturate pentobarbital (Nembutal) depends upon the hour it was injected. The same dose causes fifty minutes of sedation at one time of day, but at another hour it brings ninety minutes of sleep. Mortality curves for heavy doses of barbiturates also follow this rhythm. Rodents are most vulnerable to sodium pentobarbital in the early part of their activity cycle, which is comparable to very early morning for humans. This point of susceptibility may be a factor in the hangovers and unintended suicides that are reported among heavy barbiturate users. These people may carelessly take a heavy dose if they awaken from sleep in the morning, and many people with depression do awaken in the predawn hours. If people are particularly responsive to hypnotics at a certain time of day, the doses ought to be determined by the time of day they are taken. Time of day does not refer to external clock time, but to the time on the individual's cycle of activity and sleep.

We might ask the same question about nicotine and the stimulant amphetamine which many people use to kill appetite or compensate for fatigue and depression. Here we might expect a dramatic time-of-day difference, judging from rat experiments of Scheving and Pauly, who injected potentially lethal amounts of amphetamine at two-hour intervals. Around 6 A.M. mortality was low—6 percent, but at midnight (the peak of activity) 77.6 percent of the rats died. This meant that there was a period of very high resistance to the drug and a period of great vulnerability. They also evaluated toxicity rhythms under various conditions for a number of substances, including pentobarbital, strychnine, nicotine, and the anti-anxiety drug chlordiazepoxide (Librium), which was most lethal to rats when given in the middle of their activity span.

It seems clear that drugs have their maximum impact on the nervous system at different hours and that time-of-day information should be obtained for them. Drugs affecting the nervous system are being bought in ever-increasing volume and are not accompanied by literature that specifies timing. Some medications are not to be taken on an empty stomach, some are given *ad hoc* for pain or motion sickness, and hypnotics are usually prescribed before bedtime. Apart from the kind of practical advice that would suggest that a person retire at once after taking a rapidly metabolized barbiturate such as hexobarbital, the doctor presumably is not given any statement by the drug manufacturer, citing hours of activity or rest when a medication should attain its greatest effect, or hours when a heavy dose might be toxic. It is widely known that insulin might cause symptoms of shock if given at a time when blood sugar supplies are low, but what about adverse reactions to tranquilizers? We may also discover that the mania and psychosis sometimes caused by amphetamines, especially when abused over long periods of time, is biased by the time of day the drug is taken. Pharmacologists are beginning to notice that morphine—and presumably heroin—does not have the same effect at all hours. In 1971 it was estimated that 40,000 Americans would die from the overuse of narcotics. These deaths are not likely to occur randomly at all hours of day and night, and there is the distinct likelihood that heroin and other psychotropic drugs are more dangerous at certain hours than others. In 1971, as in each year thereafter, hospital emergency wards expect a large number of comatose people and corpses, people who committed suicide, although perhaps not by intention. Some of them will die from prescribed drugs, and others will simply report that the drug that helped yesterday, today causes dizziness, shortness of breath, trembling. These are "unexpected" effects. In the absence of data about the temporal effects of drugs, it is often assumed that the patient needs the same amount of antihistamine, barbiturate, antibiotic at all hours of the day. A few intuitively gifted clinicians have seen that it was otherwise, and have deliberately timed drug therapies to achieve a better effect.

STRATEGY FOR DRUG THERAPY

Some years ago, Dr. Heinz Lehmann observed that a number of his psychiatric patients were not sedated by the hypnotics they took at bedtime. He and his staff experimented, giving a fraction of the dose in mid-afternoon, a fraction in evening, and a final fraction before bed. Under this regimen, patients who had been irrepressibly agitated were eased into sleep on less sedation than they had been taking before. Perhaps with care drugs can be tailored to the beat of the body.

ENZYME RHYTHMS

Much of our response to drugs or toxins appears to be due to the activity or inactivity of enzymes, biological catalysts that break down toxins in the liver and the kidneys. Beginning in Halberg's laboratory, a number of these enzymes have been time-charted. The rhythms are sensitive to changes in light-and-dark scheduling. In many instances, they are influenced by diet, since a vitamin deficiency or protein deficiency can change the amount of available enzymes or smaller molecules known as coenzymes, often derived from vitamins. The kidney enzyme transamidinase, for example, is important to energy storage; the laboratory found that it had a pronounced circadian rhythm. Moreover, two strains of inbred mice differed in the phase of the rhythm; transamidinase activity rose and fell earlier with respect to the light-dark schedule in one strain, although the period was the same in both. This suggested that there might be a genetic basis for differences in time responses to drugs.

Circadian enzyme rhythms have been revealed in a number of laboratories. Radzialowski and Bousquet described circadian rhythms in a liver microsomal enzyme system known to break down steroid hormones and compounds such as drugs in rats and mice. Since this enzyme system controls the intensity and duration of certain drug responses, studies of drug metabolism need to be conducted in a way that accounts for circadian rhythms. This means that pharmacologists must maintain animal colonies under strictly controlled light-dark cycles when testing for drug response or toxicity.

Drs. H. von Mayersbach and R. P. Yap have demonstrated that there are enormous differences in the activity of esterase, an important liver enzyme that exhibits an unmistakable twenty-four-hour rhythm. They had been interested in the mechanisms by which the body detoxifies succinylcholine, a muscle relaxant that had been used instead of curare during surgery and which had caused fatalities by stopping respiration. They injected rats with a dose of succinylcholine that was estimated to kill about half of the animals. If the same dose of the relaxant were injected toward noon or midnight, the mortality was about 10 percent, but if the drug were injected around 8 A.M. or 8 P.M. mortality rose to about 60 percent. As they discovered, the activity of the liver esterase enzyme was the opposite of the mortality curve—most active at noon, with a decline in activity around 8 A.M. and 8 P.M. This rhythm seemed to determine how rapidly the muscle relaxant would be detoxified.

Rhythms of vulnerability to toxic compounds may be predicted by studies of enzyme rhythms, which also may predict when drugs could entail some risk of toxicity and how to time doses for least risk. There are many ailments, such as diabetes or Addison's disease, in which drug therapy is used to replace hormones lacking in the body. For these ailments drug therapy can be made more effective through a knowledge of normal hormone rhythms.

ADRENAL HORMONE TREATMENT

The adrenal hormone deficiency of Addison's disease frequently leaves patients feeling fatigued. Drs. Alain Reinberg and Jean Ghata in Paris asked several Addisonian patients to apportion their daily drug dosage according to one of three treatment schedules that made them feel best. One patient, a wall painter who had been a patient of Dr. Ghata for ten years, began to take his cortisol so that he had only a third at bedtime and two thirds upon rising. Without being instructed, he had approximated the concentrations that would be found in a normal person at these times of day and night, creating in himself a normal circadian rhythm. Since then, a number of Parisian patients have been allowed to regulate their own dosage in a manner that effectively diminishes the feeling of fatigue. Ordinarily these drugs would be meted out in constant doses with no regard to the normal hormone rhythm.

ALLERGY

Similarly, if patients with allergies were permitted to allocate hormones and anti-allergens according to the intensity of need and the greatest relief, many of them would indicate that allergic symptoms also show a circadian rhythmicity. Asthma and related allergies affect about one out of every ten Americans.

Asthma is particularly harmful and causes about 9,000 deaths a year. The asthmatic swelling of the bronchial tubes and membranes may be caused by allergy to plant or animal proteins, drugs, pollutants, house-cleaning materials, or insecticides, but some forms seem to be emotional.

Many asthmatic patients have attacks only at night and awaken from sleep gasping for air and feeling that they are about to suffocate. A dose of cortisone or cortisol can diminish these symptoms. In attempting to see how the adrenal steroid levels might be related to the symptoms, Dr. Reinberg studied eight asthma patients and four healthy subjects. Both groups showed lower levels of adrenal hormone excretion at night and higher levels in the morning. During the study the asthma attacks occurred only when potassium and adrenal corticoid excretion levels were low in the early part of the night. This is when many asthmatic people anticipate their most serious attacks.

Children with severe asthma are relieved of their terrible symptoms by adrenal hormones, but unfortunately the hormones also stunt growth and delay maturation. A study has been conducted at a special research hospital for asthmatic children in Denver, Colorado, the Children's Asthma Research Institute and Hospital, in hope that the side effects of hormones might be diminished by giving smaller doses at strategic times of day. Over a four-month period, Falliers, Reinberg, and Halberg gave the children prednisone, a synthetic derivation of cortisone, on specific time schedules. One measure of the drug's effect was the time of their peak expiratory flow rate. The boys blew into a respirometer every two hours, before and after taking hormones. Hormones shifted the time of the peak lung capacity.

Youngsters who received prednisone at 1 A.M. showed their peak about two hours earlier than they had before, and those who received it around 1 P.M. showed their crest about six hours later. The medical staff noticed that children who received their medication at 1 A.M. or 7 A.M. seemed to benefit more than the others. Further research may offer a more precise way to choose the best time of day to administer hormones so that they can be given in far smaller quantities.

Like asthma, other allergies seem to torture their victims at particular times of day, and this is partly due to a rhythm in histamine response. Histamine is one of the substances in skin that causes a reaction to insect bites and to burns. It is an amine that helps to cause a flush in the skin during an allergic reaction.

Dr. Reinberg and his associates put six healthy adults on a standardized routine of sleep, waking, and eating, then injected them under the skin with histamine at fixed hours, day and night. The largest histamine reaction and the biggest reddened weal on the skin came after injection at 11 P.M. The sensitivity of human skin to histamine or to a chemical that liberates histamine distinctly follows a circadian rhythm, reaching its peak around the hour of the night when adrenal corticosteroid hormones are dropping to their lowest levels. This is the time when insect bites or poison ivy itch the most intensely. Antihistamine drugs were tested the same way. Volunteers were first injected with histamine. Then they swallowed a constant dose of antihistamine. Some received the drug at 7 A.M., others at 7 P.M. Judging by the shrinking of the red welt, the morning dose had a far greater impact than the same dose at evening.

Under the same controlled conditions, Dr. Reinberg studied five patients who were extremely allergic to penicillin. Penicillin scratch tests produced the greatest allergic response and skin irritation at 11 P.M. Thus late evening may be a time when penicillin and other antibiotics should be administered with special care to patients who do not know if they are allergic. The pattern in these several allergy studies indicates that the circadian rhythm of allergic symptoms and reactivity may be related to the rhythm of adrenal hormones.

Only a few drugs have been tested for rhythmic response in people. At the time this was written most of these had been executed with meticulous care by Alain Reinberg and his colleagues. Needless to say, it was important to use innocuous drugs, so toxicity was not studied. Other criteria were used to differentiate drug effects—such as the number of hours that the compound could still be detected in urine.

The circadian properties of only a few drugs have been demonstrated in human beings. Sodium salicylate, a compound similar to aspirin, may linger longer in the body if taken around 7 A.M. then if taken at 7 P.M. The duration of effect might be valuable in fighting fever. Of course, any data on drug responses gathered under carefully controlled schedules must be revised considerably after a phase shift. Thus a person traveling across time zones should not be surprised if he reacts differently to a hormone, antihistamine, aspirin, or sedative that he usually takes every day. On the first few days after a trip or switch to a different work shift, a person should be cautious about using his customary drugs.

PHASE SHIFTS BY DRUGS

Just as many drug effects are influenced by the circadian rhythm of the body, drugs may change that rhythm, affecting the body's time structure. Barbiturates are a case in point. Drs. Dorothy and Howard Krieger found that sodium pentobarbital, given at any hour, would suppress the adrenal hormone rhythm in animals. A fast-acting barbiturate would block the morning rise in hormone levels only if animals received the drug in the evening. However, if barbiturates depress the morning rise in blood hormone levels in human beings, this would help to explain why these hypnotics can leave a person with a hangover. Biologists have also found that antibiotics such as actinomycin-D can shift the circadian rhythms of DNA and RNA synthesis. Thus a rhythm of cell synthesis is altered, shifting the time at which affected cell populations reach their peak of division. This might change responses to other drugs and even influence behavior.

Occasionally it is desirable to interfere with time structure. Dr. William Zung has shown that tricyclic antidepressant drugs improve both mood and sleep by lengthening the sleep cycle. Other scientists are seeking to lengthen the activity-sleep cycle to forty-eight or even seventy-two hours by counteracting a brain enzyme that continually destroys monoamines in the central nervous system. Monoamine oxidase inhibitors have lengthened the activity period in animals. Similarly, the Syntex Corporation hopes to see whether certain adrenal hormones can be given to travelers to produce an instant adjustment to phase shifts. However, the body's many systems adjust at different speeds and not all of these can be entrained by adrenal steroids.

Unfortunately, many of the temporal effects of drugs are unwittingly incurred. Most people do not expect to get nightmares and other withdrawal symptoms from hypnotic or tranquilizing drugs as late as four to seven days after they have stopped taking them and even a month later. Effects that are not immediate and obvious may never be discovered.

Somewhat at random, throughout waking hours, people take tranquilizers, hypnotics, stimulants, antihistamines, antibiotics, hormones, and other common drugs. Some of these medications may be producing long-term effects that elude our current methods of diagnosis. Dr. Curt P. Richter has used drugs to alter the circadian cycle of activity and rest in rats. Sulfamerazine, commonly used against infection, was added to the diet of adult female rats who had regular daily running cycles; every four or five days as they went into estrus, they normally became more active than usual, always becoming active at the same time of day. During sulfamerazine treatment, the daily rhythm remained, but later on, these animals began to show very long cycles of running and food consumption, and their peak activity occurred every twenty to thirty-five days instead of every four to five days. The abnormal long-term cycle did not appear until after sulfamerazine was removed from the diet. Then the animals began to behave like manic-depressives. They became very active, lost weight, and showed less appetite, then lapsed into a long inactive period when they became very inert. At this point they ate huge amounts of food, gained weight, and showed vaginal smears that were no longer coordinated with the four-to-five-day estrus cycle.

Dr. Richter speculated that the rats were responding to the action of the sulfa drug on the thyroid, since experimental radioactivity in the thyroid gland also produced long, regular activity cycles. Therefore, it may be possible that a patient could take sulfa or antibiotics and eventually suffer changes due to effects on thyroid glands. If so, the effects might be interpreted as psychiatric emotional problems. Society tends to be moralistic about people who lose and gain weight, and who cannot maintain a steady state. But clinicians have always recognized that thyroid malfunction can lead to problems in maintaining a normal weight, appetite and activity level. Some problems of uneven behavior and weight regulation actually may be created by drugs.

Richter tested numerous drugs: thyroid-affecting thiourea and thiouracil; a pain-killer, aminopyrine; a sedative, sodium barbital; an adrenal hormone, cortisone; and female hormones, progesterone and estradiol. In each instance, he saw no abnormal effects while the animals were taking the drugs. Only later, after the drug had been stopped for quite a while, did an impressively large number of animals exhibit abnormal activity and eating cycles. These cycles would never have been detected except in a laboratory where the activity rhythms of the animals were being recorded every day by an automatic recorder. Eighty percent of the animals that received thiouracil showed abnormal subsequent cycles; estradiol left an aftermath of abnormal activity cycles in 66.6 percent of the group of test animals. This study was done in the late 1950s before the widespread use of estradiol and other female hormones in contraceptive pills—which raises questions about subtle aftereffects from contraceptive pills in women who show no symptoms while they are taking the pill. Only observations over long periods of time will reveal after-effects and changes.

Female hormones effectively "reschedule" the menstrual cycles of many women whose periods were either irregular or not the average twenty-eight to twenty-

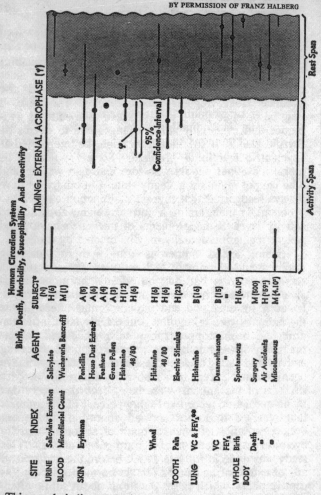

This graph indicates the phase of day or night that a person is apt to be most allergic to dust or pollen, the hours when most human births and deaths from various causes occur. The subjects are designated as healthy (H), sick, which is to say, morbid (M), allergic (A), and asthmatic or suffering from other bronchial illness (B).

The dots show the peak phase, the time of maximum response. **Vital capacity is represented by VC, and one second of forced expiratory volume is FEV.

nine days in length. (Menstrual cycles can vary from sixteen to seventy-five days.) It is possible that the imposition of a twenty-nine-day cycle would affect a woman with a twenty-eight-day cycle differently from one with a spontaneous cycle of thirty-five days. Individuality in response to drugs has been studied along a number of modalities, but never before did we have to consider individuality in time structure. Now that drugs affect millions of people it may be essential to analyze their after-effects. The simple use of diaries and calendars could provide a start by revealing obvious long-term effects.

A NEW STRATEGY IN DRUG USE

It is amply clear that timing must become a factor in pharmacology and drug therapy. At present circadian rhythms of susceptibility are not mentioned in pharmacology texts, nor are time-series studies demanded by the Food and Drug Administration. There is no mention of rhythms on the protocols of new drugs. Thus neither manufacturer nor physician knows to what extent a drug response may vary in the same individual over twenty-four hours. In discussing the metabolism of drugs, medical texts do not mention the amount of variation in enzyme activity that may make a dosage of a drug like succinylcholine fatal at one hour but not at another. The daily rise and fall of allergic responses, of pain tolerance, of adrenal and other hormonal symptoms call for timed medication, but the time-table of symptoms is only beginning to be explored in human beings. We can expect that time data will revolutionize the strategy of drug therapy, and patients should be receiving desired effects from doses much lower than currently prescribed. The pharmacology of jet travel and of people on work shifts will involve some computations. People who have made phase shifts should estimate biological time of day before taking drugs. In the future, for instance, doctors and travelers will probably have time-tables, indicating about how many days it takes a specific enzyme system to shift after a change that delays the cycle four hours, and thus when to ingest a drug that the enzyme metabolizes.

As data accumulate we will begin to incorporate the idea of internal time structure into our body image—as we have absorbed the role of DNA, of viruses, or of vitamins. As the balance of internal rhythms begins to seem real, we will treat ourselves more kindly with regard to preserving inner harmony, whether this means declining social invitations to obtain rest, or following prescriptions that ask us to consult time charts.

In the future hormone replacement will undoubtedly mimic the body's hormone rhythm. Moreover, drugs may be given periodically at specified hours to help restore rhythmicity in people whose illnesses involve a desynchronization of internal rhythms. Dr. Charles Stroebel has done this by administering antipsychotic and antidepressant drugs to exceedingly sick monkeys at twelve- and twenty-four-hour intervals, rapidly restoring circadian rhythmicity. On the other hand, a drug that shifts the phase of a hormone cycle out of its usual phase relationships could in principle have the effect of stress and begin to generate illness. Some scientists think that desynchronized cycles are the links by which our emotional distresses and habits could lead to a variety of ailments.

7 TIME AND THE CONSEQUENCES OF STRESS

Time is the school in which we learn
Time is the fire in which we burn.
Delmore Schwartz

There is absolutely no question that one can overshoot the stimulation of the endocrine system and that this has physiological consequences that last throughout the whole lifetime of the organs.

Rene Dubos,
MAN ADAPTING

In classical times, more than at any other period until a few decades ago, the doctor was more concerned with healthy people than with invalids. The branch of medicine treating of health went under the general name of hygiene, and its main consequence was "diet"—which meant, for the Greeks, not only the regulation of a sick person's food, but the man's whole routine of living, especially the rules governing his food and the exertions demanded of him. Hence it was inevitable for the physician, working on a teleological conception of the human organism, to undertake a great educational task.

Werner Jaeger,
PAIDEIA (Volume III)

7 Time and the Consequences of Stress

WE DO NOT YET HAVE A SCIENCE OF ADAPTA-
tion, but it is becoming a matter of necessity. Using
methods like those of ecology, doctors will someday
evaluate the attributes of a person's life and their effect
upon his own specific constitution, his unique personality, and his equilibrium. This mode of preserving health
was the ideal of Greek medicine four centuries before
Christ, and a restoration of harmony between individuals and their environment is, today, the aim of healers
and medicine men among many native tribes throughout the world. Navaho medicine men do not understand how American doctors can expect a person to
recover fully from a gall bladder disorder, merely by
removing the diseased gall bladder, unless they first
touch the emotional and symbolic origins that caused
the trouble. Western societies have not evolved institutions for total medicine nor has western science syn-
thesized rules for adaptation and prevention of illness.
At present, an American doctor would be baffled and
paralyzed if he had to help create a harmonious living
pattern for a patient whose economic, social, and family pressures had battered him into a state of disease.
The doctor would not know where to start. Nor was
this the role he learned in medical school. Instead he
was trained to focus on the symptoms of illness in an
analytical and specific manner, even though he recognized that receptivity to virus infection or Cushing's
disease might evolve out of the patient's relationship
with a demanding family, an aggressive boss, or a
neighborhood cracking with competition and racial
strain.

Urban people, especially, pay a toll for the richness of their lives, for their range of choices, speed of communication, their job mobility, along with noise, crowding, and pollution. The price includes a variety of psychosomatic and mental illnesses. A recent Public Health Survey (No. 1000, Series 11, # 37) of 6,672 people showed that one out of five had either just had a nervous breakdown, or felt one coming on. Sixty percent had suffered from some nervous distress. Studied separately, each mental or physical symptom might appear to stem from different mechanisms, for they are extremely diverse. After all, high blood pressure, colitis, and diabetes differ just as do neurosis and psychosis. In the past medical researchers would attempt to localize physiological events that would produce specific symptoms, such as an ulcer or catatonia. Although everybody acknowledged that stress must play some role in the development of the illness, no one theory ever indicated how similar experiences of stress could evoke such an array of human miseries. We appear to be approaching such a synthesis now, for in the past there was one common dimension that was missing from all these researches—the dimension of time.

Today, a tentative model drawn from animal experimentation may help to reveal why the same stress or continued pressures might lead one person to become psychotic, another to develop asthma, colitis, or ulcers, while in a third it might affect the process of emotional learning, generate a severe and reverberating phobia, a debilitating neurosis, or a character disorder. It now appears that some mental illnesses and the many diseases we call psychosomatic may be generated by improper timing in a number of circadian endocrine cycles.

There are numerous unstudied time cycles in the temporal architecture of the human being—microseconds in brain cells, minutes, hours, weeks, and months. Although we know very little about these cycles and have concentrated on circadian rhythms, the accumulated data on circadian cycles is sufficient to show links between external events and the etiology of illness. We now know that we are transformed, hour by hour, as our nervous systems, metabolism, and vital organs fluctuate in circadian rhythmicity. Thus it is not surprising that our abilities, our vulnerability to harassment, trauma, or infection, the acuity of our senses and our symptoms of disease all vary, as well, in circadian fashion. It is no longer surprising that the drugs we take affect us differently, depending upon the time we take them. This same circadian rhythmicity has implications for the way we learn, and what memories influence our lives.

At present a few scientists are reshaping our concept of memory, and showing the path by which an emotional experience might be transformed into immutable memories or even into physical illness. These developments have come about as medical thinkers began to give up the last remnants of a bothersome belief—the archaic idea that it is possible to treat the body separately from the mind, or the mind as separate from the body.

The unity of body-mind has been clear for centuries, but we had a religious prejudice against acknowledging it. Without this unity a physical compound, a drug, should not be able to alter the experience of pain. A hallucinogenic drug should not evoke visions, phantasmagoria, and memories. The physiological underpinnings of the soul are dramatically bared when a selfish, apathetic, despairing person takes an antidepressant compound and becomes lively, affectionate, and outgoing. Depression is, at once, a state of feeling, behavior, and biochemistry.

Just as drugs or illness may influence our biochemistry, we now know that we can change it by mental activity in a manner that once seemed beyond our control. As Dr. Neal Miller has shown at Rockefeller University, people can learn to control their blood pressure, and to lower it at will. Hindu fire dancers in Ceylon dance on hot coals without blistering the soles of their feet, and people in hypnotic trance states have produced blisters when they were merely told they were touched by fire. What we think produces physical changes in our bodies. Conversely, however, the human mind is fragile. A flaw in metabolism, not now understood, may condemn a person to live out his entire life in the nightmare of psychosis or with dimmed intelligence—a fact that should give us new compassion for all people whose physiology has damaged their ability to function and to enjoy living.

Each person is, of course, a unique composite of subtle inherited characteristics, who is moreover shaped by his experience. As we have learned from the work of such people as Jean Paiget or Jerome Bruner, there are critical stages in development when children are ready to learn certain concepts, such as the relation between the apparent size of an object and its distance. There are critical stages in infancy when visual stimulation enhances coordinated movements, and when warm but firm parental attention is particularly crucial. There are periods, beginning around age six, when languages can be learned with particular ease. The idiosyncrasies of the family, and the brutalities, neglect, or rejections during childhood may predispose an individual to neurosis or to psychosomatic illness. The roots of such illnesses usually extend deep into the past, and in the hierarchy of influences, circadian rhythms may not seem very important. However, the twenty-four-hour day remains our major social unit. All of our experience is related to this clock, whose cycle is reflected throughout our endocrine system.

We rely upon this intricate system of brain and glands whenever we are in stress, whenever we anticipate a change, when we laugh, when we ruminate, confront anxiety or anything that asks us to adapt. Because our neuroendocrine system is rhythmic, the timing of a particular stress will influence the way we react, and how vividly, how strongly we may remember it. A few recent experiments with animals suggest that what we might call "gut learning," the learning of highly emotional responses, is modulated by circadian rhythms. They suggest that an emotional trauma, or a very tense and frustrating task, do not have the same impact at all times of day. Not even laboratory mice learn at a completely stable rate, nor is their memory as firm at all hours.

MEMORY

Some of these new facets in learning have come about as psychologists have tried to pin down the small but precise interval in which an experience is registered in the brain, and then programmed into permanent memory. A certain amount of evidence has indicated that there must be a brief period after an experience when its memory is not yet stored in a permanent way. Retrograde amnesia after an accident or trauma is not uncommon. A man's car skids on an icy road, and he crashes, full speed, into the buttress of a highway overpass, killing his wife and two children. When he regains consciousness in the hospital, he remembers the family bundling happily into the car and setting off, but no more. The drive, the road conditions, the events just preceding the fatal crash are not there. Within the laboratory, researchers have used drugs and electroshock to deliberately interrupt the memory process of animals in order to piece together the timetable, location, and biochemistry that causes experience to leave a lasting and retrievable trace in the brain. How long does it take before experience leaves a temporary memory trace, and how long after that before it enters what we call permanent storage? By interrupting memory at different intervals (after an experience) Drs. James L. McGaugh and Gwen Stephens have been trying to decipher the timing of the process. Learning and memory are physiological processes, so the researchers anticipated that they might be influenced by circadian rhythms.

Stephens and McGaugh kept their rats and mice on a fixed light-and-dark schedule so that their rhythms of nervous and metabolic change would be predictable. At certain hours during the day and evening, mice were given "learning trials." Each trial consisted of placing a mouse on a cantilevered platform outside a small hole in the side of a box. The little animal would immediately try to climb inside and escape the bright laboratory lights. However, the instant it climbed through the hole it received an electric shock. After this had been repeated several times the mouse would learn to huddle on the platform without trying to climb inside. If the animal managed to stay there for thirty seconds, his sign of restraint was interpreted as an indication that he had learned an association between climbing inside, and shock. Now, at a predetermined interval after the learning trial, the animal was given an electroconvulsive shock and again returned to the platform. If the creature waited there for thirty seconds, it was assumed that he had remembered. The number of seconds the mouse managed to stay there, and not climb through the forbidden hole, was defined as his retention latency.

When this experiment was repeated at different hours of the animal's light-dark schedule, the researchers discovered that electroconvulsive shock produced the greatest retrograde amnesia if it occurred in the middle of the animal's activity cycle when body temperature was at its peak. When the light-dark schedule was rotated 180 degrees, the animals entered a transitional phase shift in which the same training and shock produced different results. This strongly suggested that the brain processes and protein syntheses underlying formation of memory traces and what is known as consolidation of memory, must fluctuate in a circadian rhythm.

EDUCATION

Since an animal is more susceptible to amnesia at a particular phase of its cycle, one inevitably wonders whether human beings also vary in their tendency to forget what they have just learned. Would accident statistics show that people who suffer concussions in the middle of the day suffer more retrograde amnesia than those who are hit at night? Circadian rhythmicity in memory and forgetting may also have important implications for education, and for the understanding of neurosis. Discoveries of the biological bases of learning have had remarkably little effect upon educational practices. Although we know that a challenging environment in early infancy will influence the maturation of the adrenal system, and will alter brain chemistry and the ability to learn, babies are often left by themselves in dull cribs. If environment alters learning ability and physiology, we also know that individuals differ genetically in their talents and learning ability. Yet we overlook all these distinctions and dump students into classrooms where they all receive the same uniform program of teaching. Those who do not fit the method are left behind. This is ironic since the demands of a technological society make a high level of general education imperative. The continued social evolution of mankind will depend upon a cooperative and educated populace, making education a necessity, not a privilege. In this context it seems foolish to use techniques that leave out the so-called slow learner. Professor Willard Madsen, at UCLA, has performed studies indicating that retarded youngsters with low IQs may have poorer short-term memories than children with high IQs. However, the pacing of teaching materials may be made to compensate for this. Madsen found that when he allowed a relatively long interval between presentations of material, the low IQ children learned almost as efficiently as their bright counterparts.

Since the waxing and waning of attention among young children suggests a "biological hour" shorter than that of the adult, the effective unit for lessons might be under thirty-five minutes, rather than an hour. In addition, there may be optimum hours for learning, a bias that could be used to help the slow learner. Certainly people show consistent, lifelong predilections for morning or night activity. Physiological differences may be found in the circadian rhythms of the so-called lark people, who are most alive by morning, and the owls, who perform at their best late in the day, yet the owls are generally penalized by the usual scheduling of school hours. An early school day benefits the larks, but an afternoon session might be tested for the owls. Fortunately for coming generations, the burgeoning education industry is ushering in an age of home learning, in which a variety of devices from computers to television cassettes will permit a child to select his optimum time for learning. Whatever skills, sciences, images of the past, and artistic visions a child may learn during school hours, there is another kind of learning he does at all hours, which will influence his behavior for life. It is almost entirely uncontrolled although it is the bedrock of the personality, the emotional coloration that will resonate and shadow the actions of the adult.

FEAR AND EMOTIONAL LEARNING

Studies of animals have begun to reveal that emotional learning is not the same at all hours of the day. A frightening experience is more profoundly frightening at one phase of the circadian rhythm than another, and its imprint is more lasting. In a series of extraordinary experiments, Dr. Charles F. Stroebel at the Institute of Living has begun to show the unmistakable influence of time of day in the inculcation of fear. If man resembles his experimental stand-ins, rodents and monkeys, the timing of experience will have ramifications in dealing with emotional traumas, the crises of children, psychotherapy. Dr. Stroebel found that the hour of conditioning biased the speed with which an animal could learn that a clicking sound was the harbinger of a painful shock. Moreover, the animal's lasting anxiety, after the shocks had been discontinued for a while, also depended upon the time of learning. The experiments uncovering circadian rhythms in the acquisition of fear will advance our understanding of neuroses and phobias, and some of the unforeseen factors that bias memories and the intensity of feelings.

Animal studies have always required some ingenuity. Creatures who cannot talk must be coaxed to reveal their inner feelings by responses developed in conditioning. Bar-pressing is a convenient procedure with rats and monkeys; the animal learns to press a bar at a certain rate of speed, lured into continuous activity by rewards. Once it becomes a conscientious bar-presser, it is possible to measure how shocks, stimulation, and other maneuvers will affect its bar-pressing. This is an operant conditioning procedure, in the sense that it uses some of the animal's own natural motions. Usually, when a rat enters a new cage, it will explore hungrily or thirstily with its paws. Ultimately, if there is a lever in the cage, it will press it by accident, and if a pellet of food or a drink of water is released as a reward, it will take it and press again. At first, a reward follows each press, but eventually the rewards are spaced out, arriving periodically, and the animal learns to press the lever at a steady rate. New conditions can be super-imposed; a light or a sound or a shock can be associated with the reward. As the animal becomes conditioned to the added stimulus, a measure of its reaction is the change in its easily quantified bar-pressing.

These operant conditioning methods may sound very cut-and-dried, and too uninteresting even for a rat—until one remembers the frustration of placing a dime in a vending machine, and waiting for the coke that never appears. Not only do we use similar rewards on ourselves, often in the form of paychecks, but we become quite emotional when a vending machine doesn't work, a check is delayed, or we have to pay a traffic penalty.

EMOTIONAL CONDITIONING AND TIME OF DAY

Initially, thirsty rats were trained to press a bar for a drink of water. They lived in a rigidly controlled environment in which the schedule of light and darkness was used to align the animals to the same biological time of day, which was judged by body temperature or adrenal steroid levels. As soon as the rats became proficient bar-pressers, they were divided into three groups, each destined for the same training but on a different schedule.

Within the first four hours of darkness, the most active part of a rat's "day," an animal was placed in a training cage where it had to press the bar for water. Now it heard clicking sounds as it worked. When the clicks stopped, the rat received a brief electric shock.

Then the rat would be left unmolested a while and would resume bar-pressing. The clicks would start again; it would halt and be shocked. This happened repeatedly at the same hour each day. Typically, the animal would press the bar for water until it heard the clicks, when it would "freeze," defecating, urinating, breathing more rapidly, showing an accelerated pulse and signs we would call anxiety or fear.

Nothing the animal could do would avert the shock, and soon the mere sound of clicks caused the creature to stop bar-pressing and show signs of extreme "anxiety." Now the rat was placed in the training cage where it heard clicks but was never shocked. Initially the creature would freeze and stop bar-pressing with signs of anxiety. Then, later the clicks no longer scared the creature, and it would begin to bar-press again. When the rat virtually ignored the clicks and bar-pressed rapidly for water, it was said to have extinguished its fear response. Extinction was defined by the rate of bar-pressing.

In one group, each rat was extinguished at precisely the same hour it had been trained. The second group had been conditioned during the first four hours of the dark period, but went through extinction in the light period. After conditioning the third group was placed on an inverted light-dark cycle and tested at the same hour of conditioning. However these rats were now twelve hours out of phase with the other rats. After the animals extinguished, they were given a three-week rest and tested again. Sometimes a strong emotional response seems to disappear during extinction, yet reappears later, indicating that a "fear" memory persists and the response was not really extinguished.

Human beings may learn anxiety responses in a similar way. For instance, if a parent scolds a child before spanking him, the child may become anxious when he hears a certain scolding tone of voice. Years later, a similar tone of voice may evoke anxiety. One of the patterns that is known as neurosis is the inability to abandon a learned feeling after it has become inappropriate.

Normally, if a conditioned stimulus is repeatedly experienced with no consequence, an individual's emotional response eventually dies away.

Extinction is one of the aims of psychotherapy. By this process people try to unlearn inappropriate responses. A man who had a cruel mother may have to unlearn his hostile response to all women. A child, badly frightened by the sight of coins scattering from the hand of an accident victim, can go through life obsessively placing a cover over all loose change, unless he manages to extinguish the conditioned terror and revulsion evoked by coins. Presumably, if the original learning were weak, extinction would occur rapidly. If the original conditioning were strong, both emotion and behavior might persist, long outlasting the cause.

In his animal studies, Dr. Stroebel found that timing entered into the strength of conditioning. The repeated tests gave startling results. Rats showed strongest "fear" responses at the biologic time of day they had been trained. If a rat had been trained at 8 A.M., its fear responses were stronger then than at any other time of day. If tested at other hours, it would show less fear. The rats that were trained and untrained at the same hour took longer to extinguish, but when these animals were retested three weeks later, they showed no resurgence of fear. The rats that had undergone extinction trials at a biologic time of day different from the time of their original training appeared to extinguish very rapidly but on a retest showed a substantial resurgence of fear.

The time-lock of fear responses was too striking to believe at first, for laboratory results are not usually so clean. Goaded by cautious excitement, the researchers repeated the experiment with both rats and monkeys. They also tested other learning situations, involving escape, avoidance, and discrimination. They found that these "more cerebral" learnings showed no influence from biological time of day, at least none that could be discerned with their instruments. However, fear conditioning was clearly time-locked. When they conditioned animals at random times of day, the animals acquired fear responses very slowly. Moreover, these animals exhibited an unusual resistance to extinction. Even when trained at random times of day and extinguished at precisely the same hours, biologically speaking, they showed a distinct and stubborn persistence of fear.

PSYCHOTHERAPY

When anxiety is learned at random hours, it may have to be unlearned on a random schedule. This possibility has interested several therapists. The timing of psychotherapy sessions has no relation to biological time. If neurotic fears and anxieties are time-bound, the combination lock to a personality disorder may require "extinction" therapy at biologically relevant hours. Many patients in psychotherapy seem to fluctuate wildly, improving and then apparently relapsing into their old emotional habits. Although this uneven process, typical of much of life, has been accepted by long-term patients and their analysts, it may only reflect our current ignorance about the relevant time to apply the tools of psychiatry to the unraveling of crippling emotional responses, the process of extinction.

Behavior therapy, a potent and increasingly popular form of therapy, explicitly sets out to extinguish the unwonted responses of the patient. Dr. Joseph Wolpe and others have used some of the underlying principles of operant conditioning to train people out of their destructive emotional habits. Particularly successful in treating phobias, behavior therapists need to make a shrewd analysis of the patient's basic problem. They then teach him methods of relaxation, while gradually exposing him to the object of his fear, in a manner that makes him progressively less sensitive to it. The phase of the patient's circadian cycle may be relevant to this desensitizing process, for patients improve somewhat erratically, with occasional resurgences of fear and revulsion.

In the future perhaps blood tests will be used to schedule therapy, since the time when stress is most likely to leave a strong impression may be the time when certain adrenal hormones reach their daily peak. In experiments the rats were most susceptible to "fear" training at the beginning of their dark period of activity, when adrenal hormones reach peak concentration. Dr. Stroebel conducted a study to find out whether there was any real relationship between emotional conditioning and the adrenal hormone cycle.

LEARNING AND THE ADRENAL CYCLE

Animals trained at the end of the activity period, or the beginning of the light period, took twice as long to learn fear at the sound of the premonitory clicks. Adrenalectomized animals took somewhat longer to show fear, but even they showed the same circadian pattern. On the other hand, when animals were injected with metyrapone, a drug blocking the synthesis of adrenal hormones, they showed an almost uniform rate of conditioning, whatever the time of day. The drug virtually eliminated their rhythm of susceptibility, possibly by interfering with central nervous system activity related to the rhythmic release of adrenal steroids and other hormones. As an examination of control animals suggested, the rhythm of fear vulnerability paralleled the levels of the adrenal steroid, corticosterone, in the blood. The greatest susceptibility came at the peak, with lesser susceptibilities corresponding to lower levels. This correlation does not mean that the hormone level causes emotionality. However, the adrenal rhythm does offer a means of predicting when an animal may be most vulnerable or resistant to emotional stress and conditioning.

If human beings have a similar "clock" of vulnerability, then blood levels of steroids might guide us in the scheduling of unpleasant or painful medical procedures, not to mention the timing of examinations and other events that might be considered an ordeal for an adult and particularly an ordeal for a child. High levels of adrenal corticoids in distressed patients might be taken as a signal to avoid stressing them further at that particular time, or drugs might be used to shift the rhythm.

DRUG EFFECTS

While studying the circadian fluctuations of animal learning Dr. Stroebel discovered that an animal's rhythm might be shifted by a drug. The tranquilizer chlorpromazine and the antihypertensive drug, reserpine, were used to shift the rhythm of fear susceptibility in a rat. Rats are most vulnerable at the peak of adrenal steroids in the blood; injection of the antipsychotic drugs reserpine or chlorpromazine shifted the phase of the animals so that they became susceptible at an earlier point on their cycle. Electroshock produced a different reaction, delaying the susceptibility cycle, shifting greatest fear vulnerability to a later time. After ten shocks, animals behaved almost as if their previous emotional conditioning had been erased.

Since human beings are diurnal, we might expect maximum vulnerability to fear roughly between 4 A.M. and 8 A.M. when adrenal hormones reach their peak. It has never been demonstrated that man's emotional susceptibility is related to his concentration of adrenal hormones; however, in 1963 Dr. Stroebel and his team did show that monkeys had fear responses and physiological vulnerability in the early morning hours, coinciding with their peak levels of adrenal hormones. These monkeys were trained and tested in the same manner as the rats while under continuous examination for physiological changes. Implanted tubes sampled blood without disturbing the animal, while blood pressure, temperature, heart rate, and respiration were continuously measured.

PSYCHOSOMATIC SYMPTOMS AS MEMORIES

As the monkeys learned to fear the clicks, they stopped bar-pressing and began breathing hard, showing heightened pulse rate and other physiological changes. Weeks after the conditioning was over the experimenters noticed that the acidity of the monkeys' blood rose at the hour when they had been conditioned. Even twenty-eight days after the study had ended, one monkey showed disturbances in the acid-base balance of the body at the original times that he had been trained with clicks and shocks.

In 1965 the experiment was repeated. Now monkeys had a very small internal catheter implanted in the right atrium of the heart, as well as devices to measure heart rate, respiration, and brain waves. Emotional conditioning took place at noon each day for eleven consecutive days. Later, during a rest period, the animals showed an increase in pulse rate, rapid shallow breathing, and rising blood acidosis just before 11 A.M. For the next twenty-two days the monkeys continued to show blood acidosis around the former time of conditioning.

It seems that the body may "remember" a time of fear and continue to anticipate and react at that same biologic time despite the fact that the provoking situation has been removed. The demonstration that blood acidity could change at a presumably learned time of day may be an important cue in psychosomatic and psychiatric illness. The acid-base balance of the blood is a delicate and highly controlled equilibrium. It affects the entire body. When the equilibrium is thrown off, as in untreated diabetes or among people who have kidney or liver disease, they suffer mental symptoms such as lethargy or stupor. Hospitals rarely initiate around-the-clock studies of patients for several days in succession, yet there may be patients in whom blood acidosis is a vestigial response to a conditioned event that occurred at a significant time of day, such as the time of an ordeal, an examination, a job, or even a class. Such people might complain of symptoms that were never in evidence during office visits to their physician. In the past such complaints might have seemed doubtful and the patients would have been told they were hypochondriacs, but it is now clear that such "ghost" symptoms may resonate as an echo of unpleasantness.

REVERBERATIONS OF NOISE

Traumatic events need not be personal crises to generate symptoms. The stresses of a modern American city with its noise and human pollution may be sufficient to cause the symptoms of illness. One implanted monkey who was exposed to an ear-splitting noise every three hours for ten days showed thereafter a three-hour rhythm of physiological abnormality. It was monitored continuously for brain waves, respiration, pulse, and behavior after the ten days of noise were over. Computations suggest that for a long time afterward its brain and body were responding every three hours to that original unpleasant noise.

A few monkey experiments are not sufficient basis for radically changing city life but they may be premonitory. Noise is only one of the pollutants stressing almost every city dweller. Vague environmental stresses may have an overall effect as disastrous as a slow epidemic, afflicting a large portion of the population with debilitating symptoms. The development of psychosomatic disease is hard to track, for it happens gradually, like the gradual accumulation of fat in the arteries of supposedly healthy young people who "suddenly" have a heart attack. Within the intricate intermeshings of the body it has been impossible to isolate a single route, for instance, from the hypothalamus to the pituitary and the adrenal cortex, as the culprit in causing "illness." Ultimately, we may conclude that we are open systems and that these illnesses are the result of the environment we have created.

FEAR AND FREE RUNNING

In attempting to verify his observations on fear conditioning, to be certain that it was not due to light or environmental events, Stroebel and his associates replicated their original experiments. A large number of rats were prepared for three weeks in a controlled light regime of twelve hours darkness and twelve hours light, so that their circadian rhythms would be in the same phase when training began. From then on they lived in constant light.

Quite as Stroebel had suspected, this group did not show so strong an association of fear and time of day. However, when he looked at the behavior of individual animals he saw that 15–20 percent were giving inconsistent responses, while 80 percent strongly and consistently showed that the strength of their fear and extinction were linked to the biological time of day they had been conditioned. What about the anomalous 20 percent?

After the experiment Stroebel took the body temperature of each animal in the study every three hours. The consistent 80 percent showed a near-twenty-four-hour rhythm; but the inconsistent animals did not. Their temperatures seemed to be free-running, diverging from the twenty-four-hour rhythm by about fifteen to thirty minutes a day. Thus each animal was biologically a little out of phase with all the others. Was it the learned anxiety or constant light that interfered with the twenty-four-hour rhythm? Was their abnormal, drifting temperature rhythm the harbinger of sickness? The researchers wondered whether emotional stress might uncouple internal cycles, incurring the kinds of illnesses that bring people to hospitals and mental institutions.

A SHOCK-PHASE THEORY OF PERIODIC ILLNESS

During a lifetime of research, physiologist Curt P. Richter observed the activity rhythms of thousands of animals, in an attempt to understand the internal "clocks" behind the regular cycles of activity, feeding, and sexual response in healthy animals. Looking at vitality levels and the distribution of energy in animals, Richter hypothesized relations between age, drive, activity, and diet. He began to manipulate diet, lighting schedules, heat, cold, and many other aspects of the environment to explore the nature of the twenty-four-hour running rhythm. The function of the adrenal glands seemed crucial, yet removal of the adrenal failed to influence the daily period of activity, merely decreasing the overall level of activity. The next step was to remove part of the pituitary, which governs thyroid and adrenal activity, yet this did not eliminate the twenty-four-hour rhythms of the rat.

Dr. Richter postulated that a "twenty-four-hour clock" must reside within the central nervous system, and he systematically began to assault regions of the brain. He deprived a group of animals of oxygen, gave electroconvulsive shock, even suspended heartbeat for fifty minutes by freezing the animals. But as soon as the animals recovered, they resumed their twenty-four-hour alternation of rest and activity. Animals were recorded during starvation, dehydration, and extremes of heat and cold. Blinded animals began to drift by a few minutes each day, showing rhythms a little shorter or longer than twenty-four hours. Drugs, anesthesia, and toxins had no effect on the "clock." However, when the hypothalamus was partly destroyed, blinded rats began to eat about every forty to sixty minutes and drink every few minutes. They no longer slept, as before, in an interval of twelve hours, but wandered around in a continuous stupor. After making lesions in the brains of over 200 animals Dr. Richter surmised that the hypothalamus or related regions were important in regulating the activity rhythm.

He also experimented with intense stresses. He forced an animal to swim for its life under a torrential jet of water for forty-eight hours. He placed two fierce male Norway rats in a cage and precipitated a vicious fight by giving them an electric shock; after returning, exhausted, to their cages, these animals exhibited long, slow swings in their levels of activity but the twenty-four-hour cycle was unchanged. The slow oscillations in body weight and activity were reminiscent of the periodic illness that Dr. Richter had seen in his human patients.

He postulated that the "clocks" throughout the body ordinarily regulate functions so that they are out of phase, giving an appearance of overall smoothness. Shocks, such as infection, allergy, surgery, and physical or emotional stresses might upset the overall coordination of phase relations among these multitudinous cycles, setting one metabolic rhythm into phase with another in a manner that would generate a periodic beat and recurrent symptoms. Although purely conjectural, this "shock-phase" hypothesis about periodic illness had interesting ramifications and influenced a number of young scientists.

BEHAVIORAL STRESS AND ILLNESS

In 1963 Dr. Stroebel used a behavioral stress (no physical stress) to generate psychosomatic and mental illness in animals and simultaneously alter the circadian rhythm. During the early 1960s, two rhesus monkeys developed a predominantly forty-eight-hour periodicity in brain temperature. This abnormal brain temperature rhythm began to show up while the animals were being conditioned in unavoidable anxiety. Stroebel and his associates wondered if behavioral stress might produce abnormal circadian rhythms.

The laboratory was arranged so that twenty-four rats could be monitored simultaneously for body temperatures and activity and analyzed by computer, thus giving the researchers data in statistically viable quantities. They also began to look at the temperature cycles of implanted monkeys during a series of learning experiments. Prior to training, the rhesus monkeys had shown body temperatures with a clear, pronounced peak every twenty-four hours. It was a predictable rhythm that repeated each day and persisted under constant light in the early weeks of the experiment. However, after four weeks one monkey began to show peak temperature at intervals of forty-six to forty-eight hours.

DRUGS

There had been no change in the monkey's feeding schedule, its light-dark schedule, the cleaning of its cage, or the six hours of daily conditioning. At first the shift came about as a drift of fifteen minutes or half an hour each day. Soon its "circadian" peaks were occurring on a thirty-one-hour schedule, then abruptly it leaped to a forty-six-hour, then to a forty-eight-hour temperature rhythm. At this point the animal lost all interest in eating. The experimenters were amazed, but they wanted to protect their valuable subject. Monkeys are delicate and in the laboratory they often die very swiftly. Instead of studying this monkey further, its abnormal rhythm was suppressed by a series of timed injections of a tranquilizer during the subsequent four weeks. When the drug was discontinued, the normal twenty-four-hour temperature rhythm reappeared. The members of the laboratory had earlier made particular note of the monkey's behavior during intervals of abnormal temperature cycles, for it became noticeably neurotic. When the tranquilizer was administered, it grew less agitated, and several weeks later when the drug was discontinued and the twenty-four-hour rhythm reappeared, the animal seemed well again. The relationship between abnormal temperature rhythms and abnormal behavior demanded a series of experiments.

BEHAVIORAL STRESS—LOSS
OF A SECURITY SYMBOL

Dr. Stroebel and his associates began using seemingly mild behavioral stress to produce disturbances in monkeys. For six weeks of adaptation each day the monkey sat in a restraining chair facing a panel surrounded by four lights and a hopper that delivered pellets of food. A projector screen, capable of projecting twelve images, was just below, and on the left and right were two retracted levers. At the end of six weeks of training, each animal was surgically implanted with many electrodes and spent two weeks recuperating. Then they were returned to their chairs in the training chambers.

The monkey was not allowed to see other monkeys; it saw human beings only at 6:30 A.M. and 4 P.M. For twenty-four hours around the clock, the monkey saw images on the panel, and by using the right-hand lever, it could solve the problem and be rewarded. The left-hand lever was always extended, but pressing it produced no effect. Then began a ten-day program of what might be called escape training. The temperature in this testing booth was made uncomfortably warm. At this point, an accidental press of the left lever produced a gust of cool air. Once this initial task was mastered, the monkey quickly realized that he could escape loud noises, flashing stroboscopic lights, and mild shocks by pressing the left-hand lever. As it worked problems, the animal could rid itself of any annoyance by pressing the left-hand lever. It soon developed a habit of keeping its left hand on the left lever, apparently associating that lever with a feeling of security and refusing to let go.

After two to four weeks in this situation, the experimenters retracted the lever into the wall. There were no further annoyances, no high temperatures, loud noises, or lights. But now the monkeys could see the left-hand lever and not touch it. They became frantic. Initially, the animals spent hours trying to get at the lever. From this point on, twelve out of thirteen monkeys became increasingly disturbed. By the fourteenth day after the retraction of the lever, these twelve monkeys showed two trends. They were living under a regimen of twelve hours light and twelve hours dark, with regular feeding times, yet five animals showed a tendency to desynchronize or to be free-running. Their temperatures still showed circadian rhythm, but like men in isolation, they were desynchronized from the dominant twenty-four-hour cycle of the environment and their peak temperature came fifteen to thirty minutes later each day (in two cases it came earlier). The animals continued to perform their discrimination tasks, but were inefficient. They also developed symptoms that could be described as neurotic and psychosomatic.

ABNORMAL RHYTHMS:
ABNORMAL SYMPTOMS

Two of the monkeys developed asthmatic breathing. Two developed duodenal ulcers and later died of them. They all showed gastrointestinal disturbances, eruptions of the skin, and developed sores that did not improve under antibiotics. They drank much more than their normal amount of water. In addition to their other symptoms, three also began to show high blood pressure and blood in their stools. The five psychosomatic animals barely managed to function, but they did press the right-hand lever erratically to solve the problems that were continuously presented.

The other seven animals reacted very differently. They began to show a predominantly forty-eight-hour cycle of brain temperature after the recessing of the lever.

At first the peak came at sixteen-hour, then at thirty-two-hour and forty-eight-hour intervals. With the disturbance in the brain temperature rhythm, this group of monkeys began to show a distinct lassitude and weakness. They no longer groomed themselves and their fur became mottled. They began to lose interest in food. They performed unpredictably, if at all, on the right-hand-lever problems. Instead, they napped and their behavior became bizarre. Two monkeys spent hours catching what seemed to be imaginary flying insects and one masturbated almost continuously. Three convulsively pulled out their own hair. All of them tended to show very little interest in their external environment, and sometimes rocked or pulled at their fingers or pulled at their fur in the manic and stereotyped repetition of some psychotics. There were long periods when these poor animals seemed despondent and enrapt in their own bleak world. They resembled human psychotics in mental hospitals.

The differences between the "psychotic" monkeys and the "psychosomatic" group were clear. The psychosomatics showed desynchronization from the environment, a free-running temperature pattern like that of individuals in isolation. But the animals with psychotic symptoms shifted to a cycle of thirty hours or more, then jumped to forty-five- and forty-eight-hour brain temperature rhythms.

INSOMNIA

The sleep cycle also became abnormal and animals began to resemble the insomniac patients who toss and turn, lonely and agitated, in the night hours in mental hospitals. Normally, a rhesus monkey sleeps about nine hours at night in specific cycles of EEG activity. But the psychosomatic or neurotic animals drowsed about 60 percent of the time, slept lightly, and had very little deep sleep or rapid-eye-movement sleep. The sleep patterns found in these sick monkeys parallel human studies that indicate a number of abnormal sleep patterns during the beginning of mental illness. Like human patients who often nap during daylight but sleep fitfully and poorly at night, the animals frequently slept by day instead of night. Out of kilter with the routine of activity and eating, the psychotic monkey may have an apparent disinterest in his surroundings because of a need to protect himself from the demands of "daytime" which he cannot handle with a "nighttime" body.

DRUGS AND RECOVERY

The study of abnormal temperature rhythms and symptoms could not be fully explored because the animals were too sick. Monkeys are expensive, delicate, and require considerable care in the laboratory, so they were studied for six to ten days at most, then restored to health with drugs. Catheters in the monkeys' abdomens permitted a continual infusion of medicine that the animals would never perceive. For four weeks a tranquilizer was infused into the psychotic monkeys with remarkable impact. The forty-eight-hour rhythm of brain temperature vanished and there was an astonishing change in sleep patterns. The monkeys began to spend an enormous amount of time in deep slow-wave sleep. For three weeks they showed continuous improvement, but in the fourth week they became despondent and refused to eat. This despondency paralleled a stage in recovery from psychosis when people often go through a period of deep depression.

The depression was so devastating to the monkeys that an antidepressant was added to the infusion. Within seventy-two hours their behavior improved and a circadian temperature rhythm began to re-emerge. The monkeys started to behave normally again. Since the antidepressant appeared to enhance the circadian rhythm, it was decided that the effect might be further reinforced by administering the drug in pulses every twelve or twenty-four hours. When drugs were pulsed at twelve-hour intervals, the temperatures began to show small twelve-hour peaks, and larger peaks every twenty-four hours. At this point the monkeys again began to press their lever for food rewards.

RETURNING THE SECURITY LEVER

At a phase of the experiment before drug treatments were about to begin, Dr. Stroebel selected two psychotic monkeys and two neurotic monkeys. In their cages the security lever was protruded back within reach. The neurotic animals quickly recovered. Their temperatures resynchronized with the light schedule, their somatic problems abated, and so did their neurotic behavior. But the return of the lever had no observable effect on the psychotic monkeys even over a five-week period.

There is a strong human parallel, for psychotic reactions to stress are not as reversible as the emotional crises of normal or neurotic people. Psychotics are out of contact with reality. Compensating for the loss that precipitated his illness would not improve a psychotic.

Yet ulcers have been known to disappear "miraculously" in a wife whose husband was not going to leave her after all, and in a man whose insecure job was made secure again. Although a neurotic person may become very sick and distressed, the tragic and mysterious figure in psychiatry is the psychotic person whose grief or stress plunges him into an unreachable remoteness. Psychotherapy or a favorable change in environment may help the neurotic person out of his crisis, but they are not likely to touch the psychotic unless he has been made more accessible by drugs. After drug treatment, psychotics begin to resume communication with the world around them. The difference in stress responses is probably very fundamental. In numerous studies of schizophrenic interactions and family traits the lists of traits and stresses have not explained why some people become neurotic instead of psychotic. Researches on children of schizophrenic mothers and schizophrenic twins, and on some biochemical factors found in psychotic patients, suggest that the tendency to react psychotically rather than psychosomatically after extreme stress may be a genetic inheritance.

DIFFERENCES IN TIME STRUCTURE AND SYMPTOMS

Differences in time structure in the monkeys were notable. Most of the neurotic monkeys showed a circadian rhythm that was uncoupled from the environment by only fifteen to thirty minutes. They drifted, living a day slightly longer than twenty-four hours. Over forty to fifty days they would drift twelve hours, entering a nighttime phase when it was "daytime" in their cage. Then they would slowly drift back into phase with the light. Two of the psychosomatic monkeys showed a cycle shorter and faster than twenty-four hours; these were the two that died of duodenal ulcers. In human isolation studies a cycle faster than twenty-four hours has been exceptionally rare, and judging from responses on personality tests, it accompanies notable maladjustments in the individual. The evidence is still slim, but a fast free-running cycle seems to be an ominous sign. Moreover, the difference between a free-running, nearly twenty-four-hour cycle and a forty-eight-hour cycle exhibited by the psychotic monkeys is too striking to overlook. The mysterious differences between the withdrawn, remote, psychotic animal and the neurotic creature with his many physical ailments is not simply explained by the difference in body temperature rhythms. Still, circadian rhythms represent a complex harmony between inner functions and interaction with the environment. The organization we inherit will change during stress, and one outward sign may be the temperature rhythm, perhaps representing metabolic rhythm within. It is not known but it seems plausible that deviations from the external environment may produce internal dissonance, equivalent to a lack of vital biochemicals in the proper amounts and places or to being inundated with unnecessary constituents. It takes little imagination to envisage the kind of biochemical disorder this could produce.

Moreover, it is not hard to imagine that the result of a free-running rhythm (almost twenty-four hours in period but always shifting with respect to external day and night), would entail a very different internal disorder than would a forty-eight-hour rhythm. At present little is known about temperature, but even less about other physiological rhythms in man, and particularly in psychiatric patients. Psychiatrists have not been trained to look for temporal symptoms, whose waxing and waning give important information.

TEMPORAL SYMPTOMS IN MENTAL PATIENTS

At the Institute of Living, for instance, Dr. Stroebel's experiments have alerted the staff, who have discovered that several patients in the hospital show agitated symptoms and disturbed sleep-waking cycles like those observed in the desynchronized monkeys. One young man entered the hospital with signs of a peptic ulcer and a bizarre sleep schedule that had worried his family for two years. He would go to bed about a half an hour later each night, drifting slowly around the clock—thus performing a roughly three-week cycle in which he would sleep by day, then slowly revert to sleeping by night. Doctors had attempted to force him onto a twenty-four-hour sleep schedule by giving a tranquilizer at night and amphetamine by day. It didn't work. The boy continued his cycle. Like the stressed monkeys, his strange desynchronization from the everyday world began during a period of adjustment, when his family moved from his home town to another city and a new house. Current studies are beginning to show the internal desynchronies in this young man and other patients. Psychiatric records resemble X-rays—it is hard to find anything unless you know what you are looking for. Thus the animal studies so ingeniously performed by Dr. Stroebel's laboratory have offered some of the first clues of what to seek in psychiatric patients.

Indeed, on round-the-clock study, the adrenal steroid rhythms of the young ulcer patient gave a vignette of his distress. Unlike the normal pattern, his blood levels would drop low, then rise very high in a forty-eight-hour cycle, then in seventy-two-hour and 120-hour rhythms. Every two days or so there would be a "beat," a time when the steroids were exceptionally high and his symptoms became extreme: he was confused, could not concentrate, and would be wracked with stomach cramps, nausea, and vomiting. If judged by his confused, estranged behavior, such a patient would probably be classed as schizophrenic. The usual treatment would involve "antipsychotic" drugs, such as chlorpromazine. Treatment would not take into account the underlying undulations, abnormal tides of adrenal hormones suggesting that the illness involves mistiming in regulation of the endocrine system. In the future, Dr. Stroebel speculates that such patients might benefit from mild electrotherapy, sometimes called electrosleep, and from regularity of life as it used to be arranged in the old spas of Europe. Sleep studies of this same young man have indicated that he is trying to conform to the hospital schedule, but his body is not beating to a twenty-four-hour rhythm and he is therefore unable to sleep at night, but tosses and turns with agitated insomnia.

Most psychiatric patients are neither observed nor diagnosed over time. Indeed, it requires not only the willingness to make observations around the clock for days and weeks, but an investment in special methods and instruments.

COMPUTER NURSING NOTES

Ironically enough, it is the computer that may finally allow psychiatrists to see how all the factors of light, behavior, mood, and biochemistry fit together. A number of mental hospitals have installed computer systems that will allow them to track the minutiae of change in patients with a precision that was never before possible. The system began at the Institute of Living in Hartford, Connecticut. The Institute staff evolved a way of analyzing a detailed daily description of each patient. The procedure is simple: nursing notes, recorded by all nurses and aides, are automated. They consist of a checklist of traits, actions and descriptions, a comprehensive evaluation of the patient that is filled out every twelve hours. This checklist is distilled from years of research and many personality inventories, and in order to fill it out, the nurse or aide is forced to observe the patient closely.

The printed nursing notes carry 215 descriptive statements, with items on fastidiousness or sloppiness of the patient's dress, whether he groomed himself, ate, slept, read, went to classes. Did he seem irritable, sad, tearful, preoccupied, angry or hilarious? Did he take his medication? No nurse could write such a description of each patient on every shift, and even if she could, no doctor would have time to read it. But the computer can accumulate a changing profile of a patient's behavior over days or weeks. In the history of medicine, no psychiatric patients ever received such informed treatment. Most psychiatrists have to judge patients on the basis of little information, and have no picture of the patient in their absence.

The quality of psychiatric care can be greatly improved by this system. Like behavioral chromatography, the computer analysis gives a sensitive gauge of the patient's progress and his reaction to drugs. Many patients show rhythmic fluctuations in mood and behavior. Moreover, on close inspection, their recoveries indicate that there is a good deal missing from classical descriptions of mental illness. One depressed patient, for instance, showed a roughly three-day fluctuation as he improved. The initial sign of improvement was a decrease in his disorientation and disorganized way of doing things, although he remained anxious and depressed. Next, he was less anxious. Finally, he became less depressed. Like the paper chromatogram that separates an organic compound into its components and makes them visible by colors, automated behavior analysis is beginning to distinguish the many behavioral components of an illness like depression.

The computer is doing what "personal" attention cannot accomplish, and medical staff at the Institute is now able to predict when a patient is about to succumb to minor illnesses, a head cold, or the flu. Since the computer routinely analyzes daily habits, it has been discovered that the regularity of bowel movements is a good index of gastrointestinal health. If the timing should change for three or four days, it is the harbinger of a cold or other minor ailment. Although the automated checklist does not sound friendly and solicitous, it provides a medical staff with sensitive analysis of each patient, and automated notes could be filled out at home by clinic patients and their families, allowing the clinic doctor to see what happened to his patient between visits. If many people have feared depersonalization of medicine with the advent of computers, the opposite seems to be occurring, and the quality of medical treatment is radically improved. At least the doctor is informed to a degree that was previously impossible, and the rest is up to him. At the Institute of Living, descriptive profiles are revealing that quite a few patients suffer from desynchronies, like the young girl who stays awake all night pulling her

hair out, and who sleeps all day; the rhythmic nuances
of their actions resemble those of the stressed monkeys.

STRESS AND RATE OF CHANGE

Many of these patients cannot identify any
single event as a source of their bizarre symptoms of
helplessness and withdrawal or of anxiety and confusion. Stress may not be an event. Illness may result
from the cumulative impact of the environment rather
than from a specific factor. In America today the signs
of stress are everywhere, in the polluted air, the din of
cities, the crowding, pressure, social violence, and economic insecurity. For most individuals the most difficult aspect of life is probably the rate of change, for
whether events are good or bad, they require the individual to adjust.

Dr. Thomas H. Holmes, of the University of Washington School of Medicine, was among the first to
demonstrate that the rate of change in a person's life is
predictive of his health. Working with Dr. Richard
Rahe, Holmes created a scale to measure life changes,
and to rate each of the common events with a number
indicating the amount of impact it would have upon a
person's life. As they validated the scale, by questioning thousands of men and women about how they
would rank a vacation, the death of a spouse, or a
change of work hours according to the amount of adjustment each would require, there was astonishing
agreement. It was possible to assign a numerical weight
to a list of over fifty items, ranging from the relatively
minor (change in church activities would rate nineteen
points, a vacation would rank thirteen), to the monu-
mental change that occurs with the death of a spouse
(100 points, and the top of the scale). Not all changes
are unpleasant, but even the birth of a child (39) or
marriage (50) entails considerable adjustment. Holmes
and his associates, Minoru Masuda, Allen Wyler, and
Robert Casey, began to collate the life-change scores
of thousands of Americans and Japanese, with their

medical records. The pattern was so striking that the authors initially hesitated to publish the results.

In 1967 it was clear that people with high scores on the life-change index were more likely than their peers to undergo some serious illness in the following year. When the life-change scale was applied to 3,000 Navy men, the score was used to predict illness within the next twelve months. Indeed, men in the top 10 percent with the most changes of life style suffered about twice as much illness as the individuals whose lives had hardly changed, and who were in the bottom 10 percent. Moreover, the higher the score, the more severe the illness was likely to be. Even though the pace of life was quickened by a job promotion, outstanding achievement, buying a new house, or settling of business claims, the total amount of change was tightly correlated with amount and kind of illness in the subsequent year. The index would predict whether a person might have a stroke, cancer, or depression, rather than something minor, such as hemorrhoids, warts, or gastrointestinal upsets. Perhaps the person who is constantly exerting himself to adjust to a new condition exhausts some of his resistance to the infections that are always hovering about us. Perhaps the sickness of grief, the well known proneness of widows to illness and sudden aging, results not only from loss and sorrow, but from the need to compress a number of major life changes into a short period after the death. Adaptation has a physiological, a biochemical meaning and every time we cope with something new the endocrine system must supply extra energy. Viruses and bacteria are widely available: but not all people in contact with them get sick. It is the pace of life, the rate of change that has predicted illness.

CANCER

Cancer itself appears to be a disease of mistiming, in which cell division does not seem to follow the rule of circadian rise and fall that dominates the rest of the body. The beat of time in our tissues and cells was dramatically illustrated by Dr. Janet Harker when she joined together two cockroaches, with activity cycles that were out of phase. Brain tissue from animals that were in phase produced no tumors, but as the reader will recall the recipient of material from a donor with a different activity rhythm led to the development of tumors. Although this work remains somewhat puzzling, the phenomena suggest that time is a relevant property of living tissue. Cancer sometimes appears in the aftermath of emotional strain, perhaps through mechanisms similar to those that produce ulcers, colitis, hypertension, and metabolic illnesses. Judging from the Stroebel experiments, a purely emotional distress may lead to internal desynchronization. When a person's sleep and waking rhythm is out of phase with the rest of his circadian systems, he will ultimately ask parts of his sleeping anatomy to perform for his waking will, as if they were geared for daytime activity. Small displacements in the phases of internal rhythms might conspire to produce swells of biochemicals in the wrong places at the wrong times. Small displacements of circadian rhythms might, in theory, account for the entire range of psychosomatic and emotional illnesses. Certainly there is an implication in this new information that our own behavior, and the way we schedule our actions, has physiological potency.

PREVENTIVE MEDICINE

Our endocrine systems have limits, and the flexibility of our nervous systems is not infinite. If we are to live in a civilization that subjects us to accelerated change, that places our lives in ever greater flux, we may have to take prophylactic measures to protect our health. The Holmes data suggest that individuals must moderate the shifting and change in their lives. If there are major personal changes in one's family, one may have to minimize other adaptation such as the changing of jobs. After bereavement, divorce, retirement, or an accumulation of changes, an individual may think twice before setting off on a long vacation trip that itself requires continual coping. One may have to evaluate even the purchase of a new car or redecoration of a house for the amount of disruption it may introduce into an already fast-paced life. The external world will generate even greater accelerations, and the individual must examine the ecosystem of his own life to preserve a modicum of essential serenity. Otherwise the environment will overwhelm him, luring and cajoling him into constant transition—which, as we have seen, is destructive to basic health.

Medicine must again begin to consider the entire individual and his life style. Because today's medicine falls far short of that classical ideal, the patient himself must summon greater discrimination in choosing therapists and trying to ascertain why he got sick, assessing his own schedule, drug habits, and life style. People may discover, for instance, that they have uneven dispositions, undulating moods, which change their outlook or wellbeing, and bring periodic symptoms of gastric or emotional distress. Such symptoms might be generated if one of the person's circadian systems were desynchronized from the twenty-four-hour rhythm by only a few minutes. These undulations are likely to become legitimate criteria for diagnosis in the future, although fluctuations are not even recorded today, and most physicians do not have time to listen to details of their patient's everyday routines. Until a greater volume of research has focused medical attention on the consequences of timing, individuals must listen carefully to their inner whisperings, preserving some quiet and constancy, and considering how their own schedules of sleep, work, eating, and drug taking may be influencing their health in the long run.

8 PERIODIC SYMPTOMS IN SICKNESS AND HEALTH

I know a Gentleman of a tender Frame of Body, who having once, by over-reaching, strained the Parts about the Breast; fell thereupon into a spitting of Blood, which for a year and a half constantly returned every New Moon, decreasing gradually, continued always four or five days. . . .

Epileptical diseases, besides the other Difficulties with which they are attended, have this also surprising, that in some the Fits do constantly return every New and Full Moon; the Moon, says Galen, governs the Periods of Epileptick Cases. . . .

Richard Mead,
A DISCOURSE CONCERNING THE ACTION OF THE SUN AND THE MOON ON ANIMAL BODIES (1704).

It was the hand of Edward Hyde.

I must have stared upon it for near half a minute, sunk as I was in the mere stupidity of wonder, before terror worked up in my breast as sudden and startling as the crash of cymbals; and bounding from my bed I rushed to the mirror. At the sight that met my eyes, my blood changed into something exquisitely thin and icy. Yes, I had gone to bed Henry Jekyll: I had awakened Edward Hyde.

Robert Louis Stevenson,
DR. JEKYLL AND MR. HYDE

Men have expended infinite ingenuity in establishing the remote rhythms of the solar system and the periodicity of the comet. They have disdained to trouble about the simpler task of proving or unproving the cycles of their own organisms.

Havelock Ellis

8 Periodic Symptoms in Sickness and Health

EACH OF US PRESERVES A VERY PRIVATE AND complicated self-image. It is a portrait we agree to live by, and the people closest to us expect us to maintain the image, and to feel and behave today as we did yesterday and the day before. Children loudly resist such consistent expectations, yet ultimately most people grow up to accept the portrait. Who, indeed, seeing his reflected face in the morning, looks behind the geography of features to recognize the trace of a dream, to admit that the eyes are unfamiliar, hiding a sea of moods, antipodes of character, and shadows of forgotten essences in the infant face behind that in the mirror? A look in the mirror is not at trip in time. Most of us do not see a true image of ourselves, for the mirror reflects what we expect, and not how we are changing. One can know oneself better from a diary, a calendar.

The calendar can mirror continuous change and also reveal the predictability of supposedly "unpredictable" changes. It may be one of our most overlooked yet valuable means for self-knowledge and also for medical diagnosis. Most people go through palpable undulations of mood, health, vitality, food tastes, weight, even intelligence. Some of these recurrent yet unexplained changes and moods may stem from a slight exaggeration in some normal endocrine cycle, as do the premenstrual tensions of women. However, we do not usually think of normal people as undulating in their outlook. If anything, we demand that people be consistent and are intolerant of changeableness. In our unrealistic expectation of constancy, we look for a specific cause to "explain" every change in a person's behavior. Sometimes this habit of thinking generates discord, as people blame external events and those around them for any trouble, responding blindly without looking inward to their own transformations. The mere expectation of change would be helpful.

If you know that a person becomes irascible every fourteen days, you no longer take his outbursts personally nor provoke him at the peak of irritability. It is possible to cope with alterations that are predictable, even if these are serious changes such as symptoms of periodic illness. Many people with periodic illness have simply marked off certain days on the calendar when they will be unfit to carry on their usual lives. One excellent athlete from Cambridge University had a painful swelling of the knees every nine days, so regularly that his team would schedule games months in advance, avoiding dates on which he would be incapacitated. Many periodic ailments such as this one would not be helped by surgery, yet people with such illnesses have undergone surgery and medication unnecessarily because their periodic symptoms were never properly diagnosed. Medical mistakes and a good deal of social friction and domestic turbulence might be prevented if people were to keep diaries of their own undulations of mood, appetite, symptoms, and energy. Unfortunately in modern times the diary has gone out of fashion and our linear habits of thought make us seek an immediate cause for what may be cyclic human events.

Ancient peoples, lacking an explanation for events in nature and particularly within their bodies, looked to the stars for answers. In cosmology they observed major periods of recurrence, and they related human behavior and physiology to cosmic influences. We still reverberate to some of their myths, and suspect there may be some truth to the idea that lunacy, a word deriving from a description of strange behaviors at the full moon, may ultimately be explained. This is a time when psychiatric hospitals see a rush of new arrivals. We also tend to relate the phases of the moon with the menstrual period. In Italian folklore, for instance, a neuralgic

pain around the socket of the eye was called a *"chiodo
lunare"* or moonstroke. It was believed to begin when
the moon rose and to disappear as it set. Skin eruptions
and swellings also were thought to intensify with the
waxing of the moon, and improve with its waning.
Hippocrates and other ancient physicians always made
note of recurrent symptoms. Indeed, when treating a
long illness the Greek physician would employ a three-
day cycle, alternating the types of food and recreation
the patient should receive. The Hippocratic school believed that change itself is the only reality. They saw
that the patient could not be considered apart from his
environment, and that one country wasn't like another,
nor was one season like another. Thus diet and medication were varied according to region and season. Acute
diseases seemed to come from outside the patient, but
the physicians were ignorant of what it was that came
from outside and how it harmed a person, so they emphasized prolonged observation. Epidemics did change
with the seasons, and so did recurrent symptoms.

It is much more difficult for an American doctor in
the 1970s to detect periodic symptoms than it was in
ancient Greece. Neither patients nor doctors today in-
vite long periods of observation without any treatment.
Drugs are administered promptly, yet drugs mask
symptoms and may even change their periodicity. It is
therefore hard to know whether periodic illnesses are
growing increasingly common. There is some reason to
expect an increase. For example, experiments with animals have indicated that drugs and stress may leave
an aftermath of abnormal periodic symptoms. However, periodic symptoms are not always abnormal.

THE MENSTRUAL CYCLE

One of the best examples of a normal cycle in
which slight imbalances enlarge into a variety of symptoms is the menstrual cycle. Many other endocrine
cycles are experienced by normal people, with occasional symptoms, but none are so well-marked and
therefore so easy to study. The approximately lunar

rhythm of menstruation probably has its subtle counterpart in men, for in at least one study there have been signs of a monthly hormonal rhythm, and there are monthly mood cycles as well as monthly psychoses in men and adolescent boys. All of these other rhythms are likely to be illuminated by the study of women, for understanding symptoms and corresponding endocrine cycles in menstruation may create a model for understanding the quirks, idiosyncrasies, rashes, bursts of acne, changes in vision, and other expressions that perfectly healthy people feel as the result of other, less obvious cycles. Menstruation is just becoming a focus of study, as a cycle in which all women undergo major hormonal changes that permeate tissues throughout the body and inevitably influence the mind.

Premenstrual tension is a catchall phrase for a variety of symptoms that may occur at several phases of the cycle. Usually they happen in the four to five days just before onset of menses. It is estimated that 60 percent of all women experience some palpable change at this time; it may be just mild irritation, depression, headache, decline in attentiveness or in visual acuity. Numerous women experience a day or so of great energy, followed by lethargy that abruptly vanishes with the onset of menstrual bleeding. Some women become jittery, others weep or suffer insomnia, vertigo, and even nymphomania. Some women get respiratory ailments. Others are revisited by the symptoms of chronic illnesses such as arthritis, ulcers, or gastrointestinal ailments. For some women, this is a time when they feel a gustatory surge, a craving for sweets, while others entirely lack appetite.

Monthly changes in water retention may account for headaches and blurred vision. The high proportion of viral and bacterial infections that occur around menstruation have been postulated to be related to the effects of estrogen and progesterone on adrenal hormones. The pervasive social impact of premenstrual tension comes from psychological and behavioral change. This is the time of month in which women are most likely to be admitted to psychiatric wards. In *The Premenstrual Syndrome,* Dr. Katharina Dalton has summarized many studies of behavior change; some have shown that a large portion of crimes (63 percent in an English study, 84 percent in a French study) are clustered in the premenstrual interval along with suicides, accidents, a decline in the quality of schoolwork and in intelligence test scores, visual acuity, and response speed.

Dr. Oscar Janiger, a Los Angeles psychiatrist, began to notice that some of his women patients went through extraordinary spells of depression or belligerence. Sometimes in extreme cases even a transient psychotic was seen. The patients' reported quarrels with husbands and behavioral changes could not be explained purely psychiatrically, and when Dr. Janiger inquired, he almost always found that his patient was in the premenstrual period. It was common twenty years ago to suggest that premenstrual symptoms came from a denial of femininity or a resistance to sexual roles. It was also thought that cultures shaped attitudes toward sex and femininity, thereby enhancing or reducing menstrual symptoms. In searching the available anthropological literature, Dr. Janiger and his associates found no information that would allow a comparison of cultures, so they compiled their own questionnaire to elicit information about age, occupation, and social status with a listing of symptoms from mild to severe. They inquired about parental attitudes toward discipline, home, religion, sex, and menstrual matters. They also used items that would rate each woman on emotional maturity and a masculinity-feminity scale. Originally, they expected that they might see different symptoms in different cultural groups or even in subgroups.

There are many taboos about menstruation and the potency of menstrual blood, and menstruation is profoundly relevant to rites of passage and initiations into the adult role. In order to capture the possible differences, the questionnaires were given to extremely diverse groups of women: Turks in the American College in Beirut, Japanese students in Tokyo, Greek students, women in a Nigerian mission school, Apache Indians, and American women. The similarities were greater than the differences, and premenstrual tension seemed to be universal. These women reported a hierarchy of symptoms with abdominal bloating, irritability, nervousness, depression, fatigue, allergies, backache, headache, moodiness, and other symptoms that strongly suggested a physiological cycle rather than a cultural behavior. Premenstrual tension is a cycle also observed in primates. Dr. Janiger wrote to zookeepers and found that premenstrual symptoms of lethargy, belligerence, and irritability had been observed in rhesus monkeys, chimpanzees, and gorillas.

Dr. Janiger has assembled an enormous world literature on premenstrual symptoms for a monograph (in preparation) that will be part of a research program on the menstrual syndrome as a prototype for understanding less obvious cycles. His survey suggests why normal endocrine changes might produce physical and emotional symptoms. Roughly every four weeks an ovum is formed and dropped into the uterus where it degenerates; it is then expelled along with the uterine secretions and the process begins again. Although the pituitary gland plays a major role the process involves the thyroid, the adrenals, and several regions of the brain.

The cycle consists of several hormonal stages. The hormone that triggers the cycle in FSH or follicle stimulating hormone, which is secreted by the anterior lobe of the pituitary gland at the base of the brain. This hormone incites development in the tiny follicles of the ovary in which the ova develop. The follicles release estrogen to prepare the uterus for the coming ovum. FSH is sensitive to external, environmental changes, and this may be a source of irregularity with some women.

After the follicles are developed, another pituitary hormone, LH or luteinizing hormone, makes possible the final maturation of the ovum and its release through the rupture of the follicle. LH makes a rich yellow lining around the ovum. The ruptured follicle now becomes transformed into what is known as the yellow body—corpus luteum—that secreted progesterone to complete the preparation of the uterus for the coming ovum and develop the environment for the implantation of the fertilized egg.

During the cycle, estrogen rises to a peak twice, once during the midpoint at ovulation and again in the subsequent period known as the luteal phase. These estrogen peaks may have an effect on the adrenals, increasing the amount of active cortisol in the blood, although researches on this point do not agree. Cortisol is one of many hormones from the adrenal cortex that affects the nervous system, and increased levels of cortisol might be responsible for mild depression.

After ovulation, in the luteal phase there are increased levels of progesterone. Therefore progesterone is high between five and eight days before menstruation. It is also high in early pregnancy, and has been shown to have sedative effects, possibly causing depression as well as somnolence. Progesterone remains high until the first day of menstruation when it suddenly drops. But its effects are ramified. For instance, it may indirectly cause the increase of the hormone aldosterone at this time, which causes salt retention, leading to retention of fluids in the body. Among the most common premenstrual symptoms are abdominal swelling, weight gain, headaches, and problems with vision. All of these may result from increased fluids. Aldosterone reaches a peak level one to five days before menstruation and drops abruptly during onset of the period.

It would be impossible to enumerate all the important biochemical changes that occur as a result of the chain of hormones in the secretory phase just before menstruation. The hormonal cycle alters the levels and the rate at which electrolytes are excreted; these are charged metals that influence activity throughout the nervous system, thus affecting the senses, the heart, and all muscles. Changes in electrolytes have been observed by a number of researchers. Sodium retention increases before menstruation, but potassium, which helps metabolize sugar, may be lost, which may play a part in the cravings for sweets that can often be alleviated merely by adding potassium salt to the diet. Sodium salt, on the other hand, increases edema and in extreme cases may help to cause a cyclic mood imbalance so serious that it is stabilized only by medication such as lithium salts. Calcium, which appears to play a role in muscle function, drops radically with the onset of menstruation. This may be one cause of cramps, and some women have apparently prevented all discomfort by taking supplementary calcium along with vitamin D and magnesium, as indicated by nutritionist Adelle Davis.

The trace minerals, sodium, calcium, potassium, magnesium, copper and others, all bear electric charge, and in charged form they perform many services, such as holding water within cells or helping cell metabolism. Muscle contraction may be dependent upon a stream of calcium ions. Just as the body uses and excretes these elements in a circadian rhythm, there is a monthly rhythm in the amount excreted. This means that a woman who pays attention to her monthly symptoms may be able to decrease her salt consumption before the feeling of bloat occurs, or may add potassium salt or calcium to her diet in advance of her symptoms. In the very near future—because of current research—it should be possible to time treatments, with hormones, dietary minerals, and other substances, so that the abnormal symptoms of the menstrual cycle are unobtrusive, imperceptible, and merely the ghostly reminders of internal change.

Clearly, slight amplifications in important sex hormones such as estrogen and progesterone have their echoes throughout the nervous system and metabolism, in body and mind. Since 60 percent of all women do feel some cyclic symptoms, these symptoms must be considered normal—except when they overmaster the woman by their severity. When one considers how many functions, chemistries, and intermeshed cycles must cooperate to produce an ovum each month, it is astonishing that the cycle proceeds as smoothly as it does.

EMOTIONAL CYCLES IN MEN

The menstrual cycle is an excellent example of an almost monthly rhythm, and may have a less conspicuous counterpart in men, although less is known about rhythmic change in males. Dr. Christian Hamburger, a Danish endocrinologist, became interested in fluctuations of adrenal hormones known as 17-ketosteroids, sex hormones that are affected by gonadal secretion and can be detected in the urine. Dr. Hamburger collected and analyzed his own urine daily for sixteen years. When later analyzed by Halberg, a near-monthly rhythm appeared in the levels of 17-ketosteroids. This rhythm also has been studied by Japanese researchers who have been trying to understand psychoses that occur in adolescent boys and men in cycles of about a month.

In a variety of periodic psychoses, signs of oscillating behavior may parallel oscillating hormone balance. Dr. Hobart Reimann has cited the case of a young man, classified as a paranoid schizophrenic, who underwent cyclic alternations between feeling and acting male or female. He would be male for three or four days and then female for three or four days in extremely regular alternation. Some other patients have had attacks of homosexual feelings every four weeks, suggesting that there might be considerable oscillations in the output of sex hormones.

Emotional rhythms usually pass unnoticed in normal men. One of the few attempts to tabulate emotional undulations in the "average" working person occurred in a factory under the auspices of an industrial psychologist, the late Rex B. Hersey. In 1929–1930 he began to find that economists and psychologists were omitting an important attribute in describing the working man who was always treated as if he were invariant, as stable and immutable as a robot. Dr. Hersey thought there might be cyclic or rhythmic fluctuations in behavior.

He spent a year observing management and workers in industry, concentrating on a selected group of twenty-five industrial workers who seemed average in intelligence, who liked their jobs, and who seemed adjusted and "normal" in all overt respects. For thirteen weeks he watched and interviewed each man four times a day. He examined each man physically and then stopped the incessant questioning for a time. Meanwhile, he asked each person to rate himself on an emotional scale. After this recess, he began another series of observations and interviews with the families. Charts plotted for each worker showed that emotional tone varied within each day. Moreover, there were typical longer trends in each individual. One happy sixty-year-old, who claimed that he never changed, actually exhibited a nine-week cycle with a mood decline so gradual that he didn't realize he was refusing to joke with his fellows, withdrawing, and criticizing his superiors.

One twenty-two-year-old man showed a four-and-a-half-week cycle with no greater variation than a woman's menstrual cycle. During low periods he was indifferent and apatheic both at work and at home; an avid hobbyist in his elated periods, he temporarily abandoned his artwork when depressed. Another more temperamental person with a cycle of four-and-a-half to six-and-a-half weeks tended to be irritable and to magnify minor crises out of all proportion during the depressed part of his cycle. A third man with a five- to six-week cycle had manic periods of great vigor and energy during which he felt confident and outgoing. However, in his low periods, he found work a burden, he slept more, and was happy to be left alone to sit quietly. Typically, he weighed less and slept less in his high periods.

There are many indications that undulations of mood underlie the state we accept as normal in men as well as in women. Whenever these fluctuations become pronounced enough to be detectable, they may seem to be a chronic disease. Periodic illnesses probably include many symptoms that, like the menstrual syndrome, are an exaggeration of a normal glandular rhythm. There are some diseases, such as malaria, in which the periodicity comes from the reproductive cycle of the parasite. Yet others may result from the interaction of a normal rhythm with other normal internal cycles when they are slightly out of their proper temporal adjustment; for instance, a person whose body temperature was drifting in a cycle fifteen minutes longer than twenty-four hours would face the daytime world with a nighttime metabolism roughly every forty to forty-eight days. Unfortunately, these illnesses are not being studied extensively and there is little chance that most of these periodic symptoms would be correctly diagnosed, since the sufferer would be likely to receive drugs shortly after his first visit to the doctor.

PERIODIC ILLNESS

Periodic illnesses intrigued some of the great research clinicians of the early twentieth century, Drs. Werner Menzel, Curt P. Richter, and Hobart Reimann, who have summarized a wealth of case histories in their books. In *Periodic Diseases,* Dr. Reimann suggests that many of these illnesses represent the effects of sudden excitations within primitive brain regions such as the hypothalamus. In periodic illness there are changes sometimes in numbers of certain blood cells, fluid retention, local swelling of tissues and skin, recurrent fevers, and oscillations such as manic-depressive swings, intermittent psychosis, migraine, epilepsy, and periodic catatonia.

Some periodic illnesses can be inherited and have been known for centuries. Periodic peritonitis, a recurrent inflammation of the lining of the stomach or intestines, was described graphically in a seventeenth-century diary as a most terrible bellyache and vomiting that lasted about twelve hours every fortnight, with a cycle that spaced out to a month, and finally to six months. Although peritonitis may involve intense pain and even high fever, the symptoms are sometimes mild enough that members of a family have had this genetic illness without noticing it. It occurs in a number of forms, leaving the person healthy between bouts, which may occur weekly, biweekly, or monthly, and which may begin at any age. The most effective way to diagnose the disease is by registering the symptoms in a diary for weeks or months, a procedure that would prevent useless surgery and drugs. When periodic peritonitis goes undiagnosed, there is no way of advising vicitims against passing the disease on to another generation; it appears to be transmitted by a recessive

gene among certain ethnic groups from the Mediter-
ranean, and is most prevalent among Armenians, Jews,
and Arabs. Periodic edema, by contrast, seems to be
linked with a dominant gene and affects Caucasians
almost exclusively. This retention of excess fluids may
involve swellings in the hands, legs, or abdomen, is
sometimes painful, and can be serious when it occurs
in such regions as the throat. Here, too, a diary is
necessary to help clarify the recurrent cycle of illness
and prevent unnecessary surgery or medication.

Unfortunately, symptoms rarely are recorded graphically or on a calendar, and the medical nomenclature
is confusing. This means physicians and patients usually
do not realize the periodic nature of an ailment, especially when there are symptoms affecting the mind and
many parts of the body. Each symptom may be interpreted as separate, and many patients may go the round
of specialists, seeing various internists, surgeons, derma-
tologists, hematologists, and psychiatrists without diagnosis or relief. Lack of adequate records is particularly
sad among people with hereditary illness who cannot
therefore be advised against passing their illness on to
another generation.

Dr. Reimann's exhaustive compilation of cases and
medical lore includes examples of the curious role of
the periodic illness, purpura, the disease of mystics.
Medieval chronicles offer many accounts of mystics who
showed the stigmata, the legendary wounds of Christ,
quite regularly on days of the Christian calendar; a
number of people capable of showing the stigmata on
the proper dates were rewarded with canonization.
These people bled regularly on Fridays from all the
parts of the body where Christ had bled on the cross,
where nail holes had been made in the palms, the back
of the hands, and the feet. Some of these people also
fell into trances, experienced pain, enjoyed a "communication" with their Savior, and were healed the
following day. It is not known whether severe trauma or
self-induced trance induced the appearance of this seven-
day cycle. However, blood platelets have a life cycle of
about seven days, and the ailment may be an interaction between emotion and biological rhythm. Pur-

pura induces various kinds of internal bleeding and hemorrhaging into the skin. It may simply resemble recurrent wounds or bruises on the surface skin, but bleeding can be serious, even fatal, when it occurs in vital organs.

Less impressive than recurrent bruises, but irritating and painful, are recurrent ulcers, sores in the skin and the mucous membranes of the mouth, or the genitals, or other parts of the body. Usually they are preceded by detectable decreases in white blood cells and sometimes by fever. The disorder may start when a person is quite young, recurring throughout life about every twenty-one days. Quite a few periodic illnesses get diagnosed as allergy. One of them is the pain and swelling of joints found in periodic arthrosis. Swellings can occur in the salivary glands, and the first episode is often mistaken for mumps or tonsillitis.

One complex and baffling periodic illness is a form of periodic hypertension. In 1953 a shy, slight Irish nun came to the attention of Dr. Reimann. She had suffered distressing episodes of fever, initially lasting only a few minutes, but later recurring about every five days and lasting for twelve or more hours. Her fevers and headaches were given several tentative diagnoses, among them malaria, migraine, anxiety neurosis, and trichinosis. Finally it was observed that she had hypertension solely during the episodes of fever. Her blood tests, urine, and electroencephalograms revealed no abnormalities. Nothing explained her sudden malaise, chills, and the throbbing headache in the back of her head, which came with fever and an increase in pulse rate. Her blood pressure would rise from 130/80 to as much as 170/110, and the headaches would become very oppressive. An analysis of her fevers by Halberg showed that the episodes recurred about every eleven days. Diagnosed as a periodic hypertensive, she was sent to the National Heart and Lung Institute in Bethesda, Maryland, to be studied by Drs. Frederic Bartter and Sheldon Wolff. A forty-day study showed that she underwent sweeping changes in the concentrations of aldosterone and of several adrenal steroid hormones. Since these hormones play an important role in the retention of water in the body, their levels can create the edema that causes headache and high blood pressure.

MENTAL ILLNESSES: CYCLIC PSYCHOSIS

Most dramatic of all the periodic illnesses are the recurrent emotional or mental illnesses. Some plunge an individual through rapid alternations of normalcy and symptoms of illness every forty-eight hours, while others span weeks or months. By way of example, Mary Lamb, the sister of the great English essayist Charles Lamb, suffered a cyclic psychosis for fifty years, beginning at age thirty. During one of her psychotic attacks, she killed her ailing mother of whom she was very fond. A lawyer friend was fortunately able to save her from prosecution and placed her in her brother's custody where she lived a long and fruitful life to the age of eighty-three. Between her thirty-eight attacks, she was normal. The attacks were regular and at the first sign of a slight irritability in her manner, her brother would rush her to a hospital or put her in a straitjacket. Immediately after recovering, she went on her usual round of entertaining literary friends and writing books or stories until the next attack.

This famous case is of interest because Mary Lamb showed no signs of physical or mental deterioration, except that of old age later in her life. It is possible that some signs of deterioration in mental patients derive from interference with normal development and stimulation. The routine of hospital life deprives a person of his usual modes of expression and fulfillment; it is often humiliating, and the impairment observed among mental patients may be a result not only of illness but of the way we treat the mentally ill. Diary information might be used to restrict hospitalization for mental patients in the way we restrict it to the acute phases of physical illness. Chronic patients might lead more normal lives in the interstices between bouts of illness if the calendar of attacks permitted. Sometimes, however, the intermission is too brief, and then a hospital setting becomes crucial.

PERIODIC CATATONIA

A number of patients who alternated between a few weeks of normalcy and a few weeks of psychosis have been studied throughout their adult lives in what may be the single most thorough long-term study of an illness. In Oslo, Norway, at the community hospital, Dr. Leiv Gjessing and his father, Dr. Rolv Gjessing, before him, have been trying to discover what biochemical mechanisms cause periodic catatonia, an illness in which people swing from a normal state into one of hyperexcitability and violence or into a frozen state resembling paralysis.

The Dikemark Sikhus where the Gjessings studied these patients is the Oslo community hospital and was founded in 1905. The old stuccoed pastel buildings have high arched windows and towers, and the setting, on steep, wooded hills with lawns high above a small lake, is unusual for a mental institution, at least by American standards. Among farmland and lakes, the hospital grounds have an atmosphere of nineteenth-century New England. Patients are not isolated from the surrounding life of the community. Many of them work on the hospital farm or in its small industrial shops, treating the place as a home where they live, paint, practice the piano, construct furniture, and assist in the laboratories.

In the 1920s, Dr. Rolv Gjessing observed that some of his patients had fortnightly stupors interspersed with normal periods of behavior, and that when behavior changed radically, so did the physical appearance of the patient. During stupor, one man had sputum so thick it could be drawn out like chewing gum. His skin became very oily. Using the instruments available at the time, Dr. Gjessing measured nitrogen retention and other physiological functions, maintaining his patients on a controlled diet, and training nurses to get exceed-

ingly accurate measurements. With his own funds, he
furnished a biochemistry laboratory in one of the men's
wards, for he suspected that metabolic flaws involving
the thyroid gland underlay the illness. His work has
been continued by his son, Leiv Gjessing, who has had
the advantage of studying and caring for old men who
once knew him as a little boy. Exacting around-the-
clock studies have won extraordinary cooperation from
these patients, who treated him as a young nephew.

Since catatonic patients have normal periods, they
develop pretty much in pace with their peers. The
periodic psychosis often begins in the early twenties,
sometimes abruptly following a stress. Dr. Gjessing has
speculated that stress, brain damage, or perhaps a
metabolic shock due to some auto-immune reaction
might damage a metabolic regulator and thus produce
the clocklike symptoms of catatonia. When catatonic, a
patient may seem to be out of contact, mute, and immobile for several days at a time, but according to the
diaries and reports of such patients they are internally
experiencing an implosive intensity. One man, who has
been hospitalized since 1935, always begins to talk to
himself during his transition; for a day or two he would
babble aloud in a manic fashion, reclining with his head
and feet raised. He would stay for several days in a
position that is practiced a few seconds at a time by
gymnasts. Eyes open and frozen, his hands clammy,
skin oily, he lost his appetite, and had a high pulse rate
and blood pressure. He looked like a wax doll until he
began to recover.

This paralyzed state masks an intense hallucinogenic
state resembling experiences under mescaline, as can
be seen in these recollections of one patient:

> In the stupor many strange events enter the soul.
> The soul is bewitched. [Ordinary experiences, such as
> being washed, displeased him, and the sensation was
> strange.] Everything was polar. . . . In order that the
> sun should shine, the soul had to have psychic trouble,
> the trouble corresponding in strength in proportion to
> the strength of the sun. . . . Like the Tree of Knowledge,
> everyone who eats the fruit must die.

If you ask a simple question, I hear it, but it's as if from outside the room. People help but the people become transformed into words, and from words people are transformed into a kinemagraphic picture . . . thought stops but for a few fixed points that act as a lighthouse. . . .

Asked why he did not move in bed, he answered:

The soul and thinking prevent moving, prevent muscles from doing what I want them to. Impulses are not carried out, and this seems natural. Not to want anything and to have no interest in anything is important. Former interests do not penetrate.

This state suggested a kind of intoxication to Dr. Gjessing, the kind which might come from mishandled nitrogen. Over years of daily biochemical studies, it has become clear that nitrogen metabolism is faulty in these catatonic patients. Nitrogen is a key element of all protein and all body tissue. It is absorbed from plant and animal protein and metabolized in the liver. In general, the body maintains a balance, excreting about as much as it takes in. During intervals between stupor attacks, the urine shows a retention of nitrogen, but the balance is shifted noticeably during attacks of illness. In patients with catatonic excitement, nitrogen was over-excreted during the normal interval and retained during the phase of excitement. Thus, urinary ammonia was higher at the beginning of an attack than at the end. The electrolytes, phosphate and sodium chloride, are excreted more during attacks.

Graphs of daily temperature or of urine pigmentation in individual patients taken over ten years show such regular changes that one could predict, to within a day, when an attack would fall in the coming year. The oscillation between normal behavior and illness has been found to correspond to major oscillation in many metabolic functions. The periodic catatonic swings between phases resembling certain aspects of patients with underactive or overactive thyroid glands. Thyroxin, a thyroid extract, has prevented nitrogen retention and has successfully ameliorated the symptoms in a number of patients. These people have lived normal lives for years. When they stop thyroid treatment, however, they relapse.

MANIC-DEPRESSION

During the late nineteenth and early twentieth centuries in Munich and Vienna, a number of doctors kept careful diaries of mood change in patients. These showed weight and behavior fluctuations over many years, sometimes revealing a manic-depressive trend unfolding over fifteen months or two years. The person who has manic-depressive symptoms today is fortunate if his mood changes swiftly, for he is likely to be diagnosed and studied. Dr. Curt Richter has written about the famous case of a man with forty-eight-hour manic-depression. A foremost salesman in the Washington, D.C., area, he would be so morose and apathetic during his depressed twenty-four hours that he would drive to a customer's office and find himself unable to move from the car, sitting miserably there for hours. Yet, on good days, he was the epitome of the aggressive, garrulous salesman. He finally adapted to his illness by accepting appointments only on alternate days.

Manic-depressives with long cycles are likely to go undetected and may do themselves harm, for in their manic phases they are prone to serious misjudgments and grandiose illusions. Such people seem to go through a transformation of character, from normal diffidence and activity to superconfidence and unbounded energy, often coupled with pretentious business plans and outrageous gambles. The ceaseless activity of a person in an elated phase involves an astonishing output of energy.

At present a number of forty-eight-hour manic-depressive patients are being studied at various hospitals around the world. Dr. F. A. Jenner in Sheffield, England, has been watching a former boxer from Yorkshire who became manic-depressive after a bad accident in the 1950s. For twenty-four hours he is overactive, talkative, sometimes testy, with grandiose ideas about science and the world; typically, at some time in his sleep he changes. He awakens feeling lethargic and bleak, rises reluctantly, later than usual, and falls asleep earlier that night. On his sluggish days he urinates and excretes more but eats and drinks less than on manic days.

For eleven years this man has lived in a clinic, eating a controlled diet and being measured and tested every day for physiological changes that might match behavior. He has taken performance tests; his urine and blood are repeatedly tested for a variety of hormones, sugars, and amino acids. When he stayed in bed on a liquid diet, he showed a forty-eight-hour alternation of weight, urine volume, and volume of red blood cells. It appears that the amount of fluid within and around cells was shifting with his moods. Fluid retention within and around nerve and other cells has been thought to be controlled by a balance of charged elements. The sodium and potassium content of this man's saliva and urine did coincide with his alternating moods. On depressed days, the saliva sodium was very low and saliva potassium was very high; on manic days it was exactly the opposite. The influence of electrolytes on behavior did not, however, seem very strong in the light of a subsequent experiment.

In 1963 Dr. Jenner took his patient into a hospital isolation room where a team of observers supplied meals and collected urine samples from both of them. The lighting was regulated so that the day was twenty-two hours long, but neither Jenner nor his patient knew the exact day length. The experiment lasted eleven real days in which they lived twelve cycles. Throughout this period, Dr. Jenner, living in the compartment, took notes on his patient while unseen observers outside made behavior and physiological notes on him and his patient. His patient, meanwhile, alternated between morose silence and an uncontrollable railing, scheming, and incessant shouting; when manic he yelled and thrashed about in an agitated manner that was almost too much for Dr. Jenner to endure. Curiously enough, the patient's moods adapted to a twenty-two-hour day;

he alternated from lethargy to mania in a forty-four-hour cycle. Yet, excretion of water and electrolytes largely remained on a twenty-four-hour cycle, and did not explain the adaptation of his moods to a twenty-two-hour day.

Since the balance of electrolytes in the nervous system seems critical to the function of nerve cells, the effects of lithium, an alkali metal, have attracted great interest among psychiatrists. In 1967 Dr. Jenner gave his patient lithium salts, and for the long period when he was taking them, the man remained essentially normal. When he stopped taking the drug for a couple of weeks, the hints of his old alternation began to show through. One day he was articulate, even over-talkative, and responsive. The next day he was slow at finding words, less ebullient, and less volatile. His manic-depressive cycle had been obliterated by lithium, yet when he was given doses of sodium, the alternating mania and depression returned. Similar results have been seen with lithium use throughout the world. It is the one medication that seems to be effective in "normalizing" people with manic-depression and it also works with other cyclic psychoses. The mechanisms by which lithium effectively damps these mood cycles is not fully understood.

UNDETECTED CYCLES

The pieces of the puzzle are likely to be fitted together in animal studies, and in studies of patients with remarkably regular shifts in mood. However, it would be unfair to leave the impression that most manic-depressives are so clocklike in their alternations, for that is not so. Several years ago, a group of psychiatrists led by Dr. J. Angst collaborated on an international study of cyclic depression and manic-depression. They unearthed no formula that could describe the timing of attacks, which were in some cases irregular. It is difficult, perhaps impossible, to evaluate the regularity and spacing of attacks in people who have been taking antidepressant and antipsychotic drugs, and it goes without saying that almost every patient in a psychiatric hospital today is maintained on medication. This has made it possible for many patients to live at home, and immediate treatment is a blessing to the person in throes of psychosis, panic, or depression. Nonetheless, drugs that alleviate symptoms do not cure the illness, and they do obscure its calendar of occurrence, hiding the mysterious biochemical fluctuations that cause a normal, bright photographer to take on more and more assignments, working excitedly night and day, speaking rapidly, urging his wife to consider buying a new house, urging his partner into a new field of advertising. Over the months this prodigious outpouring of ideas, vitality, disconnected fragments of creation or speculation, reach a fever pitch in which the person sleeps less, shows weight loss, and near-derangement, when gradually it subsides. But a year later, for reasons that all seem plausible, the man is apathetic and moody, business goes badly, and he can no longer concentrate, being enrapt in a sour denunciation of his own failures and hopeless of the future. In miniature, we are all familiar with the long roller-coaster of energy and mood, but we usually do not recognize that it is a recurrent cycle.

Similarly, a person may find that he gets skin ulcers repeatedly or migraine headaches. He may even have a mild peritonitis, that he ignores as "stomach troubles." Today, however, it is unlikely that a doctor will diagnose periodic symptoms, since the person is likely to have received drug therapy, or perhaps in some cases major surgery. Mild undulations that reappear over a time course of three to six months generally are not identified as such. A calendar survey of the symptoms of healthy, normal people would probably disclose that an astounding number of us show regular undulations in weight, vitality, optimism, work output, pessimism, appetite, sleep, undulations in vibrancy and dullness, endeavor and apathy, moodiness and imperturbability, malaise and robust well-being. To our linear habits of thought, each of these changes often seems to stem from a specific event. Yet such oscillations may be our normal state: when exaggerated slightly they impair our functioning and constitute illness. Were we to identify these cycles by keeping diaries of our many dimensional changes, a yearly calendar of aches, pains, joys, weight, and other "trivia," we could anticipate many of the ups and downs, accommodating ourselves to the "bad" days and taking full advantage of the "good" ones. Indeed, it seems likely that a number of illnesses are mere exaggerations of these normally unobtrusive cycles, and like premenstrual symptoms could be dealt with more effectively if the symptoms were anticipated. At present many people respond to a slight symptom by medicating themselves at once, with sedatives, tranquilizers, stimulants, antibiotics, antihistamines, and other drugs. Many people, for instance, do not imagine that their migraine headaches may occur in cycles. According to a study conducted by Dr. F. Sicuteri and his co-workers in Italy, these headaches often recur periodically, and may involve an inability to handle the amino acid, tyramine, which is abundant in cheese, bananas, and many other foods. People with migraines often attribute them to current tensions, although they may be part of a complex of symptoms that are periodic, and in some cases appear to be genetic.

Since medical schools do not train doctors to search for signs of periodicity in illness, they, too, expect linear relationships of cause and effect, and they tend to treat patients *ad hoc*. People who suspect that they have recurrent symptoms ought to be vociferous about it when they consult a doctor, and try to document the periodicity by keeping a calendar record. Diagnoses in the future will be vastly more precise: it will be possible for each individual to keep a computerized record of his entire medical history. A doctor need not rely on a patient's memory of previous symptoms and treatment, since he will have access to the total memory of the computer, and its swift digest of information. At present, in our mobile society, the physician and specialist are at a great disadvantage in trying to identify recurrent symptoms. The American suburbanite is likely to move at least once in five years, and some populations of executives, engineers, and other professionals do even more shifting around. After arriving in a new job, home, and neighborhood, people seek a nearby doctor, a physician who on first encounter has no more suspicion than the patient that the problem is not a new one. Often the physician makes what seems a sensible diagnosis, and prescribes a drug. Neither he nor his patient realize that the pain would have abated without help, if they had just waited. In some instances, more dire symptoms might lead to a laparotomy in which tissue may be removed from the abdomen, offering some temporary relief until the cyclic recurrence. Needless drugs and surgery could be prevented if individuals would keep records of their stomachaches, edema, fevers, headaches, and swollen knees. As Dr. Reimann lamented, in preparing his richly informative and documented monograph on periodic disorders, no foundation or agency seemed interested in subsidizing collations of case histories, nor did they seem to understand that periodicity itself might give clues to the nature of the malady. Dr. Reimann and a handful of men like him were many years ahead of their time. Society now has at its disposal—if it cares to use the tool properly—a means for discovering unprecedented information about disease and health in the population. The infinite memory and rapidity of data analysis by computer now offer a bank into which we can deposit the most detailed account of our health and medical histories. No doctor could know, or even keep on file, all that a computer can rapidly summarize about a patient.

In the near future, as people begin to sense the ecology of their lives, their biological rhythms, and their diseases, there is likely to be a kind of cultural outburst, in which people will become self-aware, conscious of their periodicities. Research on such illnesses as periodic hypertension, periodic catatonia, and manic-depression may begin to give a new picture of these ailments, and reveal the meaning of the interval between attacks, the origin of the periodicity itself.

There is only a hair's-breadth between health and illness, normalcy and derangement. It is often a matter of degree. Like women with their monthly cycle, men will discover that they too undergo rhythmic monthly or bi-monthly changes in mood, weight, and intellectual performance. As these patterns become widely known they may change the expectations and customs of society so that there is leeway for the elusive changes and inconsistencies that are at the heart of being human. For those whose periodic symptoms outstep the limits of control, we may take a more understanding and restorative attitude, treating their periodic physical or emotional symptoms so that they can lead normal lives between attacks. Many researches in progress may eliminate the abnormal cycles; for example, studies of electrolyte balance and the use of lithium carbonate may constitute a first step in eliminating disastrous manic-depressive mood swings.

SEASONAL TRENDS

Many tides of mood and of allergies and ulcers seem to undulate with the seasons. Dr. Angst and his team found seasonal trends in depression that might be related to hormone regulation. People with endogenous depressions or manic-depressive illness tend to be most sick in autumn and spring. Long ago the Greeks noticed seasonal trends in symptoms, for they considered health to be part of a harmony with nature. The ancient treatise, "On Airs, Waters, and Places," advises that the medical scholar must first study the effects of the seasons of the year, for ". . . human diseases change along with the seasons." As Aretaeus long ago wrote,

The melancholic cases tend towards depression and anxiety only . . . If, however, respite from this condition of anxiety occurs, gaiety and hilarity in the majority of cases follows, and this finally ends in mania. Summer and autumn are the periods of the year most favorable for the production of this disorder, but it may occur in spring.

Presumably there are many subtle changes in our metabolism that are consonant with seasonal change. As automatic data analysis reveals unsuspected rhythms in man, we may begin to see cycles with very long periods that are not now documented. There are annual symptoms, and even psychoses that seem to be related to our glandular adaptation to the seasons. For instance, we secrete something known as "summer hormone," a thyroid product that helps to reduce body heat. But little is known about it or about how the secretion is triggered to anticipate the hot summer months.

Until recently, only sketchy statistics and anecdotal reports hinted that there were annual rhythms in the number of suicides and suicide attempts, and that deaths from arteriosclerosis do not occur evenly throughout the year. Statistics from the Minnesota Department of Health have been analyzed by Dr. Halberg, and suggest that there are cycles in these events. There is an increase in the number of deaths from arteriosclerosis that peaks in January, a peak in suicides around May, and a peak in accidental deaths around July and August. Some of these apparent rhythms may be explained by social customs, in which throngs of summer vacationers, for instance, may be hurtling around the countryside exposing themselves to unusual physical dangers and highway traffic. However, some of these statistics more likely disclose seasonal changes within us, and may help to solve some of the mysteries of medical and psychiatric disorders.

ARCTIC WINTER MADNESS

Travelers to the Arctic Circle, to Norway, Finland, or Russia have heard of a strange affliction, a transient madness that occurs among the Eskimos, Lapps, and Finns. It is sometimes called Arctic hysteria, or "winter madness."

Many Eskimo rituals were evolved to confront this yearly crisis, so beautifully described by Sir James Frazer in *The Golden Bough*.

In late autumn, when storms rage over the land and break the icy fetters by which the frozen sea is as yet

but slightly bound . . . the Esquimaux of Baffin Land
fancy they hear the voices of the spirits who people the
mischief-laden air. Then the ghosts of the dead knock
wildly at the huts, which they cannot enter, and woe to
the hapless wight whom they catch; he soon sickens and
dies. Then the phantom of a huge hairless dog pursues
the real dogs, which expire in convulsions and cramps
at sight of him. All the countless spirits of evil are
abroad striving to bring sickness and death, foul weather
and failure in hunting on the Esquimaux. Most dreaded
of all these spectral visitants are Sedna, mistress of the
nether world and her father. . . .

In 1969, Joseph Bohlen, who was then a venture-
some graduate student at the University of Wisconsin,
found what may be clues to the winter psychoses of
people in polar latitudes. The malaise may come on
rapidly, with dramatic symptoms resembling psychosis
that last for only a few days, a few hours, or a couple
of weeks—always in winter. Dr. Bohlen, aided by his
wife, lived among the Eskimos of Wainwright, Alaska,
and observed that there was also an annual physiological rhythm.

The Bohlens studied ten individuals around the clock
for ten days, during each season of the year. It took a
heroic effort to gather information, for they had to visit
their subjects' houses every two hours. They took oral
temperature, blood pressure, pulse, samples of urine,
and made tests of hand-grip strength, and of eye-hand
coordination. Because Eskimos live in almost unchang-
ing darkness in winter and nearly perpetual light during the summer months, many people had wondered
whether, on strict examination, they would show circadian rhythms like those of people in temperate zones.
They did indeed show twenty-four-hour rhythms in
body temperature and urinary potassium. However, it
was the rhythm of excreted calcium that drew the interest of the Bohlens.

Like sodium and potassium, calcium has a profound
influence upon the functioning of the nervous system,
since it appears to be essential in the transmission of
nerve messages. Calcium deficiencies are known to

affect the parathyroid and thyroid glands, and thus indirectly influence the entire endocrine system. When people have had too little free calcium they have shown symptoms like those known as "anxiety neurosis." Thus calcium may play an indirect role in emotional disorder. As the Bohlens discovered, Eskimos excreted eight to ten times as much calcium in the dark winter months as they did in summer. It was a pronounced annual rhythm.

Sunlight plays a role in modulating the amount of calcium in the body, since sun forms vitamin D on the skin, and the vitamin enhances the absorption of calcium from food. Sizable excretion of calcium during the winter, when absorption is likely to be diminished, gives a possible clue to the seasonal emotional disorder of the Eskimo, the Arctic winter madness. Buried in the time cycles of man's physiology, as they are entrained and influenced by the environment, we may begin to learn why certain seasons bring increases in suicides, or in symptoms of such ailments as ulcers or asthma, which rise in spring and fall. Even normal people experience seasonal changes, feeling a vibrant anticipatory restlessness in spring and fall, as if internal cues were perforating consciousness with signs of metabolic adaptation to the changes in the world of nature. We cannot extricate ourselves and our symptoms from the cycles of the natural world, for we are part of that vast ecosystem even if we live in electrified, steam-heated, glass-plated, chrome-striped honeycombs in modern cities. Even if we never have to adapt to warm weather or cold, the seasons enter through our eyes.

Perhaps, as the next chapter may indicate, our own cycles are synchronized with those of earth, for like birds, plants, and other mammals we respond to the effects of light, the transition from long to short days. Some of our periodic symptoms, whether they are the springtime melancholy or the stirrings of love, may be synchronized by the seasons, as our activity and rest is synchronized by night and day.

9 LIGHT—A LINK WITH THE RHYTHMS OF EARTH

Linnaeus Flower Clock

 6 A.M. — Spotted Cat's Ear opens
 7 A.M. — African Marigold opens
 8 A.M. — Mouse Ear Hawkweed opens
 9 A.M. — Prickly Sowthistle closes
10 A.M. — Common Nipple Wort closes
11 A.M. — Star of Bethlehem opens
12 noon — Passion Flower opens
 1 P.M. — Childing Pink closes
 2 P.M. — Scarlet Pimpernel closes
 3 P.M. — Hawkbit closes
 4 P.M. — Small Bindweed closes
 5 P.M. — White Water Lily closes
 6 P.M. — Evening Primrose opens

Carolus Linnaeus (1707–1780)

In spring a young squirrel's fancy turns because the days are getting longer, and exposure to longer light periods sets off a chain-reaction involving the brain and pituitary gland, resulting in release of hormones that affect sex hormone levels and in turn cause the sex glands to enlarge and produce their sex hormones.

Joseph Meites

Love everything in the universe, because sun and the earth are but one body.

ANCIENT CHINESE MAXIM

9 Light—A Link With the Rhythms of Earth

LIKE INFINITESIMAL FILAMENTS, RESPONSIVE to the gargantuan impulses of the universe, we are calibrated to the rhythms of nature partly by the senses that we know, and perhaps also by senses we only suspect to exist. One of the most important cosmic forces in our existence is sunlight, which may tune us to the rhythm of our planet. We are only beginning to find out how light itself affects the physiology and behavior of man and beast. Primitive people greeted the daily rebirth of the sun with rituals and worship. It was at the heart of the Taoist religion of China. As one ancient writer said, "The Tao ... which is revealed by the sun's course through the heavens is also revealed inside man's heart. ... It is the vital energy which lends existence to being." The Taoists purified themselves with fasts and meditation, attempting to perceive the vital energy of the heavens and understand its meaning for man.

Knowledge often begins in magic. Man's first attempts to decipher how he fit into the cosmos started perhaps some thirty thousand years ago in the magic science of astrology, with Paleolithic incisions on the bones of reindeer and mammoth, marks now believed to be notes of lunar cycles. All over the earth—in the Middle East, in Mexico, and in South America—ancient Mesopotamians, Aztecs, Maya left behind them the remains of their watch towers, giant pyramids, ziggurats, once the observatories of kings and priests. Egyptians and Chinese, Indians and Babylonians, Aztec and Maya noted carefully that the cycles of the planets and stars corresponded to changes on earth. They could not explain why they were affected by the stars but they knew their health lay in some form of harmony with the celestial panorama above and the earth around them. The epitome of a sense of wholeness came with the Greeks, who created an entire way of life, uniting man's love life, diet, and thoughts, his recreation and exercise in a "hygiene" balanced for his stage in life, his location, the climate, the season, the year. Constantly watching cloud-lines and winds, lints of sky and its gradual star-dance, our ancestors sought the mysterious order of which they knew they were a part, but hadn't the instruments to discover.

By the time astronomers were turning giant radar dishes toward distant galaxies, meteorologists were predicting weather, and biologists developed the methods to strip the first veils from the mystery, modern society had begun to forget that man was a natural animal. A dominant social elite could pick their season, and by short flight discard winter for summer. Crystal City near Washington, D.C., and Lefrak City in New York have become symbolic of the change—indoor cities, capitals of the retreat from nature. These structures, capable of housing twenty thousand people or more, are the forerunners of "mile-high" buildings in which a person might work, shop, swim, dine, go to theatre, and live out his life without any contact with the skies, winds, smells, or tempests of changing seasons. In such bastions of concrete, steel, and glass, light may still enter, and people will still be permeable to winds of magnetic change and perhaps to other cosmic messages of seasonal change. But were they perfectly insulated, what principles would these sky-dwellers use to maintain the internal order, the clockwork of their own bodies? How would they retain some consonance with the ancient echoes in their bodies—those cycles of the earth and the moon?

If we are to engineer and construct an artificial environment for human life we shall need to know more than we do at present. We have only begun to glimpse the meaning of light in our lives, a few clues to the way day and night, sunlight and darkness, may integrate us into the changing seasons. There may be a survival value in gradual acclimatization to seasonal change, just as there is probably a survival value in the fact that we are usually asleep during the hours when our gamma globulin is low, and with it, immunity to infection. Light is an important synchronizer.

Throughout the millennia people timed their work and sleep, their social activity by the alternation of day and night. Artificial light was expensive and rare until very recently. From ancient times until now, people have always accepted light as an axiomatic part of the environment. It is necessary for vision. It is essential for plant growth. On occasion poets have written hyperbolic lyrics to the potency of light, but no one seriously considered that light might be altering our physiology, entering into the brain, causing hormonal changes, and "insidiously" influencing our behavior. This realization has come about gradually. It began with the careful observations of botanists, natural scientists who noticed that plants and animals responded to the daily alternation of light and darkness, and that they were differently affected by seasonal change.

Why plants and flowers might droop or bloom, open or close, at different hours of the day nobody could explain, but in nineteenth-century Europe, the empirical information was used in designing elaborate formal gardens, that were sometimes planted to form a clock face with flowers in each bed blossoming at a different hour. On a sunny day one could tell the time to within a half hour by glancing at the garden. The famous eighteenth-century Swedish naturalist, Carolus Linnaeus, was the first to notice that various flowers opened at different hours and to use them in a flower clock.

Anyone who has tended house plants or a garden realizes that not all plants thrive where it is constantly light. Some flowers can be seen only at night; some plants flower in summer, others in winter, guided by mysterious internal mechanisms that determine when they will bloom, and whether they will bloom at all. Within each plant there seems to be a kind of time sense related to the alternation of light and dark. Linnaeus noticed that plant leaves and flowers changed position at night in what he called "plant sleep."

This time sense is not surprising, since light is a major physical component in plant life. Light is radiant energy. A molecule that absorbs a quantum of light may become excited in a manner that can be transmitted as a resonance, re-radiated as fluorescence, or transformed into heat. The action of light involves color (wavelength), intensity, and duration, which we now realize may stimulate or inhibit plant cells, thus governing rhythms in a manner known as photoperiodism.

PHOTOPERIODISM

The way in which the changing light of the seasons affects plant and insect rhythms has been explored by a stream of biologists, beginning with eighteenth- and nineteenth-century scientists, including Charles Darwin, who was fascinated by plant sleep. This aspect of a twenty-four-hour rhythm has been observed in plants since the time of Androsthenes, who noticed the nightly closing of tamarind leaves as he marched through India with Alexander the Great. Many people have noticed that the mimosa (related to the tamarind) folds its delicate leaves at night, as if injured, but they are open again the next morning. Recently, time-lapse photography has made the circadian dance of plant leaves quite visible. Dr. Erwin Bünning, like some of his scientific predecessors, demonstrated that this solar rhythm of twenty-four hours did not persist exactly when plants were kept in total darkness or light.

Dr. Bünning found that he could give plants ten hours of light and ten hours of darkness and they would show a twenty-hour cycle of leaf movement. Light and darkness were clearly important in determining their cycles. By a variety of experiments he found that plants could adapt to many different light-dark cycles. However, when they were left in total darkness, they would revert to a circadian rhythm of leaf movement that was almost, but not precisely, a twenty-four-hour cycle. The precise period length— whether twenty-four, twenty-five, or twenty-six hours— varied from plant to plant. Dr. Bünning crossed plants and discovered that the hybrid had a circadian rhythm with an intermediate period. Thus, the rhythm seemed to be inherited.

When Dr. Bünning raised seedlings in darkness, the young plants exhibited no rhythmicity, yet a single exposure to light instigated the circadian rhythm of leaf movement. He performed countless tests of the stability of this rhythm and found that within limits it was not altered by temperature variation or by many kinds of poisons. After some thirty years of research, he concluded that a plant must undergo periodic structural changes in its protoplasm, related to processes of cell division, although the exact nature of the mechanism remains a mystery. Plant rhythms and their responses to light suggested that they inherit a kind of time map of their environment—a time map giving them flexibility, yet preparing them for oncoming seasonal changes of temperature and light.

All children know that plants foretell the season. When crocuses poke through the snow, spring is on its way. When chrysanthemums bloom, summer is over and autumn is arriving. Of the crocus or chrysanthemum children ask, "How does it know when to blossom?"

It would seem that plants can anticipate the season by responding to ratios of light and darkness as the days grow longer in spring, and shorter in the fall. Dr. Karl Hamner and his associates in the Botany Department at UCLA have illuminated this timing mechanism in many plant experiments. Often they used a hardy Biloxi soybean, which flowers in fall, and "appreciates" a short day. If they gave it a long day, such as eighteen hours of light, the soybean plant would not flower. However, if returned to a "short day," it would soon bud. The number of buds was directly proportional to the number of short days the plant enjoyed, suggesting that light could be inhibitory and might prevent flowering.

On various light-dark schedules it became clear that

the plants required very small amounts of light every twenty-four hours. The only requirement seemed to be that light had to come every twenty-four hours or in multiples of twenty-four hours. The plants seemed to possess a rhythm of light sensitivity, and it was possible to stop a plant from budding by interrupting the darkness with light at critical periods. (A similar effect has also been found in animals.) Light in one twelve-hour period inhibited flowering, yet during the next twelve hours would stimulate flowering. The plant seemed to be "counting" by an inherent rhythm of light receptivity, perhaps within its daily cycle of enzyme manufacture, metabolism, and photosynthesis.

Time counters in plants and insects enable them to get ready for the seasonal change in weather. Both plants and insects go through intervals of dormancy, or diapause, when reduced metabolism gives them resistance to cold, to heat, or to drought, and prepares them for a cycle of growth to be followed by flowering and breeding. This annual schedule affects the entire cycle of plant and animal ecology.

SEASONAL CHANGES IN ANIMAL AND MAN

In a more complex fashion, it is clear that birds and mammals undergo cycles related to shortening or lengthening of light. Some animals, like the bear and certain squirrels, hibernate in winter. Weasels change the color of their fur. These changes do not wait for the weather. Among all the conditions which an animal must survive—temperature, food, humidity—light seems to be the most important synchronizer of animal activity. How else do huge numbers of birds all manage to go through the essential reproductive development—simultaneously—so that they can breed? Migratory birds gradually respond to the shorter days of fall by increasing their fat deposits, and becoming nocturnal; then they migrate, and breed, and once more go into molting and a period of inactivity as they accumulate fat for the return migration. It is believed that seals, whales, and other migrating animals may show a similar sequence.

As yet there is no body of scientific data to demonstrate that human beings go through seasonal changes, perhaps almost as profound as those of migrating seals or birds. Profound human changes are likely to take the form of moods, emotions, energy levels, illnesses, or weight fluctuations. Most people have a favorite season, some are more active and vibrant in fall, and a great many people sleep more in the dark winter months than in summer, blaming a sedentary indoor life for the additional weight they accumulate. In spring, reducing salons lure customers with quick courses to pedal and jog away that extra winter fat, lest it be exposed in a bathing suit. It does not seem to be just the harshness of winter weather that has caused people from time immemorial to welcome the prospect of longer days.

WINTER SOLSTICE

After December 22, when the days have been shortening, they lengthen again. People are glad not to go to work in darkness and return home in darkness. In western societies the celebration of the change takes the form of Christmas holidays, but there may be a hidden universal meaning in the celebration of Christ's birth. A vast number of cultures, ancient and modern, have celebrated the winter solstice. Ancient Egyptians and Syrians used to hold midnight ceremonies from which they emerged shouting hymns to the waxing of the light; it was the nativity of the sun, and fittingly they bore images of an infant—the newborn sun. December 25 was reckoned the winter solstice in the Julian calendar, the turning point. The Eskimos and many people in high latitudes had rituals to welcome the return of the sun. In January, the Iroquois held their festival of dreams, a week-long saturnalia, a festival of liberation to be found in many cultures. May day rituals and the Swedish and Eskimo ceremonial contests express the war of winter against summer, of darkness against light. Although human beings have adapted to all the regions of earth, man appears to be a truly diurnal animal. We not only welcome the lengthening of days and the return of light, but many people find themselves rising earlier, more willingly, as the light grows brighter.

LIGHT AND ACTIVITY

A great many experiments have been performed on the diurnality of birds, mammals, and man—and on the nocturnality of mice, rats, and cats. There is no doubt that light (or darkness) is a primary synchronizer of activity rhythms. As Pittendrigh and his associates discovered, small arctic animals can detect an infinitesimal change in light level. Thus there are cues of day-night change even in what might appear to be the Arctic sameness of summer or of winter. Dr. Jürgen Aschoff has conducted studies with birds, animals, and people. He found that diurnal creatures oriented their activity around the time of light, shifting toward it when it was delayed in the laboratory. In continuous light a diurnal creature could be expected to accelerate his activity cycle, while a nocturnal creature would delay. As days lengthen in spring and the light intensity increases, nocturnal animals delay their activity period, while diurnal animals awaken progressively earlier. Thus the phase and period of the activity cycle changes somewhat as the relative length of day and night gradually shifts.

Most of us have accepted this pattern of seasonal existence without wondering why light was central to behavior. How could light affect physiology so as to cause migration or mating? Out of his many studies of rodents, Halberg had a hunch that light (or in nocturnal animals, darkness) might trigger a region of the brain, perhaps the hypothalamus, which would stimulate the pituitary to stimulate the adrenals. In this way, perhaps, adrenal steroid levels might anticipate awakening, and allow the awakened creature to face the world, prepared. Today we know that light does affect the brain and the neuro-endocrine system.

LIGHT AND THE HUMAN ENDOCRINE SYSTEM

Drs. David N. Orth and Donald P. Island of Vanderbilt University indicated that rescheduling light might influence the rhythmic outpouring of adrenal hormones in the blood. Five healthy volunteers lived in a light-proof suite in the hospital, having adapted to the sleep schedule for ten to fourteen days beforehand by sleeping the same eight-hour period of each day. Hourly blood samples were taken through a small implanted catheter. On one schedule the volunteers awakened in a room that remained dark for four hours. Although they were awake, the hormone rhythm (17-OHCS) did not show its usual peak in late sleep, but occurred four hours later, coinciding with the turning-on of the lights. It should be emphasized that the shift was not instantaneous: blood was sampled after the person had adapted to the schedule for almost two weeks. On another schedule the volunteers had to be awake all day in darkness, receiving only one hour of light in twenty-four hours. This time the adrenal hormones showed peak levels around the time of awakening, and again at the hour of illumination.

BLINDNESS

If light acts upon the endocrine system, the blind may be missing something more than just vision. Dr. F. Hollwich, of Munster, Germany, has indeed found that people who have severe cataracts or who are blind, do not show the adrenal hormone rhythms observed in normal people. In fifty people with severe cataracts he could not find the normal amplitude of circadian rhythms in adrenal hormone metabolites, or in certain blood cells. However, the rhythms appeared after the cataracts were removed and the patients could see again. As he continued to examine 250 people with cataracts, Dr. Hollwich examined water balance, urinary electrolyte levels, carbohydrate metabolites, adrenal hormones, fat and protein metabolism. Before surgery the metabolism appeared to be abnormal, yet it became normal after successful surgery restored vision. Dr. Hollwich noticed that people who had lost their vision in early youth often showed disorders in water and glucose balance, and a lower-than-normal insulin tolerance. Perhaps visual perception of the alternation of light and darkness may synchronize or in other ways influence the intermeshed cycles of the endocrine system, affecting all our metabolism.

Do our endocrine systems also gradually respond to the changing ratio of light and dark as the year shifts from winter to summer? When a person feels the vibrant restlessness of "spring fever," and a "young man's fancy turns to thoughts of love," are these glandular responses to the messages of seasonal change? Perhaps the delicious sentiments of springtime are part of our linkage to the rhythms of earth, and can be explained in part by a look at the animal world.

SEASONS FOR MATING: BIRDS

Early in the 1920s, Dr. Vernon Rowan performed a startling experiment when he captured some migrating juncos in Saskatchewan, Canada. The birds had been on their way south, heading for a warm climate. Rowan kept them in aviaries in the zero-degree cold of the Canadian winter, but at sunset he turned on a few electric bulbs, for a little longer each evening. The bulbs did not raise the temperature, but they did extend the daylight. By mid-December the birds were singing the mating calls of their species, and when he released them in the icy mid-winter, the birds headed north instead of south. Light had certainly influenced the gonadal development of the birds, and as more recent research indicates, the direction of migration is determined by hormones.

Dr. J. Benoit, another pioneer in exploring the impact of light upon sexual reproduction, removed the eyes from immature drakes. These eyeless young ducks did not show the usual signs of sexual maturation until a light was shined directly into the brain—into the hypothalamus. As Benoit and subsequent workers found, the brain was sensitive not only to light, but also responded differently to various wavelengths or colors. Light had to be primarily in orange-red wavelengths to stimulate gonadal growth, but all wavelengths stimulated growth when the light was shined directly into the hypothalamus.

HORMONAL CHANGES IN ANIMALS

Inner hormonal states, mediated by the environment, appear to help guide the migratory directions of birds. Dr. Stephen T. Emlen captured some indigo buntings in the autumn. He gave some of them a laboratory environment that corresponded to the natural light changes of the season. Others were put through an accelerated daylight in which the day length was rapidly increased as if they passed through spring and summer. This in turn accelerated their cycle of fat deposits and molting. By May birds who lived in a natural lighting schedule were in spring condition physiologically, while the accelerated creatures were already in autumn condition. Dr. Emlen tested the birds by letting them fly in a planetarium in which the star patterns were those of the spring sky. The birds in spring condition turned northward, while those physiologically autumnal headed south.

The hormonal changes taking place in these creatures have been worked out by a number of scientists in different laboratories. Dr. Joseph Meites and his colleagues found that constant light increased the hypothalamic production of FSHRF (follicle stimulating hormone releasing factor) in rats. In turn this stimulated an increased secretion of FSH (follicle stimulating hormone) by the pituitary. FSH regulates production of sperm. Constant light seemed to enhance this hormonal process, thus influencing gonadal development.

Dr. Robert Lisk and his associates implanted optic fibers that would carry light directly into the hypothalamus or pituitaries of blinded rats; these fibers give light without heat. When light was applied in cycles, the rats went into estrus in a fairly normal manner, but constant light resulted in constant estrus. This was another one of many examples indicating that the cyclicity of light may be important to normal functioning.

The alternation of light and darkness appears to trigger activity within the nervous system that in turn regulates physiological cycles involving reproduction. Scientists have long wondered how light might enter the brain and what structures in the brain would respond to light. Considerable research has now been conducted on the pineal gland which at first seemed to play some role as mediator between incoming light and the signals involving sexual reproduction, but whose function is not at all certain.

THE PINEAL GLAND

The pineal gland is shaped like a small pine cone deep in the middle of the brain between the two hemispheres. Indian mystics and yogis have referred to the pineal body as a vestigial third eye. Indeed, it does protrude like a skin-covered eye on the skulls of lizards, and it even responds to light. Moreover, it is a gland with curious biochemical properties. In 1916 pineal tissue was found to blanch the skin of a tadpole or frog. It had a powerful effect on the pigment granules in skin and was thought to be responsible for skin discolorations and blemishes. The blanching chemical was isolated in the late 1950s, and because of its influence on melanin which darkens our pigmentation, the blanching substance was called melatonin.

Subsequently melatonin injections were found to influence the function of the thyroid glands and the size of the adrenals, to modify electroencephalographic tracings, and to pass through the blood-brain barrier, the membrane that protects the brain from a bombardment of inappropriately large molecules from the blood.

Melatonin seems to be concentrated in the midbrain and hypothalamus where it may influence sexual functions.

Melatonin is a complex molecule, related to the important transmitter, serotonin. As Dr. Julius Axelrod and his co-workers have shown, serotonin is converted into melatonin by an enzyme that is found exclusively in the pineal gland in mammals. This enzyme seems to be inhibited by light in nocturnal animals and by darkness in diurnal animals. Melatonin levels fluctuate in a diurnal rhythm; serotonin, on the other hand, fluctuates in a circadian rhythm that is not dependent upon a rhythm of light and darkness. In addition to serotonin and melatonin, the pineal gland contains a number of compounds that are crucial in brain and nervous system activity. Among them are histamine, dopamine, and norepinephrine (also known as noradrenaline). The pineal is rich in norepinephrine which is stored in the saclike cell containers at the nerve endings. Wurtman and Julius Axelrod have shown that in rats, norepinephrine increases and decreases rhythmically, reaching its high point at the end of the night. Norepinephrine may play a role in driving such rhythms, and in stimulating melatonin production in the pineal.

Pineal research has involved many species of animals, and many controversies and complications, but two facts stand out. The gland seems to influence sexual development, perhaps through melatonin, and its melatonin production can be influenced by light. Judging from rare cases seen in hospitals, the pineal appeared to inhibit gonadal development. Young boys lacking pineal glands because of destructive tumors reached puberty very precociously, sometimes while in kindergarten.

The victims of these glandular catastrophes often receive world-wide fame for their grotesqueness. Sporadically the public will read about a little girl of five who has given birth to a baby, or of a small boy who is as developed as a full-grown man. Some of the precocious sexual activity has been produced experimentally in animals. Infant rats deprived of their pineals showed precocious mounting and copulating.

When Drs. Charles C. Rust and Roland K. Meyer implanted melatonin into weasels who were already beginning to turn brown for spring, the animals developed white winter coats and showed an inhibition of gonadal development. The amount of melatonin injected into animals in this and other experiments vastly exceeds the amount secreted by the pineal gland. However, it indicates that melatonin may exert an inhibitory influence on reproductive capacity and the seasonal fur color of animals. It was once thought that the pineal acted as a coupler, and using seasonal change in light, regulated reproductive development. Today, nobody is sure. But it is clear that light duration and color affect the brains of birds and their gonads. Biologists Oishi and Kato painted the heads of Japanese quail with a pigment that sent orange light into some, green into others. There must be some deep organic reason for our associations with the color red, which has been the whore's color since the time of Babylon—for the animals with orange light showed gonadal development, but those wearing green paint did not.

Light and the color of light may have a pronounced effect upon sexuality, possibly through some impact upon the pineal. Since man's pineal is not at the top of his skull as it is in birds, one might wonder whether light and darkness could affect a gland so deeply buried in the center of the brain. A possible route was found by Axelrod and Wurtman through an elaborate series of experiments. By surgeries on the brains of rats, they demonstrated that light must enter through the eyes and travel a circuitous route through the inferior accessory optic track where its light messages would be transmitted to the cervical ganglia, nerve centers at the base of the brain. From there signals might activate the sympathetic nervous system which could relay the information to the pineal. In general, glands are stimulated to secrete hormones by biochemical signals such as the ACTH from the pituitary that causes the adrenals to release its hormones. The pineal may act more like a transducer, emitting its biochemicals in response to neural messages.

THE PINEAL IN HUMAN INFANTS

Pathologists working in Nova Scotia have recently reported their findings from autopsies on human infants and from animals. Their report should cause some interest in the lighting of hospital nurseries, for it suggests that light affects the pineal gland from the moment of birth on and that it may possibly accelerate its development. Drs. N. A. Kerenyi and K. Sarkar, of the Halifax Department of Public Health, have found that there is a structural cell development in the tissue of the human pineal gland which begins at birth. The process, producing a mosaic pattern, is complete by the age of two to three weeks. By six months this pattern diminishes and by about nine months it vanishes altogether. This sequence begins at birth whether or not the child is premature, a fact that strongly suggests that tissue development of the pineal may be enhanced by light. If so, the rate at which an infant's pineal develops may be related to the amount and quality of light in his environment.

This finding was corroborated by a study in which rabbits were kept in darkness for two months after birth, before comparing their pineal tissue with that of infant rabbits normally exposed to light. The rabbits kept in darkness had pineal glands that clearly showed retarded development.

ARTIFICIAL LIGHT

Most artificial light does not give the wavelengths of natural light. Light bulbs have a color glow that is mainly cosmetic, using oranges and reds to give the skin a healthy tinge. Daylight bulbs exist—approximating natural light—but they do not flatter the human face and are not widely used. Were human beings more like birds one might conjecture that the wide use of orange lights had some remote relationship with the fact that civilized nations are witnessing an ever-earlier age of sexual maturation in the young. Such speculations inevitably cross the mind, only as wild conjecture at the present. Nonetheless, light, particularly in certain parts of the spectrum, may have potent effects upon metabolism and well-being. It is an important synchronizer of waking and sleep, and thus circadian cycles. Without the daily light alternation, as studies of the blind give witness, metabolic functions may become irregular.

At present we use light haphazardly. Despite the fact that light penetrates closed eyelids—otherwise one could not be awakened by the fresh light of morning—we leave lights on in rooms where people are sleeping. After his many studies of the pineal, Dr. Richard Wurtman predicted that light would someday be considered as potent as any drug, and that we would use both wavelength and timing deliberately. We may find means of giving light therapy to the blind, for instance, and of adapting indoor lighting to approximate the spectrum of natural light. Certainly it seems important to explore the impact of light on the human brain.

SEASONAL LIGHT CHANGE AND HUMAN GLANDS

If human beings, like soybeans, respond to some changing ratio of daylight and darkness, we may begin to understand how we anticipate the heat of summer with summer hormone. Moods, whether the bliss of spring sensuality, or the despair and loneliness of depression, are mediated by the neuro-endocrine system. It is not accidental that people feel spring fever, or that there are increases in suicides in certain seasons, and autumnal increases in ulcers and allergies. Despite the even temperatures provided by steam-heat and air-conditioning, human beings still tend to mate more in spring and summer.

The neuro-endocrine effects of light may indeed begin to explain some historic stereotypes of temperament and climate, the moody Dane or jolly Italian. Robert Burton attributed Norse melancholy to cold. "In those Northern Countries the people are therefore generally dull, heavy, and many witches ... ascribe to melancholy. But these cold climes are more subject to natural melancholy." Perhaps lack of sunlight, as much as actual cold, may dampen the spirits of people at high latitudes.

In Finland, where the winter months are dark and gloomy, and where only a few months of the year are bathed in intense sunlight, a recent study suggests that the annual rhythms of light can be detected, indirectly, in the gynecological health of women, whose pituitary glands seem to be responding to the amount of light.

This master gland governs the phases of the menstrual cycle, influencing the changes in the endometrium—the walls of the uterus—and the preparation of the ovum. Dr. Sakari Timonen and co-workers in Helsinki studied the rate of conception, incidence of cysts, and other cell proliferation taken from vaginal smears or from biopsies from a considerable number of women over a period of five years. They placed their statistics on a calendar where they superimposed the monthly measure of sunlight from the Central Meteorological Office. The results were interesting: with increased light, conceptions increased and the pre-tumorous cell growths known as hyperplasias decreased very markedly. During the dark months of the year these abnormalities increased and conception dropped. The researchers cautiously conjectured that light levels might be having an indirect effect upon the human pituitary.

Other evidence comes from observations made by Dr. Reinberg on a young woman who lived in a cave for nearly three months, relying only upon the dim light of a miner's lamp that she wore throughout the experiment. She had taken her temperature daily for a year before, and a year afterward. Before, she lived a twenty-four-hour day and had a twenty-nine-day menstrual cycle; underground her day lengthened to 24.6 hours and her menstrual cycle shortened to 25.7 days. It was about a year before her cycle returned to around 29 days.

Dr. Reinberg wondered whether the low intensity of light in the cave had influenced the menstrual cycle. He searched the literature and found a study about the timing of menarche, first menstruation, among 600 young girls from northern Germany. Menarche most frequently occurred in winter. Another study of girls in Prague also showed that a girl was more likely to enter menarche in winter. Moreover, it has been observed widely that blind girls reach menarche earlier than girls with sight. Perhaps dim light or lack of light may stimulate a phase of hormonal development in women. If the pineal is involved, lack of light may reduce the amount of melatonin, which would be like taking the brakes off the reproductive system. It is possible that the intensity, duration, and quality of light does influence the menstrual cycle and the reproductive system in general. This means that as the light changes, we, too, show seasonal influences in our bodies and behavior. Perhaps we also exhibit a variety of photoperiodism by which light at critical periods may inhibit or enhance our flowering. It is no longer farfetched to think of using light to influence our own rhythms of fertility. The first intimation that such a thing might be possible came from animal studies.

CONTROLLING ESTRUS BY LIGHT

During the late 1940s, Drs. John W. Everett and Charles H. Sawyer began a classic series of experiments with rats. They discovered that there was a twenty-four-hour rhythm in the neuro-endocrine apparatus that releases LH (luteinizing hormone) in rats. They used a barbiturate (Nembutal) to depress the nervous system and prevent ovulation. The drug prevented ovulatory action if delivered at 2 P.M. on the day before estrus; but it did not have the same effect after 4 P.M. Using a number of barbiturates, they showed that ovulation and estrus could be blocked by injections if they were delivered at appropriate periods during the sex cycle of the rat. There was a critical period of about two hours on the day before estrus in rats who lived on controlled lighting regimens. This critical period began around the beginning of illumination. If anesthetics, blocking drugs, or other depressants are applied to the brain just before the critical period, it is possible to interfere with the neural mechanism releasing LH, the signal that would ordinarily result in surges of ovulating hormone. If the same blocking is applied on the next day at the critical time, ovulation is again blocked, and so on, ad infinitum, until the ovarian follicle degenerates. There may also be a critical time of day and month in which the drugs would influence the cycle of the adult woman.

Now we come to the striking discovery that light can be as potent as drugs, and can play a similar role in blocking estrus. When rats were maintained under constant light they were constantly in estrus. More recently it has been shown that rats in darkness will not ovulate if given two hours of light during the critical period before ovulation. By turning light on and off, people are now able to turn on and off the hormonal mechanisms controlling reproduction in the rodent just as they can control flowering in the soybean plant. Light affects the male animal as well. When deprived of light the extraordinarily fertile hamster shows gonadal atrophy. In total darkness the gonads shrink to about a quarter of their usual size and the animal's fertility is significantly reduced.

THE HOUR OF BIRTH

There may be critical phases in the reproductive cycles of human beings too, when their reproductive processes might be interrupted. Although the human gestation period is nine months, the unit by which the body appears to count is the day—the circadian cycle. Statistics on the hours of human births suggest that most normal births occur at a particular phase of the circadian cycle. Dr. Jeri Malek and his co-workers in Prague examined 92,000 births and found that 60 percent began at night and 40 percent by day, regardless of season. Labor pains began twice as often at midnight as at noon, and moreover, Malek found that natural deliveries begun around midnight were the fastest and easiest. In the United States Drs. Irwin H.

Kaiser and Franz Halberg have found that 60 percent of labor began at night, with a peak around 3 A.M. Most stillbirths or neonates born with fatal complications, they found, were born in late afternoon. The statistics suggest that the circadian phase may play an extremely important role in healthy child-bearing. The Czech team noticed a possible relation between morning or afternoon births and the circadian phase when menstruation usually began. In a study of some 800 girls they found that menstrual periods usually began between 4 and 6 A.M. with a few between 8 A.M. and noon, and many fewer in afternoon or evening. This meant that the menstruation pattern might be related to the timing of labor and delivery, for most births occur in the early morning, as does the onset of most menstruation. Perhaps, as we are beginning to see, the regularity and timing of menstruation reveals something about the time structure of a woman, and the potential ease with which she will deliver a child. Perhaps the emotional shocks or irregular habits, that may unloose circadian rhythms from their usual phase relationships, begin to show themselves in menstrual irregularities and the unusual timing of onset.

MOON CYCLES

For most women the menstrual rhythm averages twenty-eight to twenty-nine days. This may be a vestige of a moon cycle. The synodical month is 29.5 days: once in a synodical month the sun and the moon rise and set at roughly the same time. Regular movements of sun and moon may be responsible for atmospheric cycles that help to synchronize the mating of many sea creatures, and may have become part of the time structure of mammals.

The swarming, spawning, mating of many sea creatures is related to the rhythms of the tides, which grow stronger when the sun and moon are in opposition or conjunction. In spring in Bermuda, at the time of full moon, the surface of the sea becomes brilliantly luminous with the swarming and breeding of the Atlantic fireworm. Along the Southern California coast, between March and August, grunions spawn on the flood tides of nights after the full moon.

It is no wonder that ancient cultures related spring and the moon to fertility. In ancient Egypt and in Africa, rites of circumcision, planting, and fertility were governed by the moon. In our times there is still a trace of moon awe, and there is almost no psychiatric hospital that cannot offer statistics and anecdotes to demonstrate that there is more unruliness at the time of full moon and more cases are admitted then. Police departments have reported that crimes involving possible psychosis, arson, kleptomania, fights, and automobile accidents would increase around the full moon.

Recently scientists have taken a fresh look at the possibility that lunar rhythms may be relevant in understanding human ovulation cycles.

CONTROLLING OVULATION BY LIGHT

For much of his professional life, physicist Edmond Dewan has been fascinated by the way in which biological oscillations become synchronized by environmental cycles. In theory, any biological oscillation can be entrained by a periodicity in the surrounding world. Dewan began to wonder whether the similar periods of the menstrual and lunar cycles could be more than coincidence, a vestige of the way in which primitive organisms were entrained by the moon. He explored the ancient myths and literature on sexual cycles of fish and marine animals. He was struck by experiments that had been conducted on sea worms by a German biologist, C. Hauenschild (whose studies are recited in the 1960 Cold Spring Harbor Symposium). Hauenschild indicated how moonlight, rather than atmospheric changes, might influence these lower forms of life. On six nights out of thirty he shone a dim light on the worms, approximating the lunar cycle. The worms showed sexual ripening in a rhythm synchronous with the light. Even among primitive organisms that show relatively precise rhythms of hormonal change and swarming, not all individuals show cycles that are in split-second concurrence with the phase of the external rhythm.

If one looks at the menstrual rhythm of women, one sees a range of periods from sixteen to seventy-five days. Although many women show regular twenty-nine-day cycles, many others are quite irregular. Emotional stress and other factors can cause irregularity, but could a signal be used to make menstruation and ovulation regular? Since light affects the neuro-endocrine system, Dewan conjectured that a light shone at a critical phase in a woman's cycle might influence the release of LH and FSH, making ovulation predictable and controllable.

In 1965 Dewan experimented with a young woman who had a history of menstrual irregularity for sixteen years. Her cycle had varied between twenty-three and forty-eight days. Throughout the four-month study, she placed a lamp on the floor at the foot of her bed and kept a 100-watt bulb burning during sleep, so that reflected light from the ceiling and walls shone on her face during the fourteenth, fifteenth, and sixteenth nights of her cycle. The first day of menstruation was counted as the first day of the cycle. To her surprise and bafflement, her periods shortened to twenty-nine days. A second volunteer found that she felt a slight pain on the fourteenth night of her cycle at the time of ovulation. She made the discovery when she began regulating her menstrual cycle with light, for it gave her an external signpost that made it easier to notice and identify the inward sensation.

It is a rare woman who can feel where she is on her monthly cycle, much less identify the time of ovulation. If further research confirms that light will entrain the ovulatory cycle, such lighting will undoubtedly become part of the education of every girl, giving her a sense of her own physiology and a means of resynchronizing herself. So far, research has been preliminary and minimal, due to lack of funds. However, the possibility that light may synchronize ovulation suggested its use to prevent conception or to enhance fertility.

Many patients at the Rock Reproductive Clinic in

Boston are women who hope to be cured of irregular menstrual cycles and infertility. Dr. John Rock, the courageous Jesuit researcher who founded the clinic, and Dr. Dewan studied seventeen of these patients under a regimen of lighting in the bedroom throughout the fourteenth, fifteenth, and sixteenth nights of their cycle, counting the first day of menstruation as the first day of the cycle. Needless to say, some of the women who had come to Rock longing to have a baby, and hoping for some miracle drug, were shocked and crestfallen when they received the doctor's prescription. "That's a prescription?" they asked. Analysis of the records of these women several months later, and comparison with a normal group, showed that the light regimen had caused all but two of them to become more regular, with a period more nearly twenty-nine days. It should be added that another light regimen on a different group did not work (light used on the eleventh to thirteenth nights of the cycle). Perhaps if light can synchronize human ovulation cycles, it must be timed for a critical period within the woman's cycle, just as light intervention in the rat's estrous cycle must occur within two critical hours.

For several of the twenty-five women who had been studied, the experiment was a gratifying success, and worth the snoopy questions of neighbors about lights burning all night, as well as the skeptical grumbles of husbands. Having almost despaired of motherhood, they became pregnant. A medical reporter who had been troubled by very irregular periods all her life covered the story for her paper and used the regimen herself, successfully maintaining a regular cycle for about three years. Since she traveled a great deal, it was sometimes inconvenient to use the lighting, and she found that the regularity persisted even if she forgot for a couple of months. After three months' omission, she became irregular again.

The data are preliminary, almost so sketchy as to be anecdotal, yet the possibility of entraining the ovulatory cycle by light, and entirely without drugs, is too exciting a prospect to abandon. The hypothesis is crude, but it suggests that we may find we are like photoperiodic plants and creatures, tuned to earth's rhythms by the potent synchronizer—light. It helps to shape our alternations of activity and rest, enters our unwary heads, and influences our circadian rhythms of adrenal hormones, our daily rhythms of metabolism. Even skimpy evidence from studies of the blind and gynecological examinations of Finnish women suggest that light affects the pituitary, the master gland of reproduction and of metabolism. Each day light may synchronize our behavior and bodies with the earth's rotation. The slowly changing ratios of daylight and darkness may guide our physiology, our hormonal systems in tune with the seasons, causing our moods, symptoms, sexuality, and the condition of our reproductive organs, to change slowly in an annual rhythm, bringing us along with the earth without sudden transitions.

We are not accustomed to thinking of time or light as potent forces in our health, nor do most of us self-consciously time our activities to affect the time structure of our bodies. A woman might think her gynecologist was irrelevant if he made a big issue of wanting to know the exact hour that menstruation began, and she would certainly think him a quack if he prescribed sleeping in orange light for three nights a month. However, in the future gynecologists will want to know about the phase of the onset of menstruation in the circadian cycle; using synchronizers, perhaps light, women will undoubtedly regularize their cycles before becoming pregnant, and will approach labor at night during the optimum hours for childbirth. If Dr. Wurtman is correct, we will use light as deliberately as we now use X-rays, and we may find some way of giving pulses of light or other brain stimulation to the blind to enhance their rhythmicity.

GENETIC ENGINEERING

How will all of this elaborate temporal harmony be programmed into those first embryos who are allowed to gestate in laboratory bottles? Genetic engineering is making rapid progress, and the day is approaching when women will not need to carry a child in the womb. Already, at the Institute for Cancer Research in Philadelphia embryos have been taken from two pregnant mice, placed together in artificial nutriment until they fused, and then implanted in the womb of a third mouse who bore pups with the fur marks and traits of the two pairs of donors. Many experiments with animal and human embryos *in vitro* suggest that parents of the future might be able to pick some of the traits they want in their offspring, and fertilize eggs and grow them outside of the body. Will the first offspring from laboratory bottles have a time structure allowing them to adapt easily? Is this rhythmicity largely programmed into the gene, or does it slowly acquire the rhythms of the womb, the mother's heartbeat, the pulsing of substances, ninety-minute cycles, circadian cycles, and monthly cycles of change, along with the movements of the mother? At this stage of knowledge, it would be easier to synthesize the nourishment needed by a growing fetus than to stimulate the delicate and complex time information, the beats of the womb.

CONCLUSION

We have scarcely begun to explore the nature of time structure in human beings, yet the accelerated development of certain lines of research and the momentum of huge economic interests are rapidly plunging all mankind unprepared and naked into the startling future. We can now create artificial cities in which day and night can be manipulated at will, where economic interests might dictate non-circadian schedules. We have already begun to see harmful effects from frequent east-west travel, phase shifts. It is one thing when weekly phase shifts shorten the lives of rodents, but serious when the cumulative effects of phase shifting begin to cause failing health in middle-aged individuals, and catastrophic when it happens to large populations. Until we understand the combination lock of our time structure, our critical periods of susceptibility to light or darkness, hours of awakening, food, infection, drugs, we can only act blindly when we detach ourselves from the natural cycles of day and night.

What of man's inheritance from his evolution on this planet and its ecosystem of cosmic pulses? Will we explore our time structure before it is too late? Sudden and superficial interest in ecology began in the United States as pollution became both dangerous and noticeable. Over a decade ago Rachel Carson had described the destruction we were causing to the grand chain of animal and fish life with pesticides. At the time President Kennedy called together a committee of distinguished scientists who, after many months of rebuff, animosity, and politicking from all sides, reported what pesticides were doing to land, fish, animals, and human beings in the United States. That was 1960, and little has changed. People can still buy lethal insecticides in hardware stores, and substitutes for DDT, even more dangerous, are dusted over the land. Lip service is given to ecology, but reform involving major economic adjustments is a long time coming.

The same delays and disputes will occur over issues of circadian rhythms, over scheduling jobs, screening people for jobs, revising the schedules of hospitals, testing drugs, changing the specifications of medical diagnoses. The ecosystem of human life is deteriorating and ultimately medicine will be forced to deal with the whole patient, and his way of life. At present, and for a long time to come, the technological world is run for efficiency. Men are considered the same, judged only by productivity. But you, the individual reading this, have only one life. You live within the tough yet fragile instrument of your body, held together by a structure of intermeshed events, cycles of physiological change. Only you, if you care to live, can protect the order and balance of your own existence. A person must learn to sense his own cycles, his own beat, and then as a matter of self-protection, adhere to it stubbornly, hear its counsel. One's behavior, one's intensities, tensions, joys, one's too great speed careening through too many encounters, or too many time shifts, all change the biochemical harmony. One simply has to listen to that inner voice, and make the decision, balancing the pleasure and stimulation of social engagements or travel, against the total equanimity of one's life. Some people may need to learn meditation and quietness to perceive the inner signals. Others may need to keep a diary, to know their own undulations of vitality, of hungers, lusts, thirsts, of weight, sleep, brilliance or stupidity, of aches, sores and other symptoms, and many moods, of elation or despair, irascibility or serenity. People will have to calculate, insofar as they can, their own stresses, confronting the dentist's chair in hours when they feel strong, gauging exams, unpleasant phone calls, surgery, whatever they consider ordeals of life. Most people know something about their daily rhythms. They know whether they fall asleep rapidly and awaken rapidly, or whether they descend gingerly and slowly into slumber, easily awakened then, yet even more tentative and gradual in the uphill climb into waking in the morning. These are basic patterns.

We know that healthy sleep is a rhythmic tide, through cycles of 90–110 minutes of descent into slow deep sleep, of ascent into the excitation of REM sleep, and of dreaming. A person who watches himself carefully may learn to awaken from dreams, recalling more of his night thoughts, and also to awaken more easily without an alarm clock. Knowing something about the rhythms of the sleep cycle, individuals may examine their daily undulations of relaxation and attention, cycles of alertness, restlessness, hunger, or daydreaming. Any person can discover the time of day he functions best, and worst. The aspect of rhythmicity over which we all have control is the timing of sleep and meals. Sleep can set the regularity of inner cycles, of circadian phase relationships.

One need only review the list of changes through which the different segments of our physiology rotate in a day to realize that the predictability of any body function requires a certain stability of the activity cycle. Timing can be potent. Heavy meals can be eaten earlier, for instance, by weight-watching people, and activities can be planned to anticipate the way a person knows he will feel. These circadian changes may explain why allergies become particularly troublesome at night, or why a teacher may be tougher and more hostile to her last afternoon class than she is earlier in the day. Fatigue and heightened sensory sensitivity are part of the daily rhythm. These circadian changes may explain many quirks that people privately discuss, surprised, relieved, even enchanted to find that another human being has had the same experience. For instance, men complain among one another that their wives or girlfriends are not interested in lovemaking in the morning when they wake up. The male of our species seems to awaken horny and eager, only to find that his tender advances are sleepily or indifferently put aside. Is a man's morning eroticism related to the fact that he awakens with peak levels of the sex hormone testosterone in his blood, and may he still have an erection from his last REM period? If these circadian rhythms are responsible for the disparity between male and female sexual inclinations in the morning, then it is likely that most of the population has experienced it.

Rhythmicity is the principle of all we do—of all movement, of walking, talking, music, dance, all sports, and even the learning of language and mathematics. From earliest infancy, the regularity of basic functions seems to play a deciding role in the ease with which a child grows up and adapts to being human. No one can say whether the irregularity seen in difficult children has a genetic basis, or comes from emotional stresses and irregularities in the mother during pregnancy. The Navahos believe that the child of a woman who sees lightning strike a man will later in his life suffer an illness. Stresses can disturb the chemistry of the womb, and indeed, when pregnant animals have received injections of male hormones, the female young have later acted like males. Can we learn enough about our responses to light and other synchronizers, to bring regularity into the newborn child? Will overcrowded societies permit people to establish the routines that suit their well-being?

The answer is probably negative. Yet the delicate phasing of hormones that predispose our vitality and our moods becomes entirely desynchronized from other functions when we keep erratic hours, when we cross time zones, rotate shifts, invert day and night. Travelers of the future may arrive in terminal lounges where they may receive either mild electrical brain stimulation or a drug to rephase them. Even if such methods did permit a person to accomplish his business, in an ultimate sense he would still need time to adapt to new air, climate, food, latitude, and temperature, not to mention a different culture.

Individuals have some control over the schedules they keep and amount of pressure they permit in their lives. For certain individuals this may be no issue. Some people are less temporarily vulnerable than others. The differences between their day or night performances are small. They show less deterioration when in isolation, or when subjected to phase shifts. Most people have an instinctive, self-preserving sense about themselves, and know whether they are impervious to a change in phase, or whether they go through several days feeling slow-witted, lethargic, and disrupted. After a fast jet trip east or west, or a booming emotional crisis, many people literally "cannot get it together."

In another decade, doctors are likely to ask patients some questions that will sound futuristic—or classical, depending upon the direction of one's gaze. A physician will want a picture of a person's life, his stress points, loves, reading, pace of work, gustatory tastes, sports and hobbies. His emotional tone and muscular coordination will be measured. His startle response to a sudden short or loud noise, his sensory acuity, and his vigilance will be relevant. Many tests that are now performed only on laboratory animals or experimental volunteers, and which are scattered throughout the behavioral science laboratories, will be drawn together as diagnostic necessities in the medical clinic. Instruments that assess rhythmicity in an individual at work and during his ordinary life may be evolved to give us an early-warning system of potential illness. It will be worth the expense of obtaining round-the-clock recordings from automatic devices, for illness is always more costly than means of prevention. Only our self-deluded manner of accounting makes good medicine seem too expensive. In the future, however, no doctor will be able to trust a blood test unless it contains many samples obtained over a period of time.

Present medical research is oriented toward trouble-shooting, yet even transplanting a heart involves the problem of sewing together tissues with two different circadian phases. Clearly, symptoms of illness, use of drugs, timing of surgery, and interpretation of blood, urine, or tissue samples for diagnosis all depend upon a greater understanding of human time structure. At present some drugs are not as safe at one time of day as at another. Until drug testing accounts for circadian rhythmicity in response, there will be surprises when a doctor, ignorant of a patient's phase and not warned about the drug, gives a drug that is marginal at some hours, but 70 percent more toxic at others. At present, too, most people with periodic illnesses are likely never to be diagnosed. A patient will receive drugs to counter the present symptoms, and after a couple of months he may feel better, believing with his doctor that the drugs actually helped—until the symptoms return. At present, odd cycles of symptoms are not likely to be judged periodic, and an individual must take note of his own symptoms and show the periodicity to his physician. To know oneself is to know oneself in time.

For the most part, time series studies are not likely to be incorporated very soon into drug testing, or into medical procedures scheduling. Research is difficult and expensive, the rhythmic nature of change is difficult to discuss, and even scientists do not agree about methodology or the language that best describes it. Predictable cycles of change seem tenuous, invisible to those who fund research, so this important area is likely to lag. People will continue to attempt to live forty-eight-hour days, to shuttle around the world in jets, or to obliterate the inevitable signs of fatigue and desynchronization with drugs. Feats of flexibility may merely exchange momentary convenience for long-term illness. Today a doctor would be dismissed if he told a frenetic executive to drop some of his accounts and alter his life style, yet physicians deeply know that a person's health is warped and strained by his life.

Tomorrow's human being will look back on all of this as we look upon Paleolithic man. Each person will be acquainted with his time structure, as we are acquainted with our temperaments.

Future people will not only know more facts about the planet on which they were born, but they will also be able to feel their connections to earth and the cosmos. A sense of ancestry is not only the genealogy of one's little family, a few generations back in history; it is a sense of kinship with the rest of earth's creatures, and with those who lived earlier in our long evolution on this rotating earth. Probably circadian rhythms, that potential to respond at this particular frequency, began as we evolved in a world of alternating light and darkness, night and day, a cycle that is believed to have been a little shorter than twenty-four hours in the early days when earth seems to have rotated faster. This important rhythm of energy, from light, must have influenced life for hundreds of millions of years. Rhythmicity was probably one of the first forces of natural selection, since the organisms that timed their activity and life processes in accord with light, temperature, and humidity cycles would have had an advantage in survival. It would be altogether strange if this long evolution had not left its trace on mankind.

Circadian cycles are only one of the beats that will be part of the consciousness of every civilized person in the future. People will undoubtedly learn something of their ratio of pulse to respiration, and the concordance between a state of high adrenal hormones and mental function. Not to realize one has time structure is analogous to going through life ignorant that one has a heart and lungs. Bees and birds seem to use their twenty-four-hour rhythms to navigate, but future man will more likely use his time sense to make life easier, more joyful, and fluid—to "set" his head for a twenty-minute nap, and fall into sleep at the time his rhythms are easing him into rest. Like the plant that flowers if given a little light at the right time, here may be a combination lock to human activity, moods, illnesses, creativity, and mental brightness. It will permit us to schedule teaching, therapy, performances, travel, medication, and many of the arts of raising children in a way that does not fight with inner timing. By understanding what we might call clockwork, we will find ourselves at a new threshold of mastery, a new consciousness of what kind of complex beasts we are, and how intimately our being pulses with that of the world around us.

If circadian rhythms bind us to the cycle of the earth on which we live, we have seen that light may slowly change our hormones and moods, in consonance with the longer annual revolution of earth about the sun. Light is only one of the many cosmic influences upon us. Earth turns in the winds of the sun, in the gravitational flux of the galaxy.

Since the dim beginning of man's history, human thought has been permeated with the belief that the movements of the planets and stars influence all earthly movement, from agriculture to health and social order. These astrological ideas were the basis for most of man's great religions, and throughout much of man's history, his most important science. The Hindu Vedas speak of the union of cosmic and social order, and accomplished Indian meditators attempt to feel the vibrations of the cosmos. From the Chaldeans to the Chinese, the Inca to the Iroquois, the great legacy of human learning and legend involved an appreciation of cyclic changes on earth, some of them well beyond the span of one or two generations. These cycles seemed influential for the future of life on earth. The object of the religions was to harmonize man with earth, and resolve how man belongs to the grander system of the universe.

With our utilitarian outlook, we tend to dismiss such metaphysical questions as irrelevant. Yet there is an entire folklore about the ways in which weather changes man's emotions and behavior. We have seen that sunlight may influence emotions by indirectly regulating the amount of calcium available for nervous activity. Gravitational changes, magnetic field changes from sun spots, or barometric pressure from lunar cycles may account for surges of excitement and agitation among vulnerable humans on earth. Our harmony with earth rhythms and the grander cosmos beyond is not a matter of philosophy, outside of our skins. Like the crab who feels the oncoming storm, and the other animals who share this planet with us, we respond to magnetic storms and changing forces. Our belief does dictate whether we shall learn to identify these external rhythms and events, or continue to be influenced unawares.

Our five senses are merely the primary receptors whose messages we consciously attend. Like the experimental inhabitants of shielded bunkers in Germany, who gave signs of response to artificial fields, unawares we are bombarded by the periodicities of earth, and in its helicoidal, screw-like course around the sun, to constantly shifting galactic fields. The cosmos has hourly, daily, monthly influence upon our existence, and subtle vibrations do indeed come from all this planetary motion in space. Unlike our astrological ancestors, we have many options and many new instruments that can expand our dialogue with the cosmos around us. Instead of being buffeted by invisible tempests of particles, and residues of galactic winds, we can choose to identify these messages from the universe and find in them our link to cycles beyond the solar system. Their echoes may be part of us.

Just as body and mind are a unity, our inner time-structure is part of our planet. What we may call a clock in ourselves may be a collection of oscillators, that tend to respond to the rhythms of earth. The time-structure of our bodies is, after all, only partly within our skins, for we are open systems, unable to detach ourselves from the beats of this nature of which we are part.

There is a season for everything
And a time for every purpose under the heaven.

APPENDIX
Notes on the Vocabulary
and Analysis of Rhythms

PLANT AND ANIMAL RHYTHMS HAVE CAUGHT the attention of astute observers throughout history, but it was not until the eighteenth century that research really began. Astronomer Jacques de Mairan noticed that mimosa and other plants opened and closed their leaves in a twenty-four-hour rhythm. The leaf movement persisted when he left a plant in total darkness. In current language, the plant seemed to be showing a free-running rhythm, that is, an oscillation that is self-sustained under constant conditions. Its rhythmic dance was not precisely twenty-four hours, as later discovered, but rather close; it was a circadian rhythm. Dr. Frank Brown coined the term "circadian," which has become defined as a cycle with a frequency of twenty-one to twenty-eight hours. A shorter cycle, occurring with higher frequency, would be "ultradian," while a longer cycle such as a week or a month might be called "infradian." In the nomenclature of rhythm study, or rhythmometry, the Greek prefix, *chronos*, indicates any specialized study in which time is the focus of interest. Thus a number of current studies bear such titles as chronobiology or chronopharmacology. Dr. Halberg and Dr. Arne Sollberger in their prolific writings about the measurement and analysis of periodic phenomena, have rapidly speeded rhythmometry into the computer age.

Some researches have not needed such help. Many botanical researches on the leaf movements of plants, for instance, have used a strain gauge and camera attached to the plant leaf so that measurements of move-

ment and time-lapse photography could be obtained
around the clock, showing the twenty-four-hour rhythm
with no ambiguity. Unfortunately, the simplicity of
time-lapse photography and continuous recordings is
not feasible for most studies of physiological and emotional rhythms in man. Simple time charts usually are
not sufficient, and scientists within the field of biological
rhythms have debated how to analyze their data. Spectral analyses and statistics have been used by some
scientists but have not been universally understood;
other scientists have doubted that the mathematics did
indeed reveal rhythmicity. These people may doubt the
existence of biological rhythms unless they are visible
to the naked eye but until the development of high-
powered microscopes they would have had to doubt the
existence of cell structure and DNA. Nonetheless, until
instruments with the resolving power of the electron
microscope become available for the continuous study
of the body's time structure, certain mathematical
manipulations are the only means of making rhythms
visible.

Light and dark, sleep and waking, social customs and
other factors may act upon the nervous system like the
resetting of a wristwatch, synchronizing internal rhythms
with the outside world. Synchronizer, *Zeitgeber,* and
entraining agent are synonymous terms for an oscillation
such as night and day that guides another rhythm such
as sleep and activity to the same frequency. In most
studies of animals and plants, light and dark are the
important synchronizers. The light-dark schedule is
frequently abbreviated L-D; a schedule of light for
twelve hours alternating with darkness for twelve hours
would be written LD 12:12; if light is turned on at 6
A.M., the schedule would be specified L 0600–1800,
D 1800–0600, while LL signifies continuous light and
DD, continuous darkness. Rhythms are influenced by
many factors, drugs, trauma, and seemingly minor
events. The crowding of animals may influence their
endocrine rhythms or, as Dr. Halberg's laboratory has
found, a single drop of blood taken from the tail of a
mouse created a shock that disturbed the animal's
circadian rhythm of certain blood cells for several days.

Thus the measuring process may interfere with the state being measured. This means that the study of biological cycles requires particularly controlled conditions with a schedule allowing measurement at suitable intervals over an appropriate duration of time and with a sufficiently large population. In animal research the population is purchasable and is genetically controlled, but studies of healthy or sick people usually involve very few subjects.

Ideally, rhythms should be charted longitudinally in one individual, who might be tested every hour for weeks or months, but it is not often possible to take blood or urine from a person repeatedly at equally spaced time intervals, especially if he is vulnerable and suffering from emotional stress or illness. Even healthy people balk at having their sleep interrupted. Many studies have therefore omitted the sleep period. In a compromise with the realities of equipment, funding, and human frailty, several researchers have devised what are known as transverse studies. They involve unequal time samples, perhaps observations done by different researchers and in different locations. Transverse studies may combine data, using unequally spaced samples and mixtures of subjects who are observed over brief periods.

In the future, biotelemetry instruments will record changes in temperature, pulse, respiration, skin conductivity, and other functions without impinging on an individual's awareness, making possible continuous data that can be analyzed by computer. For the present, time structure often must be inferred from inadequate data with huge gaps. Moreover, the observed changes are likely to be subtle, a few more cells dividing at this hour than at that, a person making a few less errors or omissions at a pushbutton task.

Scientists have solved some of their problems of sampling by testing huge groups of subjects as if they were a single individual. In animal researches, a new subgroup of animals from a larger group may be used for blood or tissue samples at each time interval; animals are not sampled twice. Insofar as they are nearly alike genetically and in age, weight, sex, and background, these laboratory animals may approximate a single individual displaying a rhythm over a long span of time. Such a study might measure functions in 400 mice over forty-eight hours. In some sense these studies would tell what periodicities to expect in a single individual over many days.

Sometimes, however, it is neither possible to conduct long-term observations of several individuals nor to muster a large group for a brief study. As a compromise, a few individuals may be studied for two or more cycle lengths. Such a hybrid study may be better than no study at all, particularly when the subjects are for some reason rare, as are astronauts in space or patients with encephalitis.

Common sense would dictate that any study of rhythms should encompass enough cycles—whether in minutes, hours, days, or weeks—to leave no doubt that the observed variation recurs at the attested frequency, but the sheer burden of time studies has induced many researchers to cut corners a little. The charting of a rhythm necessitates measures at intervals in a proper ratio to the total cycle. A roughly twenty-four-hour rhythm should not be studied by taking samples at twelve-hour intervals in the manner of many early clinical studies, nor does it make sense to sample every ten seconds. Dr. Halberg and his associates have worked out what they consider a reasonable ratio of six sampling intervals to one cycle length: 6:1. For many functions, such as adrenal hormones in blood, this is quite inadequate.

STABILITY

Measurements repeated over long periods of time assure a kind of stability that cannot be obtained from brief studies. Ten-year studies of nitrogen retention among periodic catatonics have divulged a three-week periodicity of illness that might not be clear if studied briefly, especially if that study occurred during a time when the person was irregular for a while. In human and animal life, a variety of perturbations cause local deviations in the overall rhythms, deviations that are small in the long run, but which would loom large on a short-term study. The advantages of longitudinal study are obvious, as are the costs and difficulties. Sollberger, Halberg, and others have emphasized the importance of sampling frequency in doing time-series studies. In order to discriminate between a circadian rhythm of 23.5 hours and a twenty-four-hour rhythm, Dr. Sollberger suggests that one would need something like a sample every five minutes for a month. However, there is considerable disagreement about the exact frequency needed for an accurate description of the cycle period. All methods of analysis involve the assumptions and judgments of the researcher, so the interpretation of time-series data is riven by the kind of controversy found throughout science.

MATHEMATICAL MODELS

Since the 1950s, biologists, physicists, physiologists, mathematicians, and others have speculated on the kinds of internal mechanisms, or oscillators, that might generate our many rhythms. The circadian rhythm of waking and sleep might be caused by a mechanism like that of a child on a swing constantly pumping and needing a regular push to keep the swing going. Or rhythms may be caused by endogenous mechanisms resembling other kinds of oscillators. They may partly depend upon cosmic sources, waves of energy from the sun, barometric pressure changes from the moon, magnetic field changes, cosmic rays. The oscillation may resemble the pendulum of a grandfather clock or the atomic tuning-fork which, once struck, vibrates endlessly until the expiration of the atom's energy.

All self-sustained oscillations require some energy from the environment to replace the energy lost in the course of change. When the energy loss is gradual and small the system resembles a pendulum which requires only a push now and then, but when a lot of energy is expended much energy must be injected from the environment. If the energy drain is sudden like that of the emptying heart, bladder, or bowel, the system is known as a relaxation oscillator. Extremely high frequency rhythms (such as heart rate or trains of nerve impulses) are often executed by relaxation oscillators. Many researchers feel that circadian rhythms in insects and animals cannot be relaxation oscillators.

The relationships between circadian rhythms and their synchronizers can be clarified by mathematical formulation. Experimental models suggest what will happen under the influence of light at various intensities, temperature change, food scheduling, social factors, and so forth, and postulate what should happen when activity rhythms are delayed or accelerated artificially. References in the bibliography suggest a variety of mathematical models. These may indicate why scientists want to test ready-made theories from other branches of science within the field of biological rhythms, especially in areas relevant to man, in whom time structure is least understood and hardest of all to study.

Some of these models are cybernetic models of a feedback, arising from engineering systems first devised in the 1950s. Human beings are exceedingly vulnerable creatures and, like the machines we invent, we keep a semblance of constancy—homeostasis—in part by feedback. The thermostat in our brain is constantly reading temperatures in parts of our body and, like the thermostat on our home furnace, it does not let us get too cold or too hot.

Feedback mechanisms, such as thermostats, are familiar to engineers and elaborate mathematics describe their function. Sometimes, however, a feedback system breaks down and sets up an oscillation known as negative feedback. All of us have experienced it when somebody turns up a thermostat in a room and the room becomes too hot; then a window is opened and the room soon becomes too cold as the furnace shuts off. Instead of an even temperature and an efficient use of the furnace, the room alternates between too cold and too hot and the furnace is taxed to the limit.

Feedback mechanisms are used to explain gonadal function, yet the feedback chain of female hormones, for instance, does not explain the time period of the ovulation cycle nor why estrus cycles vary in length from one species to another. If some scientists have conjectured that certain periodic illnesses might be explained by negative feedback, others have conjectured that periodic symptoms might be the result of two oscillator mechanisms that became related in such a way as to produce beat frequencies. Either interpretation suggests an expression of the data using mathematics borrowed from other branches of science. Some of the understanding of frequency distributions or harmonics has been based on prior work in physics in the analysis of sound or light.

WAVE FORMS AND HARMONICS

When we refer to the "menstrual cycle," we imply an internal process that moves in a kind of circle from a point of origin through various hormonal stages back again to that origin point in predictable repetition. Most fluctuations measured in the body are cycles in an analogous sense. Body temperature moves up and down about two degrees centigrade each twenty-four hours, presumably representing a metabolic cycle. Adrenal hormones become more concentrated and less concentrated in the blood. There is a varying amount of potassium in the urine.

Temperature does not smoothly rise and fall each day. A very sensitive thermometer would reveal that our body temperatures rise and fall some fraction of a degree in what may be rhythms of twelve hours, perhaps three hours, or even shorter intervals, as well as twenty-four hours. In describing any of these recurrences, it is convenient to describe them as circular processes, starting from a point of origin and returning to it. The time it takes to complete the cycle is the interval known as the period, whether it is an hour, day, microsecond, or year; it is the elapsed interval between two peaks or troughs. Period is often represented by the Greek letter (τ). The frequency of a rhythm is the reciprocal of the period ($\frac{\cdot}{\tau}$). The magnitude of the

Wave Forms

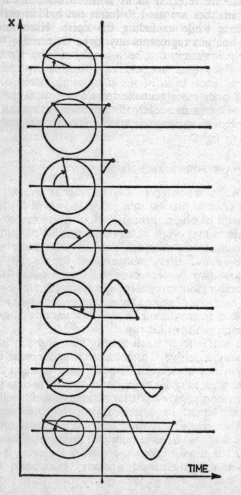

X

TIME

BY PERMISSION OF ARNE SOLLBERGER.

change, or amplitude ($\subset$), describes another dimension of the cycle. The phase (ϕ), or specific location on the cycle, is usually described with reference to some external time point.

Any rhythm will be composed of at least one dominant frequency, usually accompanied by other variations that are referred to as noise. Mathematical frequency analyses are used to ferret out hidden periodic fluctuations while excluding the noise. Harmonic or Fourier analysis represents any given time series (such as hourly temperatures for a week) as the algebraic sum of sine waves with different frequencies, phases, and amplitudes. However, harmonic analysis does not say if a rhythm is detectable from a statistical point of view, and sometimes alternative methods are used.

Analysis of variance is used to determine the significance of a rhythm. In understanding grouped data the average may indicate some central tendency, but it does not display the wide range that may exist between individual group members—the variation around the mean. One method of analyzing the amount of variation around the mean is to compute the difference of each member from the mean and to square this difference. This averaged squared deviation indicates the size of the deviation and the square root is the standard deviation often used as a yardstick in measuring the variability of data.

A similar process can be accomplished by what is known as curve-fitting. One suspects that there is a twenty-four-hour rhythm in the fluctuation of eosinophils in the blood. This twenty-four-hour period might be fitted to the hourly cell count. Then one might add derivatives of the curve, harmonics, such as a two-hourly peaking of the cell count. This composite curve would be added to the fitted curve until it became possible to significantly decrease the variance of values around the composite curve. By repeating the procedure with a number of basic periods, a series of approximations might determine which base period and harmonics best fit the data.

It is useful to talk as if body fluctuations were smooth waves, although it is not literally true. For instance, the daily fluctuation of corticosterone in human blood was long interpreted as a smooth decline to a trough around midnight and smooth steep rise to a peak before awakening. Yet the close-interval sampling by Weitzman and others has indicated that the hormone enters the blood in spurts and quickly vanishes. Over the twenty-four hours, however, the normal per-

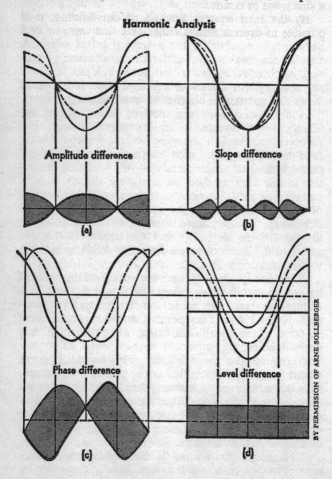

Harmonic Analysis

Amplitude difference

(a)

Slope difference

(b)

Phase difference

(c)

Level difference

(d)

BY PERMISSION OF ARNE SOLLBERGER

son shows such a regular distribution of these spurts that it can be described as a curve.

The shape of the curve over twenty-four hours, its level, amplitude, phase, and slope can be expressed by different mathematical functions. After fitting a curve to the data, so that the rhythm is characterized by its frequency and phase, this may be further abstracted as a sine wave or cosine.

By the least squares method of curve-fitting, it is possible to express results either as a sine wave or as a cosine. A cosine has its crest at the point of origin. A sine has its crest at minus-90 degrees. Since at present most scientists are interested in the peak and trough of a rhythm and a clockwise representation is easier to read, cosinor plots are easier to read than sinor plots. (The term "cosinor" was derived from *cosine* and *vector*.) If a cosine is fitted to the data to approximate a rhythm's amplitude as well as phase, the direction of the "hand" on the "clock" will indicate the phase of the rhythm at its peak, or in Dr. Halberg's terminology, acrophase.

At this writing, many biological rhythm studies involve animals, and a number of the medically oriented researchers in the field are using techniques developed by Drs. Max Engeli and Franz Halberg. By 1970, the methods of the Minnesota laboratory were being used by scientists throughout the world. These methods are sensitive enough to show up drug effects and the differential responses to drugs taken at different times of day. They have provided a means of comparing vital functions in sick and healthy persons, many of whom show circadian rhythms with the same period but differing in amplitude or phase.

Trying to determine phase relations without an agreed point of origin is like trying to run a global airline without agreed-upon time zones. In 1883, an international conference in Washington, D.C., devised a system referring all of the earth's clocks to a single point of origin—Greenwich, England. Until then, every locality set its clocks according to a sundial, so that passengers and railroaders had to make elaborate calculations to decide when, in local time, a transcontinental express train would actually arrive. In the realm of physiology and biology, a similar agreement is needed in evaluating internal rhythms. At present, each scientist chooses his own point of origin, if he specifies any point of origin at all.

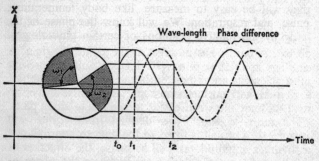

When rhythms are expressed in terms of local time of day, anyone out of that time context must translate; without this translation it might appear, for example, that the peak of the adrenal hormone cycle of people in New Guinea does not occur in the same portion of the activity cycle as that of people in Scotland. This is how it looks with reference to local time. By juxtaposing two sets of data and using a single point of origin (the midsleep time), Dr. Halberg and his associates demonstrated that there was really no phase difference. The two groups slept at different local times, but their hormonal rhythms were in the same phase relation to mid-sleep.

In studies run on a controlled schedule of light and dark (or sleep and rising), this reference point might be the middle of the sleep span. One might use the onset of light for rodents. Dr. Halberg has suggested a universal reference point: midnight (00), December 31, 1899. This point was not idly chosen. It is useful in evaluating a vast amount of already available data, including statistical surveys of birth time, deaths, and suicides in large populations. It was the beginning of a

day, a week, a month, and a year but not the century.
In the future, each individual will probably become his
own clock as, in fact, he really is. By understanding
phase relationships among cycles within the body, we
should be able to read biological time of day in individuals. It is hard to predict exactly which rhythms will be
the most convenient "hands" of the "clock"; probably
they will be easy to measure, like body temperature,
pulse, and respiration. We will know the phase of the
body by the relative positions of certain physiological
functions.

SPECTRAL ANALYSIS

Today a set of computer programs can do in
minutes work that used to take months. As a first step
the computer may print out the spectrum of temperature frequencies, that is, the frequency of occurrence of
each temperature sampled. It would also print out the
distribution of recorded temperatures along with their
mean, total variance, and standard deviation. Looking
at a histogram plotted by computer, one would immediately detect fever by a skewed distribution of temperatures. One would no longer be looking at time, but
rather at the frequency at which certain temperatures
occurred.

If one were to look at the entire picture of temperature change over a year—the thermovariance spectrum—one would see the variance at each frequency
along the entire spectrum. This would tell what proportion of the temperature fluctuation in a year was contributed by the frequency of temperature changes of a
given number of degrees over a twelve-hour period, a
twenty-four-hour period, or a weekly or monthly period.
The spectral analysis of a long series of body temperatures from a normal person would show a prominent
frequency at about twenty-four hours. Plotted loga-
rithmically, it might stand out like the Washington
Monument among the treetops. By comparing spectral
analyses of short records, perhaps of three weeks, with
records many times as long, one can see the stability

of a given component in the long record. Spectral analysis can be used to determine the appropriate length of a study. A researcher might intend to run a study for only three months, but spectral analysis might show that the cycle he was hunting was still obscured by overall variance. He might then decide to continue the study for another three months. Spectral analysis allows one to resolve the relative prominence of various frequencies (cycles) in the perspective of the record, and also to obtain statistical limits of reliability which are valid if the spectrum is fairly smooth. It is a process that can be validated by repetition and by sampling several analyses on data from the same individual.

Because so many of our functions show a circadian rhythm, their very "circadianness" may become a criterion for health or development. Dr. Halberg has devised an efficient method of computing the circadian quotient, which is the proportion of the total variance contributed by the rise and fall of a function such as temperature over roughly twenty-four hours. Rarely is a frequency absolute. Since temperature does not rise and fall in exactly twenty-four-hour cycles, one would compute a circadian quotient by using a band of frequencies. Spectral estimates for twenty-three to twenty-five hours might be summed and divided by the total variance. As an example, most babies show no perceivable pattern in their series of naps and wakeful hours in their first six weeks; it is hard to guess by looking at the usual time charts of the baby's activity how fast he is progressing toward sleeping at night, but the circadian quotient tells at once.

The Minnesota laboratory has used circadian quotients to depict responses to drugs. In one instance reserpine was given to a young girl, a hospital patient, whose temperature had been recorded at three-hour intervals before, during, and after drug administration. Her temperature, as revealed by the circadian quotient, was somewhat irregular before the drug (a circadian quotient of 25.2 percent). She was even more irregular (11 percent) during the days of reserpine administration and more nearly circadian (33 percent) after the drug treatment was finished.

Any variance quotient simply offers a single number to indicate the relative dominance of a certain frequency or band of frequencies in the overall variance. In studies of the heart or enzyme activity, an experimenter would be examining very high frequencies. In analyzing the rhythms of cell division in human cancers before and after X-ray treatment, the Minnesota team found it necessary to compute a band of frequencies with cycles around nineteen to twenty-eight hours. They found that the mitotic rhythms in tumors tended to be faster before X-rays and slower after radiation treatment.

In order to track free-running rhythms or to watch a stable rhythm as it changes in amplitude or phase, it is useful to have an equation describing a harmonic function (such as sine or cosine) that most closely approximates the actual rhythm in amplitude and phase as well as in frequency.

One may estimate the period of the cycle, then its amplitude above the adjusted level, and next its phase in relation to some time point outside the body.

The least squares method is very basic in statistics. As an extension of classical harmonic analysis, this multiple regression process can even fit cycles to data that were taken at unequal intervals, such as data from subjects who could not be tested during the night when they were asleep. For each frequency in the data, the computer matches a cosine curve in the form of an equation to the biological values. The difference between the real and abstract curves with various amplitudes, phases, and levels are squared, and the best-fit curve is the one for which the sum of these difference squares is least.

Using a geographical analogy, the least squares would represent the least wasted area between an actual mountain formation and the curve drawn to represent it. The analogy to the crest of a hill would be the so-called acrophase, or recurring peak phase, of the biological cycle over time.

Phase indicates the relation between the curve and a point of reference. The computer can calculate the extent to which the best-fitting cosine or sine curves vary from the original data. It can offer dispersion indices, for example, that are like the standard error estimates of the cosine or sine amplitude.

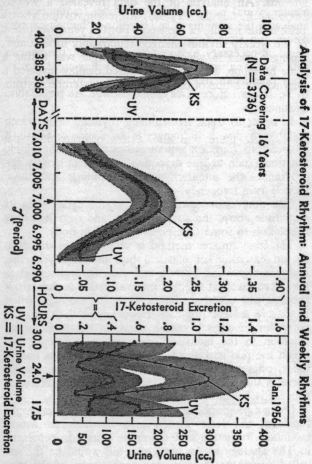

In the course of refining and testing a least squares computer program, Dr. Halberg and his associates began to reevaluate suitable data that happened to be available. Fortunately, there was an extraordinary longitudinal fifteen-year study which Dr. Christian Hamburger conducted on his own urine 17-keto-steroids. An analysis of the data revealed a weekly hormone metabolite (17-KS) excretion rhythm with a peak in the middle of the week. For ten years the phase of the weekly rhythm changed remarkably little. Later, during a span in which Dr. Hamburger was taking a male hormone, a computer-prepared display revealed a desynchronization of the weekly 17-ketosterone rhythm. A slow shift seemed to occur over a period of years, vaguely reminiscent of the drift of circadian rhythms in people during experimental isolation. Within the same data, there was also a less obvious thirty-day rhythm, suggesting that man's gonadal function may be influenced by cyclic hormonal change in a monthly rhythm.

In first applying a least squares spectrum one may not know where the prominent spectral components are located. With adequate data one can prepare a "window," choosing trial periods linearly, perhaps at six-minute intervals, in the region from twenty to twenty-eight hours. Using such a magnifying lens on some data collected in the early 1950s, the Minnesota team saw that blinded mice showed circadian temperature periods that ranged from 23.3 to 23.7 hours. Each mouse differed from a precise twenty-four-hour period by twenty to forty minutes, and the free-running periods differed from one mouse to another. Differences in phase were detected even when the individuals had the same period. Least squares analysis also can provide an index of dispersion. One knows whether one deals with a regular rhythm with a low amplitude, a near-rhythm, or with a phenomenon that reveals no rhythmicity.

POLAR PLOTS, PERIOD CLOCKS, HARMONIC DIALS

In defining a biological rhythm, spectral analysis of the data over time will reveal a series of dominant frequencies. A spectral estimate for any particular frequency will indicate how regular this cycle may be. If the cycle is stable and the frequency does not seem to vary much, then another useful analysis can be made. One may take a frequency, such as the twenty-four-hour cycle of body temperature, and use that period as the circumference of a "body clock." One of the clock "hands" might represent the phase at which the daily peak temperature occurs, while another hand indicates the peak phase of the individual's adrenal 17-OHCS; or this display could be used to compare the circadian temperature rhythms of several individuals.

A polar plot is a kind of time compass showing the timing of an individual's physiological rhythms in relation to some external reference point. The hand pointing to the peak phase of the circadian temperature rhythm could be read in terms of degrees—on a 360-degree clock. The direction of the hand, relative to the point of origin in the center, would indicate peak phase. The clock of a twenty-four-hour rhythm could be read simultaneously in ordinary time intervals of 15 degrees per hour. The plot would not show exact peaks but rather an averaged estimate, or typical phase, representing the timing of all peaks that occurred during the collection of data (there being one peak for each function represented).

Cosinor amplitudes, signifying a typical average amount of change in a unit of time, can also be expressed by the length of the hand. A computer program yields pairs of estimates of the amplitudes and phase of the particular best-fitting cosine, derived from a least squares procedure at a particular frequency. By this process, it is possible to quantify aspects of biological rhythm that are very cumbersome in graphs, charts, and tables, and it is possible to compare several individuals or to see phase relations of functions within an individual.

CONFIDENCE ARCS AND ERROR ELLIPSES

Although some strains of mice, nurtured on very rigid laboratory schedules, will show physiological and behavioral rhythms that have a machinelike regularity, the human environment is far less controlled. People inevitably exhibit individual differences. This means that a cosinor clock for a group will contain a certain variability. Just as a standard deviation depicts the amount of variation around the mean, a confidence limit estimates the extent to which the data fit the scientists' abstract summary. The cosinor plot reveals the magnitude of error in several dimensions.

The plot may show that a hospital patient, usually but not invariably, exhibited his peak oral temperature around 1 P.M. in a six-month study. Although his schedule was monotonously the same, he was not absolutely consistent from day to day. The peak phase and the amplitude of his temperature values and the slight shifts in peak phase can be summarized by an ellipse.

Circadian Rhythms in Duration of Diastole and Heart Rate of Men Experiencing Weightlessness for Several Days in Extraterrestrial Space

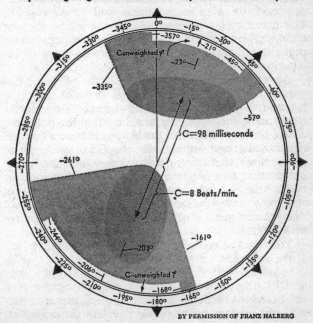

BY PERMISSION OF FRANZ HALBERG

The area within the ellipse denotes the extent of possible error.

Polar plots, also known as period clocks or harmonic dials, give a quick visual representation of temporal fluctuations in a manner that is more vivid and immediate than linear graphs or periodograms. When the hour of an ordinary "earth" clock points to twelve, we know by agreement with the rest of the world that it is noon or midnight. When the phase-amplitude hand points to 360 degrees, we know that the peak of the rhythm falls at the point of origin. This might be the middle of the sleep span or the peak of another readily measured rhythm, such as body temperature. If the phase were to shift to the right to 90 degrees, we would see that peak phase occurred six hours later. If the person were to shift another 90 degrees, he would hit his peak phase at the former time of his daily nadir.

The size of an error ellipse will indicate whether or not the original values were scattered. If they are not dispersed, the area of the ellipse will be quite small. The fewer cycles encompassed by the study, the less reason there is to be confident about the location of peaks and the estimate of the amplitudes—and this is indicated by a wider ellipse.

An error ellipse also indicates if the phase or frequency of the data is dubious. If the plot depicts a twenty-four-hour rhythm and the data contain irregular frequencies, the error ellipse will overlap the pole (the center of the circle). In essence, this indicates that the clock hand representing the purported peak phase (acrophase) could be rotated in every direction and is not pointing to any particular location on the clock for peak phase. A confidence arc thus expresses the amount of leeway within which a rhythm has been specified. The cosinor method allows a quantification of statistical confidence for the detected rhythm.

Polar plots have many advantages. For a quick look at the acrophase of any biological rhythm, this display is immediate and vivid. The polar plot conveys a great deal of information at a glance, in the manner of a wristwatch. A wristwatch never says whether it is running fast or slow, but the polar plot tells the magnitude of its own possible error. A rhythm must be detected at a certain level of statistical significance before the period, the amplitude, and the phase are quantified.

Cosinor plots have been useful in learning that physiological rhythms maintained their usual phase relationships in blinded animals while exhibiting a new frequency. The technique was used to decipher the behavior of a rhythm in respiratory function among asthmatic children as they responded to hormonal treatment; it thus allowed allergists to discover the acrophase of expiratory peak flow rate in response to drug action in the body and to see how this function changed when the drug was delivered at different times of day and night. The same technique indicated differences between skin and mammary cancer in terms of their mitotic rhythms.

Once a rhythm has been detected and its parameters described by spectral analysis, it is possible to display the stability of the rhythmic parameters over time. Thus, the amplitude, phase, and period can be visualized over a long duration, and it is possible, for example, to observe the effects of east-west flight or of drugs.

Ultimately, the methods now being developed and refined may allow medical researchers to prepare "physiological" clock graphs of patients. We may discover whether there is a normal phase relationship among the body's many rhythms. A clock might show peak phase for temperature, adrenal steroids, heart rate, eye-hand coordination, and make visible the body's time of day by exposing their phase relationships. Abnormalities of time structure may then be intercepted in medical examinations, perhaps giving us a way of detecting potential illnesses at a point at which they could be prevented.

BIBLIOGRAPHY

Books and Symposia

Ajuriaguerra J. de (ed.). *Cycles Biologiques et Psychiatrie.* Paris: Masson et Cie., 1968.

Aschoff, J. (ed.). *Circadian Clocks.* Amsterdam: North Holland Publishing Company, 1965.

Aurelianus, C. *On Acute Diseases and on Chronic Diseases.* (Edited and translated by I. E. Drabkin.) Chicago: University of Chicago Press, 1950.

Brown, F. A., Jr.; Hastings, J. W.; and Palmer, J. D. *The Biological Clock.* New York: Academic Press, 1970.

Bünning, E. *The Physiological Clock.* Revised second edition. New York: Springer-Verlag, 1967.

Claiborne, R., and Goudsmit, S. A. (eds.). *Time.* New York: Time-Life Books, 1966.

Cloudsley-Thompson, J. L. *Rhythmic Activity in Animal Physiology and Behavior.* New York: Academic Press, 1961.

Conroy, R., and Mills, J. M. *Human Circadian Rhythms.* Baltimore: Williams and Wilkins, 1971.

Dalton, K. *The Premenstrual Syndrome.* Springfield, Illinois: Charles C. Thomas, 1964.

Danilevski, A. S. *Photoperiodism and Seasonal Development of Insects.* Edinburgh: Oliver and Boyd, 1965.

Edholm, O. G., and Bacharach, A. L. (eds.). *The Physiology of Human Survival.* London: Academic Press, 1965.

Folk, G. E., Jr. *Introduction to Environmental Physiology.* Philadelphia: Lea and Febiger, 1966.

Fomon, S. F. (ed.). *Circadian Systems.* Report of the 39th Ross Conference on Pediatric Research. Columbus, Ohio: Ross Laboratories, 1961.

Fraisse, P. *The Psychology of Time.* London: Eyre and Spottiswoode, 1964.

Fraser, J. T. (ed.). *The Voices of Time.* New York: George Braziller, 1966.

Fraser, T. M. *The Effects of Confinement as a Factor in Manned Space Flight.* NASA Contractor Report, NASA CR–511, 1966.

Gauquelin, M. *The Cosmic Clocks.* Chicago: Henry Regnery Company, 1967.

Gerathewohl, S. J. *Principles of Bioastronautics*. Englewood Cliffs, New Jersey: Prentice-Hall, 1963.

Halberg, F. Symposium on rhythms. In: *Verhandlungen der deutschen Gesellschaft für innere Medizin*, 73rd Congress, Munchen: Bergmann, 1967, pp. 886–994, 1116–1117.

Halberg, F. Symposium on rhythms. Proceedings 4th Panamerican Symposium on Pharmocology and Therapy, Mexico City. Amsterdam: Excerpta Medica Foundation International Congress Series, No. 185:7–39, 1969.

Hall, C. *The Meaning of Dreams*. Second edition. New York: McGraw-Hill, 1966.

Harker, J. E. *The Physiology of Diurnal Rhythms*. London: Cambridge University Press, 1964.

Hartmann, E. *The Biology of Dreaming*. Springfield, Illinois: Charles C Thomas, 1967.

Kales, A. (ed.). *Sleep: Physiology and Pathology*. Philadelphia: Lippincott, 1969.

Kleitman, N. *Sleep and Wakefulness*. Revised edition. Chicago: University of Chicago Press, 1963.

Koella, W. P. *Sleep—Its Nature and Physiological Organization*. Springfield, Illinois: Charles C Thomas, 1967.

Kosmolinskiy, F. P., and Dushkov, B. A. (eds.); or Gurovskii, N. N. (ed.). *Papers on the Psychophysiology of the Labor of Astronauts*. Foreign Translation Division of the Clearinghouse, Department of Commerce, Springfield, Virginia, 22151: AD–684–690, 1968.

Mayersbach, H. von (ed.). *The Cellular Aspects of Biorhythms*. New York: Springer-Verlag, 1967.

Menzel, W. *Menschliche Tag-Nacht-Rhythmik und Schichtarbeit*. Basel/Stuttgart: Benno Schwabe, 1962.

Mills, J. N. (ed.). *Biological Aspects of Circadian Rhythms*. London: Plenum Press, 1971.

Ornstein, R. E. *On the Experience of Time*. Harmondsworth, England: Penguin Books Ltd., 1969.

Reimann, H. A. *Periodic Diseases*. Oxford: Blackwell Scientific Publications, 1963.

Reinberg, A., and Ghata, J. *Biological Rhythms*. New York: Walker and Son, 1965.

Richter, C. P. *Biological Clocks in Medicine and Psychiatry*. Springfield, Illinois: Charles C Thomas, 1965.

Rocard, Y. *Le Signal du Sourcier*. Paris: Dunod, 1962.

Rohles, F. *Circadian Rhythms in Nonhuman Primates*. New York/Basel: Karger, 1968.

Siffre, M. *Beyond Time*. New York: McGraw-Hill, 1964.

Sollberger, A. *Biological Rhythm Research*. Amsterdam/London/New York: Elsevier Publishing Company, 1965.

Sweeney, B. M. *Rhythmic Phenomena in Plants*. Experimental

Botany Series of Monographs. New York: Academic Press, 1969.

Symposia on Quantitative Biology. Vol. 25. Long Island Biological Association, Biological Laboratory, Cold Spring Harbor, Long Island, New York, 1960.

Ward, R. R. *The Living Clocks.* New York: Alfred A. Knopf, 1971.

Weyer, E. M., and Fischer, R. (eds.). *The Interdisciplinary Perspectives of Time,* Annals of the New York Academy of Sciences, 138(2): 367–915, 1967.

Wolf, W. (ed.). *Rhythmic Functions in the Living System,* Annals of the New York Academy of Sciences, 98(4):753–1326, 1962.

Wurtman, R. J.; Kelly, D. E.; and Axelrod, J. *The Pineal.* New York: Academic Press, 1969.

Brain

Axelrod, J.; Snyder, S. H.; Heller, A.; and Moore, R. Y. Light-induced changes in pineal hydroxyindole-O-methyltransferase: Abolition by lateral hypothalamic lesions. *Science,* 154:898–899, November 1966.

Berendes, H. W.; Marte, F.; Ertel, R. J.; McCarthy, J. A.; Anderson, J. A.; and Halberg, F. Circadian physiologic rhythm and lowered blood 5-hydroxytryptamine in human subjects with defective mentality. *Physiologist,* 3:20, 1960.

Brown, D. W., and Iverson, D. G. Diurnal variation of intraocular pressure and serum osmolality. *Experimental Eye Research,* 6:179–186, 1967.

Engel, R.; Halberg, F.; and Gully, R. J. The diurnal rhythm in EEG discharge and in circulating eosinophils in certain types of epilepsy. *Electroencephalography and Clinical Neurophysiology,* 4:115–116, 1952.

Engel, R.; Halberg, R.; Tichy, F. Y.; and Dow, R. Electrocerebral activity and epileptic attacks at various blood sugar levels (with a case report). *Acta Neurovegetativa,* 9:147–167, 1954.

Frank, G.; Halberg, F.; Harner, R.; Matthews, J.; Johnson, E.; Gravem, H.; and Andrus, V. Circadian periodicity, adrenal corticosteroids, sleep deprivation and the EEG of normal man. *Journal of Psychiatric Research,* 4:73–86, November 1966.

Friedman, A. H., and Walker, C. A. Circadian rhythms: Rat mid-brain and caudate nucleus biogenic amine levels. *Journal of Physiology,* 197:77–86, 1968.

Friedman, A. H., and Walker, C. A. Rat brain amines, blood histamine and glucose levels in relationship to circadian changes in sleep induced by pentobarbital sodium. *Journal of Physiology*, 202:133–147, 1968.

Galicich, J. H.; Halberg, F.; French, L. A.; and Ungar, F. Effect of cerebral ablation on a circadian pituitary adrenocorticotropic rhythm in C Mice. *Endocrinology*, 76:895–901, 1965.

Halberg, E.; Halberg, F.; and Bittner, J. J. Daily periodicity of convulsions in man and in mice. Report from the 5th Conference of the Society for the Study of Biologic Rhythms, Stockholm, 1961, p. 97.

Halberg, F.; Anderson, J. A.; Ertel, R.; and Berendes, H. W. Circadian rhythm in serum 5-hydroxytryptamine in healthy men and male patients with mental retardation. *International Journal of Neuropsychiatry*, 3:4379–4386, 1967.

Halberg, F.; Bittner, J. J.; and Gully, R. J. Twenty-four-hour periodic susceptibility to audiogenic convulsions in several stocks of mice. *Federation Proceedings*, 14:67–68, 1955.

Hamberger, A.; Hyden, H.; and Lange, P. W. Enzyme changes in neurons and glia during barbiturate sleep. *Science*, 151:1394–1395, March 1966.

Harding, G. F. A., and Jenner, F. A. The electroencephalogram in three cases of periodic psychosis. *Electroencephalography and Clinical Neurophysiology*, 21:59–66, 1966.

Harker, J. E. Internal factors controlling the subesophageal ganglion neurosecretory cycle in Periplaneta americana. *Journal of Experimental Biology*, 37(1):164–170, March 1960.

Henkin, R. I. Presence of corticosterone and cortisol in the central and peripheral nervous system of the cat. *Endocrinology*, 82(5):1058–1061, May 1968.

Ivanov, D. I.; Malkin, V. B.; Popkof, V. L.; Ye, O.; and Chernykov, I. N. Automatic analysis of diurnal periodic changes in human EEG rhythms. *Problems in Space Biology*, 4:642–645, Izdatelstvo "Nauka," Moscow, 1965. Clearinghouse for Federal Scientific and Technical Information, Springfield, Virginia.

Jouvet, M. Insomnia and decrease of cerebral 5-hydroxytryptamine after destruction of the RAPHE system in the cat. *Advances in Pharmacology*, 6B:265–279, 1968.

Jouvet, M. Biogenic amines and the states of sleep. *Science*, 879, 1969.

Kahana, L.; Lebovitz, H.; et al. Endocrine manifestations of intracranial extrasellar lesions. *Journal of Clinical Endocrinology and Metabolism*, 22:304–324, March 1962.

Karadzic, V., and Mrsulja, B. Deprivation of paradoxical sleep and brain glycogen. *Journal of Neurochemistry*, 16(1): 29–34, January 1969.

Krieger, D. T., and Krieger, H. P. Adrenal function in central nervous system disease. *Endocrines and the Central Nervous System*, 43:400–417, 1966.

Krieger, D. T., and Krieger, H. P. The circadian variation of the plasma 17-OHCS in central nervous system disease. *Journal of Clinical Endocrinology and Metabolism*, 26: 939, 1966.

Krieger, D. T., and Kreiger, H. P. Circadian pattern of plasma 17-hydroxycorticosteroid: Alteration by anticholinergic agents. *Science*, 155:1421–1422, March 1967.

Krieger, D. T., and Krieger, H. P. The effect of short-term administration of CNS-acting drugs on the circadian variation of the plasma 17-OHCS in normal subjects. *Neuroendocrinology*, 2:232, 1967.

Krieger, D. T., and Rizzo, F. Circadian periodicity of plasma 17-OHCS: Mediation by serotonin-dependent pathways. *American Journal of Physiology*, 217:1703, 1969.

Krieger, D. T.; Silverberg, A. I.; Rizzo, F.; and Krieger, H. P. Abolition of circadian periodicity of plasma 17-OHCS levels in the cat. *American Journal of Physiology*, 215: 915, 1968.

Makarova, L. G. Changes of EEG in a healthy individual with trigger light stimulation. *Bulletin of USSR, Academy of Medical Science, Institute of Neurology, Moscow*, 62:6–11, November 1966.

Meites, J. Releasing factors in hypothalamic control of the anterior pituitary in mammals. (Symposium on Hypothalamic Control of the Anterior Pituitary.) American Association for the Advancement of Science, December 1965.

Mink, W. D.; Best, J.; and Olds, J. Neurons in paradoxical sleep and motivated behavior. *Science*, 158:1335–1337, 1967.

Mouret, J.; Bobillier, P.; and Jouvet, M. Insomnia following parachlorphenylalanine in the rat. *European Journal of Pharmacology*, 5:1, 1968–1969.

Myasnikov, V. I. Electroencephalographic changes in persons isolated for long periods. *Cosmic Research*, 2:133–138, January-February 1964.

Nishiitsutsuji-Uwo, J.; Petropulos, S. F.; and Pittendrigh, C. S. Central nervous system control of circadian rhythmicity in the cockroach: I. Role of the pars intercerebralis. *Biological Bulletin*, 133(3):679–696, 1967.

Nishiitsutsuji-Uwo, J., and Pittendrigh, C. S. Central nervous system control of circadian rhythmicity in the cockroach. II. The pathway of light signals that entrain the rhythm. *Zeitschrift für Vergleichende Physiologie*, 58: 1–13, 1968.

Nishiitsutsuji-Uwo, J., and Pittendrigh, C. S. Central nervous system control of circadian rhythmicity in the cockroach. III. The optic lobes, locus of the driving oscillation? *Zeitschrift für Vergleichende Physiologie*, 58:14–46, 1968.

Pujol, J. F.; Hery, F.; Durand, M.; and Glowinski, J. Increase in serotonin synthesis in the brainstem of the rat after selective deprivation of paradoxical sleep. *Comptes Rendus de l'Académie des Sciences*, 267(3):371–372, 1968.

Quay, W. B. Regional and circadian differences in cerebral cortical serotonin concentration. *Life Sciences*, 4:379, 1965.

Reis, D. J.; Corvelli, A.; and Conners, J. Circadian and ultradian rhythms of serotonin regionally in cat brain. *Journal of Pharmacology and Experimental Therapeutics*, 167(2):328–333, 1969.

Reis, D. J.; Rifkin, M.; and Corvelli, A. Effects of morphine on cat brain norepinephrine in regions with daily monoamine rhythms. *European Journal of Pharmacology*, 8(1):149–152, 1969.

Reis, D. J.; Weinbren, M.; and Corvelli, A. A circadian rhythm of norepinephrine regionally in cat brain: Its relationship to environmental lighting and to regional diurnal variations in brain serotonin. *Journal of Pharmacology and Experimental Therapeutics*, 164(1):135–145, 1968.

Reis, D. J., and Wurtman, R. J. Diurnal changes in brain noradrenalin. *Life Sciences*, 7:91–98, 1968.

Scheving, L. E.; Harrison, W. H.; Gordon, P.; and Pauly, J. E. Daily fluctuation (circadian and ultradian) in biogenic amines of the rat brain. *American Journal of Physiology*, 214:166–173, 1968.

Schildkraut, J. J., and Kety, S. S. Biogenic amines and emotion. *Science*, 156(3771):21–30, 1967.

Steriade, M., and Iosif, G. Opposite changes in responsiveness of the motor and somaesthetic cortex during natural sleep and arousal. *Electroencephalography and Clinical Neurophysiology*, 25(3):299, 1968.

Strumwasser, F. Neurophysiological aspects of rhythms. In: Quarton, G. C.; Melnechuk, T.; and Schmitt, F. O. (eds.), *The Neurosciences: An Intensive Study Program*. New York: Rockefeller University Press, 1967, pp. 516–528.

Strumwasser, F. Membrane and intracellular mechanisms governing endogenous activity in neurons. In: Carlson, F. D. (ed.), *Physiological and Biochemical Aspects of*

Nervous Integration. Englewood Cliffs, New Jersey: Prentice-Hall, 1968, pp. 329–341.

Tamura, A. Changes of diurnal rhythm of Na, K, and Ca excretion in urine with disorders in brain. *Psychiatria et Neurologia Japonica,* 5:405–423, 1965.

Tepas, D. I. Evoked brain response as a measure of human sleep and wakefulness. *Aerospace Medicine,* 38:148–153, 1967.

Walker, C. A., and Friedman, A. H. Circadian rhythms in hypothalamic and caudate nucleus ultrastructure of untreated rats and those pretreated with reserpine or L-DOPA and MAO inhibitor. *Federation Proceedings,* 27:600, 1969.

Wolfe, J. W., and Brown, J. H. Effects of sleep deprivation on the vestibulo-ocular reflex. *Aerospace Medicine,* 39(9): 947–949, 1968.

Wurtman, R. J.; Axelrod, J.; and Reis, D. J. Metabolic cycles of monoamines and their modification by drugs. In: de Ajuriaguerra, J. (ed.), *Cycles Biologiques et Psychiatrie.* Paris: Masson et Cie., 1968, pp. 373–381.

Wyrwicka, W., and Sterman, M. B. Instrumental conditioning of sensorimotor cortex EEG spindles in the waking cat. *Physiology and Behavior,* 3:703–707, 1968.

Circadian Rhythms; Animal and Lower Organisms

Adkisson, P. L. Internal clocks and insect diapause. *Science,* 154:234–241, 1966.

Albrecht, P.; Visscher, M. B.; Bittner, J. J.; and Halberg, F. Daily changes in 5-hydroxytryptamine concentration in mouse brain. *Proceedings of the Society for Experimental Biology and Medicine,* 92:703–706, 1956.

Aschoff, J. Circadian activity pattern with two peaks. *Ecology,* 47(4):657–661, 1966.

Aschoff, J. Circadian activity rhythms in chaffinches (Fringilla coelebs) under constant conditions. *Japanese Journal of Physiology,* 16(4):363–370, 1966.

Aschoff, J., and Wever, R. Circadian rhythms of finches in light-dark cycles with interposed twilights. *Comparative Biochemistry and Physiology;* 16:507–514, 1965.

Barnett, A. Cell division: A second circadian clock system in paramecium multicronucleatum. *Science,* 164:1417–1418, 1969.

Barnwell, F. H. Daily and tidal patterns of activity in individual fiddler crabs (genus, Uca) from the Woods Hole region. *Biological Bulletin,* 130(1):1–7, 1966.

Bolles, R. C., and Duncan, P. M. Daily course of activity and subcutaneous body temperature in hungry and thirsty rats. *Journal of Physiology and Behavior*, 4:87–89, 1968.

Bowers, W. S., and Blickenstaff, C. C. Hormonal termination of diapause in the alfalfa weevil. *Science*, 154:1673–1674, 1966.

Brown, F. A., Jr. Effects and after-effects on planarians of reversals of the horizontal magnetic vector. *Nature*, 209 (5022):533–535, 1966.

Brown, F. A., Jr. Endogenous biorhythmicity reviewed with new evidence. *Scientia*, 103(5–6):245–259, 1968.

Brown, F. A., Jr., and Park, Y. H. Phase-shifting a lunar rhythm in planarian by altering the horizontal magnetic vector. *Biological Bulletin*, 129(1):79–86, 1965.

Brown, F. A., Jr., and Park, Y. H. Association-formation between photic and subtle geophysical stimulus patterns—a new biological concept. *Biological Bulletin*, 132(3):311–319, 1967.

Brown, F. A., Jr., and Park, Y. H. Synodic monthly modulation of the diurnal rhythm of hamsters. *Proceedings of the Society for Experimental Biology and Medicine*, 125:712–725, 1967.

Brown, F. A., Jr., Park, Y. H.; and Zeno, J. R. Diurnal variation in organismic response to very weak gamma radiation. *Nature*, 211(5051):830–833, 1966.

Bruce, V. G., and Pittendrigh, C. S. Temperature independence in a unicellular "clock." *Proceedings of the National Academy of Sciences*, 42:676–682, 1956.

Bruce, V. G., and Pittendrigh, C. S. Endogenous rhythms in insects and microorganisms. *American Naturalist*, 91:179–195, 1957.

Cardoso, S. S.; Ferreira, A. L.; et al. The effect of partial hepatectomy upon circadian distribution of mitosis in the cornea of rats. *Experientia*, 24:568–571, 1968.

Chaudry, A. P., and Halberg, F. Rhythms in blood eosinophils and mitosis in hamster pinna and pouch; phase alterations by carcinogen. *Journal of Dental Research*, 39:704, 1960.

Chaudry, A. P.; Halberg, F.; Keenan, C. E.; Harner, R. N.; and Bittner, J. J. Daily rhythms in rectal temperature and in epithelial mitoses of hamster pinna and pouch. *Journal of Applied Physiology*, 12:221–224, 1958.

Clark, R. H., and Korst, D. R. Circadian periodicity of bone marrow mitotic activity and reticulocyte in rats and mice. *Science*, 166:236–237, May 1969.

Crowley, T. J.; Kripke, D. F.; Halberg, F.; Pegram, G. V.; and Schildkraut, J. J. Circadian rhythms in monkeys:

Sleep, EEG, EMG, body and eye movement and temperature. *Psychophysiology*, 6:242–243, 1969.

Duke, M. B. Biosatellite III: Preliminary findings. *Science*, 166:492–493, 1969.

Edmunds, L. N., Jr. Replication of DNA and cell division in synchronously dividing cultures of Euglena gracilis. *Science*, 145:266–268, 1964.

Edmunds, L. N., Jr. Studies on synchronously dividing cultures of Euglena gracilis Klebs (Strain Z). III: Circadian components of cell division. *Journal of Cellular and Comparative Physiology*, 67(1):35–44, February 1966.

Eisinger, R. P. Influence of posture and diurnal rhythm on the renal excretion of acid—observations in normal and adrenalectomized subjects. *Metabolism*, 15:76–87, January 1966.

Eling, W. The circadian rhythms of nucleic acids. In: Mayersbach, H. von (ed.), *The Cellular Aspects of Biorhythms*. New York: Springer-Verlag, 1967, pp. 105–114.

Emlen, S. T. Bird migration: Influence of physiological state upon celestial orientation. *Science*, 165:716–718, August 1969.

Enright, J. T. Entrainment of a tidal rhythm. *Science*, 147 (3660):864–867, February 1965.

Enright, J. T. Temperature and free-running circadian rhythm of the house finch. *Comparative Biochemistry and Physiology*, 18:463–475, 1966.

Feigin, R. D.; Dangerfield, H. G.; and Beisel, W. R. Circadian periodicity of blood amino acids in normal and adrenalectomized mice. *Nature*, 221:94–95, 1969.

Friedman, S. B., and Ader, R. Adrenocortical response to novelty and noxious stimulation. *Neuroendocrinology*, 2:209–212, 1967.

Garcia, J.; Buchwald, N. A.; Feder, B. H.; and Koelling, R. A. Immediate detection of X-rays by the rat. *Nature*, 196 (4858):1014–1015, 1962.

Garcia, J.; Buchwald, N. A.; et al. Electroencephalographic responses to ionizing radiation. *Science*, 140(3564):289–290, 1963.

Glick, D.; Ferguson, R. B.; Greenberg, L. J.; and Halberg, F. Circadian studies on succinic dehydrogenase, pantothenate and biotin of rodent adrenal. *American Journal of Physiology*, 200:811–814, 1961.

Goff, M. L. R., and Finger, F. W. Activity rhythms and diurnal light-dark control. *Science*, 154:1346–1348, 1966.

Halberg, F.; Albrecht, P. G.; and Barnum, C. P. Phase shifting of liver-glycogen rhythm in intact mice. *American Journal of Physiology*, 199:400, 1960.

Halberg, F.; Barnum, C. P.; and Vermund, H. Hepatic phospholipid metabolism and the adrenal. *Journal of Clinical Endocrinology and Metabolism*, 13:871, 1953.

Halberg, F.; Bittner, J. J.; and Smith, D. Mitotic rhythm in mice, mammary tumor milk agent, and breast cancer. *Proceedings of the American Association for Cancer Research*, 2:305, 1958.

Halberg, F.; Peterson, R. E.; and Silber, R. H. Phase relations of 24-hour periodicities in blood corticosterone. Mitoses in cortical adrenal parenchyma, and total body activity. *Endocrinology*, 64:222–230, 1959.

Halberg, F., and Visscher, M. B. Temperature rhythms in blind mice. *Federation Proceedings*, 13:65, 1954.

Halberg, F.; Zander, H. R.; Houglum, M. W.; and Muhlemann, H. R. Daily variations in tissue mitoses, blood eosinophils and rectal temperature of rats. *American Journal of Physiology*, 177:361–366, 1954.

Haus, E.; Lakatua, D.; and Halberg, F. The internal timing of several circadian rhythms in the blinded mouse. *Experimental Medicine and Surgery*, 25:7–45, 1967.

Hayden, P., and Lindberg, R. G. Circadian rhythm in mammalian body temperature entrained by cyclic pressure changes. *Science*, 164:1288–1289, 1969.

Hayes, D.; Schechter, M. S.; and Sullivan, W. N. Biochemical look at insect diapause. *Symposium on Biological Rhythms, Entomological Society of America*, New York, N.Y., November 1967.

Hayward, J., and Baker, M. Role of cerebral arterial blood in the regulation of brain temperature in the monkey. *American Journal of Physiology*, 215(2):389–403, 1968.

Holmquest, D. L., and Lipscomb, H. S. The response of thermal and activity rhythms in the rat to cyclic variations in adrenocortical function and environmental lighting. *Proceedings of the International Union of Physiological Sciences*, 7:197, 1968.

Honjo, S.; Fujiwara, R.; Takasaka, M.; Suzuki, Y.; and Imaizumi, K. Observations on the diurnal temperature variation of cynomolgus monkeys (Macaca irus) and on the effect of changes in the routine of lighting upon this variation. *Japanese Journal of Medical Science and Biology*, 16:189–198, 1963.

Jardetzky, C. D.; Barnum, C. P.; and Halberg, F. Physiologic 24-hour periodicity in nucleic acid metabolism and mitosis of immature growing liver. *American Journal of Physiology*, 187:608, 1956.

Jerusalem, C. Circadian changes of the DNA-content in rat liver cells as revealed by histophotometric methods. In: Mayersbach, H. von (ed.), *The Cellular Aspects of Biorhythms*. New York: Springer-Verlag, 1967, pp. 115–123.

Johnson, L. Diurnal patterns of metabolic variations in chick embryos. *Biological Bulletin,* 131(2):308–322, 1966.

Kavanau, J. L., and Rischer, C. E. Program clocks in small mammals. *Science,* 161:1256–1259, September 1968.

Kuznetsova, S. S. Diurnal rhythm of radiosensitivity in mice and rats. *Biologicheskiye ritmy i voprosy razrabotki rezhimov truda i otdykha.* Materialy. Moscow, 1967, 44.

Manshardt, J., and Wurtman, R. Daily rhythm in the noradrenaline content of rat hypothalamus. *Nature,* 217(5128): 574–575, 1968.

Menaker, M. Endogenous rhythms of body temperature in hibernating bats. *Nature,* 184:1251, 1959.

Minis, D. H., and Pittendrigh, C. S. Circadian oscillation controlling hatching: Its ontogeny during embryogenesis of a moth. *Science,* 159:534–536, 1968.

Morley, A., and Stohlman, F., Jr. Erythropoiesis in the dog: The periodic nature of the steady state. *Science,* 165: 1025–1027, 1969.

Nishiitsutsuji-Uwo, J.; Petropulos, S. F.; and Pittendrigh, C. S. Central nervous system control of circadian rhythmicity in the cockroach: I. Role of the pars intercerebralis. *Biological Bulletin,* 133(3):679–696, 1967.

Nishiitsutsuji-Uwo, J., and Pittendrigh, C. S. Central nervous system control of circadian rhythmicity in the cockroach. II: The pathway of light signals that entrain the rhythm. *Zeitschrift für Vergleichende Physiologie,* 58: 1–13, 1968.

Nishiitsutsuji-Uwo, J., and Pittendrigh, C. S. Central nervous system control of circadian rhythmicity in the cockroach. III: The optic lobes, locus of the driving oscillation? *Zeitschift für Vergleichende Physiologie,* 58:14–46, 1968.

Nishiitsutsuji-Uwo, J.; Townsend, R. N.; et al. Short communication, day-night variation, the enzymatic dephosphorylation of ATP in hamster liver fractions. *Comparative Biochemistry and Physiology,* 22:319–323, 1967.

Pauly, J. E., and Scheving, L. E. Daily leukocyte rhythms in normal and hypophysectomized rats exposed to different environmental light-dark schedules. *Anatomical Record,* 153(4):349–360, 1965.

Pauly, J. E., and Scheving, L. E. The innate rhythmic nature of several processes or events involved in the total mitotic cycle of dividing corneal epithelial cells in the rat. *Third International Congress of Histochemistry and Cytochemistry.* New York: Springer-Verlag, 1968, p. 197.

Pittendrigh, C. S. Circadian systems: I. The driving oscillation and its assay in Drosophila pseudoobscura. *Proceedings of the National Academy of Sciences,* 58(4):1762–1767, 1967.

Retiene, K.; Zimmermann, W. J.; Schindler, C. J.; and Lipscomb, H. S. A correlative study of resting endocrine rhythms in rats. *Acta Endocrinologica,* 57:615–622, 1968.

Richter, C. P. Biological foundation of personality differences. *American Journal of Orthopsychiatry,* 2:345–354, 1932.

Richter, C. P. A hitherto unrecognized difference between man and other primates. *Science,* 154(3747):427, 1966.

Richter, C. P. Inherent 24-hour and lunar clocks of a primate —the squirrel monkey. *Communications in Behavioral Biology,* Part A, (1):305–332, 1968.

Roberts, S. K. Circadian activity rhythms in cockroaches. I. The free-running rhythm in steady state. *Journal of Cellular and Comparative Physiology,* 55:81–86, 1960.

Roberts, S. K. Circadian activity rhythms in cockroaches. II. Entrainment and phase shifting. *Journal of Cellular and Comparative Physiology,* 59:175–186, 1962.

Scheving, L. E. Circadian and ultradian rhythms in several physiological parameters of the rat. *Third International Congress of Histochemistry and Cytochemistry.* New York: Springer-Verlag, 1968.

Scheving, L. E. Circadian rhythms in plasma organic phosphorous and sulfur of the rat: Also in susceptibility to strychnine. *Japanese Journal of Physiology.* In press.

Scheving, L. E.; Harrison, W. H.; Gordon, P.; and Pauly, J. E. Daily fluctuation (circadian and ultradian) in biogenic amines of the rat brain. *American Journal of Physiology,* 214:166–173, 1968.

Scheving, L. E., and Pauly, J. E. Circadian phase relationships of thymidine-H3 uptake, labeled nuclei, grain counts, and cell division rate in rat corneal epithelium. *Journal of Cell Biology,* 32(3):677–683, 1967.

Scheving, L. E., and Pauly, J. E. Daily rhythmic variations in blood coagulation times in rats. *Anatomical Record,* 157:657–665, 1967.

Scheving, L. E.; Pauly, J. E.; and Tsai, Tien-hu. Circadian fluctuation in plasma proteins in the rat. *American Journal of Physiology,* 215:1096–1101, 1968.

Sollberger, A. The control of circadian glycogen rhythms. *Annals of the New York Academy of Sciences,* 117(1):519–553, 1964.

Stacy, B. D., and Thorburn, G. D. Neurosecretory cells: Daily rhythmicity in leiobunum longpipes. *Science,* 152:1078–1079, 1966.

Stephens, G. J.; Halberg, F.; and Stephens, G. C. The blinded fiddler crab: An invertebrate model of circadian desynchronization. *Annals of the New York Academy of Sciences,* 117(1):386–406, 1964.

Stephens, G. J., and McGaugh, J. L. Periodicity and memory in mice: A supplementary report. *Communications in Behavioral Biology,* Part A, 2(2):59–63, 1968.

Stroebel, C. F. Behavioral aspects of circadian rhythms. In: Zubin, J., and Hunt, H. F. (eds.), *Comparative Psychopathology.* New York: Grune and Stratton, 1967.

Strumwasser, F. The demonstration and manipulation of a circadian rhythm in a single neuron. In: Aschoff, J. (ed.), *Circadian Clocks.* Amsterdam: North Holland Publishing Company, 1965.

Sullivan, W. N.; Cawley, B. M.; Oliver, M.; Hayes, D. K.; and McGuire, J. U. Manipulating the photoperiod to damage insects. *Nature,* 221(5175):60–61, 1969.

Swade, R. H., and Pittendrigh, C. S. Circadian locomotor rhythms of rodents in the Arctic. *American Naturalist,* 101(922):431–466, 1967.

Thor, D. H., and Hoats, D. L. A circadian variable in self-exposure to light by the rat. *Psychonomic Science,* 12(1):1–2, August 1968.

Winget, C. M.; Card, D. H.; and Hetherington, N. W. Circadian oscillations of deep-body temperature and heart rate in a primate (Cebus albafrons). *Aerospace Medicine,* 39:350–353, 1968.

Circadian Rhythms: Human

Abernethy, J. D.; Farhi, L. E.; and Maurizi, J. J. Diurnal variations in urinary-alveolar N2 difference and effects of recumbency. *Journal of Applied Physiology,* 23:875–879, 1967.

Andrus, V.; Frank, G.; Gravem, H.; Halberg, F.; Harner, R.; Johnson, E.; and Matthews, J. Circadian periodicity, adrenal corticosteroids, and the EEG of normal man. *Journal of Psychiatric Research,* 4:73–86, November 1966.

Aschoff, J. Exogenous and endogenous components in circadian rhythms. *Symposium on Quantitative Biology,* Cold Spring Harbor, 25:11–27, 1960.

Aschoff, J. Human circadian rhythms in activity, body temperature and other functions. In: Brown, A. H., and Favorite, F. G. (eds.), *Life Science and Space Research V, International Space Science Symposium, 7th, Vienna, Austria, May 10–18, 1966, Papers.* Amsterdam: North Holland Publishing Company, 1967, pp. 159–173.

Aschoff, J. C.: Giedke, H.; and Pöppel, E. Tagesperiodische veranderungen der Reaktionszeit bei Wahlreaktionen.

    Zeitschrift für experimentelle und angewandte Psychologie, 1970. In press.

Bartter, F. C.; Delea, C. S.; and Halberg, F. A map of blood and urinary changes related to circadian variations in adrenal cortical function in normal subjects. *Annals of the New York Academy of Sciences,* 98:969–983, 1962.

Beisel, W. R.; Feigin, R. D.; and Klainer, A. S. Factors affecting circadian periodicity of blood amino acids in man. *Metabolism,* 17:764–775, September 1968.

Berges, D. Investigation on the extent of diurnal variations in the electrocardiogram of healthy subjects. *Zeitschrift für Kreislaufforschung,* 54:35–49, 1965.

Bohlen, J. G. Circadian and circannual rhythms in Eskimos. A Prospectus of Research Submitted to the Faculty of the Graduate School of the University of Wisconsin, 1969.

Cahn, A. A.; Folk, G. E.; and Huston, P. E. Age comparison of human day-night physiological differences. *Aerospace Medicine,* 39(6):608–610, 1968.

Cranston, W. I. Diurnal variation in plasma volume in normal and hypertensive subjects. *American Heart Journal,* 68:427–428, 1964.

Curtis, G. C.; Fogel, M. L.; McEvoy, D.; and Zarate, C. Effects of weight, sex and diurnal variation on the excretion of 17-hydroxycorticosteroids. *Journal of Clinical Endocrinology and Metabolism,* 28(5):711–713, 1968.

Doctor, R. F., and Friedman, L. F. Thirty-day stability of spontaneous galvanic skin responses in man. *Psychophysiology,* 2:311–315, April 1966.

Doe, R. P.; Vennes, J. A.; and Flink, E. B. Diurnal variation of 17-hydroxycorticosteroids, sodium, potassium, magnesium and creatinine in normal subjects and in cases of treated adrenal insufficiency and Cushing's syndrome. *Journal of Clinical Endocrinology and Metabolism,* 20:253–265, February 1960.

Feigin, R. D.; Klainer, A. S.; and Beisel, W. R. Circadian periodicity of blood amino acids in adult men. *Nature,* 215(5100):512–514, 1967.

Feigin, R. D.; Klainer, A. S.; and Beisel, W. R. Factors affecting circadian periodicity of blood amino acids in man. *Metabolism,* 17(9):764–775, 1968.

Fiorica, V.; Burr, M. J.; and Moses, R. Contribution of activity to the circadian rhythm in excretion of magnesium and calcium. *Aerospace Medicine,* 39(7):714–717, July 1968.

Frank, G.; Halberg, F.; Harner, R.; Matthews, J.; Johnson, E.; Gravem, H.; and Andrus, V. Circadian periodicity, adrenal corticosteroids, and the EEG of normal man.

Journal of Psychiatric Research, 4:73–86, November 1966.

Frazier, T. W.; Rummel, J. A.; and Lipscomb, H. S. Circadian variability in vigilance performance. *Aerospace Medicine*, 39(4):383–395, 1968.

Gerd, M. A. Human work capacity at various periods of wakefulness. *Biologicheskiye ritmy i voprosy razrabotki rezhimov truda i otdykha*. Materialy. Moscow, 1967, 20–21.

Gramvall, S., and Lundberg, U. Variations in pulse at a cycle ergometer test on Swedish Air Force pilots. *Meddelanden Fran Flygoch Navalmedicinska Naemnden*, 12(1): 4–5, 1963.

Halberg, F. Some physiological and clinical aspects of 24-hour periodicity. *Journal Lancet*, 73:20–32, 1953.

Halberg, F.; Anderson, J. A.; Ertel, R.; and Berendes, H. W. Circadian rhythm in serum 5-hydroxytryptamine in healthy men and male patients with mental retardation. *International Journal of Neuropsychiatry*, 3:4379–4386, 1967.

Halberg, F.; Frank, G.; Harner, R.; Matthews, J.; Aaker, H.; Gravem, H.; and Melby, J. The adrenal cycle in men on different schedules of motor and mental activity. *Experientia*, 17:282, 1961.

Haus, E., and Halberg, F. Circadian phase diagrams of oral temperature and urinary functions in a healthy man studied longitudinally. *Acta Endocrinologica*, 51:215–223, 1966.

Hildebrandt, G. von. Die Koordination rhythmischer Funktionen beimenschen. *Verhandlungen der deutschen Gesellschaft für innere Medizin*, 73rd Congress, 1967, pp. 921–941.

Ivanov, D. I.; Malkin, V. B.; Popkof, V. L.; Ye, O.; and Chernykov, I. N. Automatic analysis of diurnal periodic changes in human EEG rhythms. *Problems in Space Biology*, 4:642–645. Izdatelstvo "Nauka," Moscow, 1965. Clearinghouse for Federal Scientific and Technical Information, Springfield, Virginia.

Kaiser, I. H., and Halberg, F. Circadian aspects of birth. *Annals of the New York Academy of Sciences*, 98:1056–1068, 1962.

Kaneko, M., and Smith, R. E. Circadian variation in human peripheral blood flow levels and exercise responses. *Journal of Applied Physiology*, 25:109–114, August 1968.

Katz, F. H. Adrenal function during bed rest. *Aerospace Medicine*, 35:849–851, September 1964.

Konovalov, V. F.; Voronin, L. G.; and Konolalov, V. Electrographic data on the work of biological clocks. *Voprosy Psikhologii*, 12:87–94, November-December 1966.

Kraft, I. A.; Alexander, S.; et al. Circadian rhythms in human heart homograft. *Science*, 169:694–695, August 1970.

Krylov, Yu. V. Circadian rhythm of hearing in humans after prolonged exposure to noise. *Aerospace Medicine*, 39: 111–114, October 1968.

Laatikainen, T., and Vihko, R. Diurnal variation in the concentrations of solvolyzable steroids in human plasma. *Journal of Clinical Endocrinology and Metabolism*, 28: 1356–1360, September 1968.

Lipscomb, H. S. Biological rhythms in man: A correlative study. *Excerpta Medica International Congress Series No. 99*, 6th Pan-American Congress of Endocrinology, October 1965.

Lobban, M. C. Daily rhythms of renal excretion in Arctic-dwelling Indians and Eskimos. *Quarterly Journal of Experimental Physiology and Cognate Medical Sciences*, 52:401–410, October 1967.

Lobban, M. C., and Tredre, B. E. Renal diurnal rhythms in human subjects during bed-rest and limited activity. *Journal of Physiology*, 171(2):26–27, June 1964.

Meddis, R. Human circadian rhythms and the 48-hour day. *Nature*, 218:964–965, June 1968.

Nichols, T., and Tyler, F. H. Diurnal variation in adrenal cortical function. *Annual Review of Medicine*, 18:313–324, 1967.

Ojemann, F. A., and Henkin, R. I. Steroid dependent changes in human visual evoked potentials. *Life Sciences*, 6:327–334, 1967.

Panferova, N. Ye. The diurnal rhythm of functions of humans in condition of limited mobility. *Fiziologicheskii Zhurnal SSSR*, 50:741–749, 1963.

Pöppel, E. Oszillatorische Komponenten in Reaktionszeiten. *Die Naturwissenschaften*, 55:449–450, 1968.

Reinberg, A.; Halberg, F.; Ghata, J.; et al. Rythme circadien de diverses fonctions physiologiques de l'homme adulte sain, actif et au repos (pouls, pression artérielle, excrétions urinaires des 17-OHCS des catecholamines et du potassium). *Journal de Physiologie*, 61:383, 1969.

Scheving, L. E. Mitotic activity in the human epidermis. *Anatomical Review*, 135:7–20, 1959.

Serge, G.; Turco, G.; and Ceresa, F. Assay of a compartmental analysis of blood glucose and insulin relationships in man. *Acta Diabetologica Latina*, 5:242–243, October 1968.

Southren, A. L.; Tochimoto, S.; Carmody, N. C.; and Isurugi, K. Plasma production rates of testosterone in normal adult men and women and in patients with the syndrome of feminizing testes. *Journal of Clinical Endocrinology and Metabolism*, 25:1441, 1965.

Stanbury, S. W., and Thomson, A. E. Diurnal variations in electrolyte excretion. *Journal of Clinical Endocrinology and Metabolism*, 11:267–293, 1961.

Vestergaard, P., and Leverett, R. Constancy of urinary creatinine excretion. *Journal of Laboratory and Clinical Medicine*, 51(2):211–218, 1958.

Voronin, L. G. Electrographic data on the work of biological clocks. *Voprosy Psikhologii*, 12:87–94, 1966.

Wadsworth, G. L.; Halberg, F.; Albrecht, P.; and Skaff, G. Peak urinary excretion of 5-hydroxyindoleacetic acid following arousal in human beings. *Physiologist*, 1:86, 1957.

Walsh, J. F., and Misiak, H. Diurnal variation of critical flicker frequency. *Journal of General Psychology*, 75:167–175, 1966.

Wurtman, R. J.; Rose, C. M.; Chou, C.; and Larin, F. F. Daily rhythms in the concentrations of various amino acids in human plasma. *New England Journal of Medicine*, 279(4):171–175, 1968.

Young, V. T.; Hussein, M. A.; Murray, E.; and Scrimshaw, N. S. Tryptophan intake, spacing of meals, and diurnal fluctuations of plasma tryptophan in men. *American Journal of Clinical Nutrition*, 22(12):1563–1567, 1969.

Cycles: Ultradian and Infradian

Bohlen, J. G. Circadian and circannual rhythms in Eskimos. A Prospectus of Research Submitted to the Faculty of the Graduate School of the University of Wisconsin, 1969.

Bohlen, J. G.; Milan, F. A.; and Halberg, F. Circumpolar chronobiology. *Proceedings of the Ninth International Congress of Anatomists*, Leningrad, August 1970.

Buchsbaum, M. Effects of cardiac and respiratory cycles on averaged visual evoked responses. *Electroencephalography and Clinical Neurophysiology*, 19:476–480, 1965.

Chance, B.; Pye, K.; and Higgins, J. Waveform generation by enzymatic oscillators. *IEEE Spectrum*, 4:79–86, 1967.

Dubois, F. S. Rhythms, cycles and periods in health and disease. *American Journal of Psychiatry*, 116:114–119, 1959.

Fuchs, H. Seasonal and social factors in suicides. *Paper No. 96, IPU Conference*, 1961.

Globus, G. G. Observations on sub-circadian periodicity. *Psychophysiology*, 1970. In press.

Globus, G. G. Rapid eye movement cycle in real time. *Archives of General Psychiatry*, 15:654–659, 1966.

Halberg, F.; Engeli, M.; and Hamburger, C. The 17-ketosteroid excretion of a healthy man on weekdays and weekends. *Experimental Medicine and Surgery*, 23:61–69, 1965.

Halberg, F.; Engeli, M.; Hamburger, C.; and Hillman, D. Spectral resolution of low-frequency, small-amplitude rhythms in excreted ketosteroid; probable androgen-induced circaseptan desynchronization. *Acta Endocrinologica Supplement*, 103:1–54, 1965.

Halberg, F., and Hamburger, C. 17-ketosteroid and volume of human urine: Weekly and other changes with low frequency. *Minnesota Medicine*, 47:916–925, August 1964.

Halberg, F., and Reinberg, A. Rythmes circadiens et rythmes de basses fréquences en physiologie humaine. *Journal de Physiologie*, 59(1):117–200, 1967.

Hartmann, E. The 90-minute sleep-dream cycle. *Archives of General Psychiatry*, 18:280–286, March 1968.

Haus, E., and Halberg, F. Circannual rhythm in level and timing of serum corticosterone in standardized inbred mature C-mice. *Journal of Environmental Research*, 1970. In press.

Hayes, D.; Schechter, M. S.; and Sullivan, W. N. Biochemical look at insect diapause. *Symposium on Biological Rhythms, Entomological Society of America*, New York, N.Y., November 1967.

Hersey, P. Emotional cycles of man. *Journal of Mental Science*, 77:151–169, 1931.

Hildebrandt, G. von. Rhythmische Koordination als Ordnungsprinzip biologischer Funktionen. *Die Umschau*, 19:592–596, 1962.

Hildebrandt, G. von. Die Bedeutung der Unweltrezze für den Tagesrythmus des Menschen. *Bade und Klimaheilkunde*, 13:626–644, December 1966.

Hobson, A. Sleep and biorhythmicity. *Science*, 165(3896):932–933, August 1969.

Kleitman, N. *Sleep and Wakefulness*. Revised edition. Chicago: University of Chicago Press, 1963.

Kleitman, N. Basic rest-activity cycle. Abstract from paper presented at the Association for the Psychophysiological Study of Sleep, Boston, 1969. *Psychophysiology*, 1970.

Kleitman, N. The basic rest-activity cycle. In Wulfsohn, N. L., and Sances, A., Jr. (eds.), *The Nervous System and Electric Currents*. New York: Plenum Press, 1970.

Lewis, J. Some observations on narcolepsy. *Psychophysiology*, 5(2):237, September 1968.

Malek, J.; Gleich, J.; and Malý, V. Characteristics of the daily rhythm of menstruation and labor. *Annals of the New York Academy of Sciences*, 98:1042–1055, 1962.

Marotta, S. F., and Linwong, M. Excretion of urinary 17-ketosteroids and 17-ketogenic steroids. I. Effects of age, time of day and season. *Chiengmai Medical Bulletin*, 5:167–181, 1966.

Othmer, E.; Hayden, M. P.; and Segelbaum, R. Encephalic cycles during sleep and wakefulness in humans: A 24-hour pattern. *Science*, 164(3878):447–449, April 1969.

Scheibel, M. E., and Scheibel, A. B. Activity cycles in neurons of the reticular formation. *Recent Advances in Biological Psychiatry*, 8:283–291, 1966.

Spoor, R. P., and Jackson, D. B. Circadian rhythms: Variation insensitivity of isolated rat atria to acetylcholine. *Science*, 154:782, 1966.

Stutte, K. H., and Hildebrandt, G. von. Untersu-hungen uber die Koordination von Herzschlag und Atmung beim Menschen. *Pflügers Archiv für die gesamte Physiologie*, 2:289, 1966.

Thompson, M.; Panella, G.; et al. Paleontological evidence of variations of length of synodic month since late Cambrian. *Science*, 162:792–796, 1968.

Tromp, S. W. Blood sedimentation rate patterns in the Netherlands during the period 1955–1965. *International Journal of Biometeorology*, 11(1):105–117, March 1967.

Webster, J. H. The periodicity of the "sevens" in mind, man and nature: A neo-Hippocratic study. *British Journal of Medical Psychology*, 24:277–282, 1951.

Yoshimura, H. Seasonal changes in human body fluids. *Japanese Journal of Physiology*, 8:165–179, 1958.

Development: Infancy and Old Age

Ader, R. Early experiences accelerate maturation of the 24-hour adrenocortical rhythm. *Science*, 163:1225–1226, 1969.

Ader, R., and Grota, L. J. Rhythmicity in the maternal behavior of Rattus norvegicus. *Animal Behavior*, 1970. In press.

Cahn, A. A.; Folk, G. E.; and Huston, P. E. Age comparison of human day-night physiological differences. *Aerospace Medicine*, 39(6):608–610, 1968.

Feigin, R. D., and Haymond, M. W. Circadian periodicity of blood amino acids in the neonate. *Pediatrics*, May 1970.

Feinberg, I. The ontogenesis of human sleep and the relationship of sleep variables to intellectual function in the aged. *Comprehensive Psychiatry*, 9(2):138–147, March 1968.

Franks, R. C. Diurnal variation of plasma 17-hydroxycorticosteroids in children. *Journal of Clinical Endocrinology and Metabolism,* 27:75–78, 1967.

Grota, L. J., and Ader, R. Continuous recording of maternal behavior in Rattus norvegicus. *Animal Behavior,* 17: 722–729, 1969.

Hellbrügge, T.; Ehrengut Lange, J.; Rutenfranz, J.; and Stehr, K. Circadian periodicity of physiological functions in different stages of infancy and childhood. *Annals of the New York Academy of Sciences,* 117:361–373, 1964.

Hellbrügge, T. Ontogénèse des rythmes circadiens de l'enfant. In: de Ajuriaguerra, J. (ed.), *Cycles Biologiques et Psychiatrie.* Paris: Masson et Cie., 1968, pp. 159–183.

Honova, E.; Miller, S. A.; et al. Tyrosine transaminase: Development of daily rhythm in liver of neonatal rat. *Science,* 162:999–1001, November 1968.

Kleitman, N., and Engleman, T. G. Sleep characteristics of infants. *Journal of Applied Physiology,* 6:269–282, 1953.

Levine, S. Stress and behavior. *Scientific American,* 26–31, January 1971.

Levine, S. The psychophysiological effects of infantile stimulation. In: Bliss, E. (ed.), *Roots of Behavior.* New York: Hoeber, 1962.

Levine, S. Stimulation in infancy. *Scientific American,* May 1960.

Lobban, M. C. Diurnal rhythms of renal excretion and of body temperature in aged subjects. *Journal of Physiology,* 188:48–49, 1967.

Marotta, S. F., and Linwong, M. Excretion of urinary 17-ketosteroids and 17-ketogenic steroids. I. Effects of age, time of day and season. *Chiengmai Medical Bulletin,* 5:167–181, 1966.

Montalbetti, N.; Bonini, P. A.; and Ghiringhelli, F. I livelli nictemergli dei 17-idrossicorticosteroidi plasmatici nell'angiosclerosi cerebrale senile. *Giornale Gerontologica,* 13:473–486, 1965.

Othmer, E.; Hayden, M. P.; and Segelbaum, R. Encephalic cycles during sleep and wakefulness in humans: A 24-hour pattern. *Science,* 164(3878):447–449, April 1969.

Parmelee, A. H., Jr.; Akiyama, Y.; Stern, E.; and Harris, M. A. A period of cerebral rhythm in newborn infants. *Experimental Neurology,* 25(4):575–584, 1969.

Petren, T.; and Sollberger, A. Developmental rhythms. In: Mayersbach, H. von (ed.), *The Cellular Aspects of Biorhythms.* New York: Springer-Verlag, 1967.

Piaget, T. Time perception in children. In: Frazer, J. T. (ed.), *The Voices of Time.* New York: George Braziller, 1966.

Roffwarg, H. P.; Muzio, J. N.; and Dement, W. C. Ontogenetic development of the human sleep-dream cycle. *Science,* 152:602–619, 1966.

Sander, L. W.; Stechler, G.; Burns, P.; and Julia, H. Early mother-infant interaction and 24-hour patterns of activity and sleep. *Journal of the American Academy of Child Psychiatry*, 9(1):103–123, 1970.

Sollberger, A. The control of circadian glycogen rhythms. *Annals of the New York Academy of Sciences*, 117(1): 519–553, 1964.

Sterman, M. B. Sleep in the infant? In: Clemente, C. D.; Lindsley, D. B.; and Purpura, D. (eds.), *Development of Sleep Mechanisms in Relation to Brain Maturation*. New York: Academic Press, 1972. In press.

Sterman, M. B. Relationship of intrauterine fetal activity to maternal sleep stage. *Experimental Neurology*, Supplement 4:98–106, 1967.

Sterman, M. B., and Hoppenbrowers, T. Sleep and activity rhythms in the human fetus, newborn, and adult. In: Sterman, M. B.; McGinty, D. J.; and Andinolfi, T. (eds.), *Neuro-Ontogeny and Behavior*. New York: Academic Press, 1970.

Stern, E.; Parmelee, A. H.; Akiyama, Y.; Schultz, M. A.; and Wenner, W. H. Sleep cycle characteristics in infants. *Pediatrics*, 43(1):65–70, 1969.

Thomas, A.; Chess, S.; and Birch, H. G. The origin of personality. *Scientific American*, 233(2):102–109, August 1970.

Drugs, Toxins, and Stress

Albrecht, P.; Halberg, F.; and Bittner, J. J. Reserpine effects in the mouse and the adrenal. *Physiologist*, 1:6, 1957.

Baastrup, P. C., and Schou, M. Lithium as a prophylactic agent. Its effects against recurrent depressions and manic-depressive psychosis. *Archives of General Psychiatry*, 16:162–172, 1967.

Bruce, V. G., and Pittendrigh, C. S. An effect of heavy water on the phase and period of the circadian rhythm in Euglena. *Journal of Cellular and Comparative Physiology*, 56:25–31, 1960.

Christiaan, D.; van der Velde, M. D.; and Gordon, M. W. Manic-depressive illness, diabetes mellitus, and lithium carbonate. *Archives of General Psychiatry*, 21:478–485, 1969.

Cole, C. H., and Adkisson, P. H. A circadian rhythm, the susceptibility of an insect to an insecticide. In: Aschoff, J. (ed.), *Circadian Clocks*. Amsterdam: North Holland Publishing Company, 1965, pp. 344–351.

D'Agata, R.; Di Stephano, C.; Furno, C.; and Mughini, L. Sulle variazione del ritmo circadiano surrenalico doppo simministrazione oral di gli cocorticoidi. *Rivista Critica di Clinica Medica,* 68:652–657, 1968.

Davis, W. M. Day-night periodicity in phenobarbital response of mice and the influence of socio-psychological conditions. *Experimentia,* 18:235–236, 1962.

Delayed-action drugs. *Science News Letter,* 89:87, February 1966.

Dick, P.; Tissot, R.; and Pletscher, S. Influence des médicaments psychotropes sur les cycles biologiques et les cycles des psychoses. In: de Ajuriaguerra, J. (ed.), *Cycles Biologiques et Psychiatrie.* Paris: Masson et Cie., 1968, pp. 383–400.

Ertel, R. J.; Halberg, F.; and Ungar, F. Circadian systemphase dependent toxicity and other effects of methopyrapone (SU–4885) in mice. *Journal of Pharmacology and Experimental Therapeutics,* 146:395–399, December 1964.

Everett, J. W., and Sawyer, C. H. A 24-hour periodicity in the "LH-release apparatus" of female rats, disclosed by barbiturate sedation. *Endocrinology,* 47:198–218, September 1950.

Feigin, R. D.; San Joaquin, V. H.; Haymond, M. W.; and Wyatt, R. G. Daily periodicity of the susceptibility of mice to pneumococcal infection. *Nature,* 224:379–380, 1969.

Feldman, J. Lengthening the period of a biological clock in Euglena by cycloheximide, an inhibitor of protein synthesis. *Proceedings of the National Academy of Sciences,* 57(4):1080–1087, April 1967.

Friedman, A. H., and Walker, C. A. Circadian rhythms in central acetylcholine and the toxicity of cholinergic drugs. *Federation Proceedings,* 28:447, 1969.

Gattozzi, A. *Lithium in the Treatment of Mood Disorders.* National Institute of Mental Health Monograph 5033, U. S. Department of Health, Education, and Welfare, Public Health Service, Washington, D.C., U.S. Government Printing Office, 1970.

Gosselink, J. G., and Standifer, L. C. Diurnal rhythm of sensitivity of cotton seedlings to herbicides. *Science,* 158: 120–121, 1967.

Halberg, F.; Adkins, G.; and Marte, E. Reserpine effect upon the variance spectrum of human rectal temperature. *Federation Proceedings,* 21:347, 1962.

Halberg, F.; Bittner, J. J.; and Gully, R. J. Twenty-four-hour periodic susceptibility to audiogenic convulsions in several stocks of mice. *Federation Proceedings,* 14:67–68, 1955.

Halberg, F.; Haus, E.; and Stephens, A. Susceptibility to ouabain and physiologic 24-hour periodicity. *Federation Proceedings,* 18:63, 1959.

Halberg, F.; Jacobson, E.; Wadsworth, G.; and Bittner, J. J. Audiogenic abnormality spectra, 24-hour periodicity and lighting. *Science,* 128:657–658, 1958.

Halberg, F., and Stephens, A. N. Susceptibility to ouabain and physiologic circadian periodicity. *Proceedings of the Minnesota Academy of Sciences,* 27:139–143, 1959.

Hamberger, A.; Hyden, H.; and Lange, P. W. Enzyme changes in neurons and glia during barbiturate sleep. *Science,* 151:1394–1395, March 1966.

Harner, R. N., and Halberg, F. Electrocorticographic difference in D_8 mice at times of daily high and low susceptibility to audiogenic convulsions. *Physiologist,* 1:34–35, 1958.

Hartmann, E., and Bernstein, J. Effect of drugs on sleep: Long-term human studies. Presented at the Association for the Psychophysiological Study of Sleep, Santa Fe, 1970. *Psychophysiology.* In press.

Haus, E.; Hanton, E. M.; and Halberg, F. Twenty-four hour susceptibility rhythm to ethanol in fully fed, starved, and thirsted mice and the lighting regimen. *Physiologist,* 2:54, 1959.

Jones, F.; Haus, E.; and Halberg, F. Murine circadian susceptibility-resistance cycle to acetylcholine. *Proceedings of the Minnesota Academy of Sciences,* 31:61–62, 1963.

Kales, A. (ed.). *Sleep: Physiology and Pathology.* Philadelphia: Lippincott, 1969.

Kales, A.; Allen, C.; Scharf, M.; and Preston, T. A. Methodologic consideration and recommendation for sleep laboratory drug evaluation studies. *Psychophysiology,* 1970.

Kales, A.; Preston, T. A.; Tan, Tjiauw-ling; and Allen, C. Hypnotics and altered sleep-dream patterns. *Archives of General Psychiatry,* 23:211–218, September 1970.

Koella, W. P.; Feldstein, A.; and Czicman, J. S. The effect of parachlorophenyl alanine on the sleep of cats. *Electroencephalography and Clinical Neurophysiology,* 25:481–490, 1968.

Krylov, Yu. V. Circadian rhythm of hearing in humans after prolonged exposure to noise. *Aerospace Medicine,* 39:111–114, October 1968.

Lincoln, R. G., and Hamner, K. C. An effect of gibberellic acid on the flowering of xanthium, a short day plant. *Plant Physiology,* 33(2):101–104, 1958.

Lindsay, H. A., and Kullman, V. S. Pentobarbital sodium: Variation in toxicity. *Science,* 151:576–577, 1966.

Marte, E., and Halberg, F. Circadian susceptibility rhythm to Librium. *Federation Proceedings,* 20:305, 1961.

Martin, M., and Hellman, D. E. Temporal variation in Su-4885 responsiveness in man: Evidence in support of circadian variation in ACTH secretion. *Journal of Clinical Endocrinology and Metabolism*, 24:253–260, 1964.

Matthews, J. H.; Marte, E.; and Halberg, F. A circadian susceptibility resistance cycle to fluothane in male B[1] mice. *Canadian Anesthetists' Society Journal*, 11:280–290, 1964.

Mouret, J. R. Rythme circadian de sommeil chez la rat; modifications par des agents pharmacologiques et physiques. *Journal Européen de Toxicologie*. In press.

Mouret, J.; Bobillier, P.; and Jouvet, M. Insomnia following parachlorphenylalanine in the rat. *European Journal of Pharmacology*, 5:1, 1968–1969.

Nanda, K. K., and Hamner, K. C. The effect of temperature, auxins, anti-auxins, and some other chemicals on the endogenous rhythm affecting photoperiodic response of Biloxi soybean. *Planta*, 53:53–68, 1959.

Pauly, J. E., and Scheving, L. E. Temporal variation in susceptibility of white rats to pentobarbital sodium and tremorine. *International Journal of Neuropharmacology*, 3:651–658, 1964.

Pauly, J. E., and Scheving, L. E. Circadian susceptibility rhythms in response to various drugs in the rat. In: Sayers, G., and Lunedei, A. (eds.), *Biorhythms in Clinical and Experimental Endocrinology*. Proceedings First International Symposium, Florence, May 1969. *Rassegna di Neurologia Vegetativa*. In press.

Pizzarello, D. J.; Isaak, D.; et al. Circadian rhythmicity in the sensitivity of two strains of mice to whole-body radiation. *Science*, 145:286–291, July 1964.

Radzialowski, F. M., and Bousquet, W. F. Circadian rhythm in hepatic drug metabolizing activity in the rat. *Life Sciences*, 6:2545–2548, 1967.

Radzialowski, F. M., and Bousquet, W. F. Daily rhythmic variation in hepatic drug metabolism in the rat and mouse. *Journal of Pharmacology and Experimental Therapeutics*, 163:229–238, 1968.

Randrup, A., and Munkvad, I. Changes in urine volume and diurnal rhythm caused by reserpine treatment of schizophrenic patients. *British Journal of Psychiatry*, 112 (483):173–176, February 1966.

Reinberg, A., Chronopharmacology. In: Mills, J. N. (ed.), *Biological Aspects of Circadian Rhythms*. London: Plenum Press, 1971.

Reinberg, A. The hours of changing responsiveness or susceptibility. *Perspectives in Biology and Medicine*, 11(1):111–128, 1967.

Reinberg, A. Les variations circadiennes de résistance ou de susceptibilité des organismes. In: de Ajuriaguerra, J.

(ed.), *Cycles Biologiques et Psychiatrie*. Paris: Masson et Cie., 1968, pp. 145–154.

Reinberg, A., and Sidi, E. Circadian changes in the inhibitory effects of an antihistaminic drug in man. *Journal of Investigative Dermatology*, 46(4):415–419, April 1966.

Reinberg, A.; Sidi, E.; and Ghata, J. Circadian reactivity rhythms of human skin to histamine or allergen and the adrenal cycle. *Journal of Allergy*, 36(3):273–283, 1965.

Reinberg, A.; Zagula-Mally, Z. W.; et al. Circadian rhythm in duration of salicylate excretion referred to phase of excretory rhythms and routine. *Proceedings of the Society for Experimental Biology and Medicine*, 124:826–832, 1967.

Reindl, K.; Falliers, C.; Halberg, F.; Halberg, F.; Chai, H.; Hillman, D.; and Nelson, W. Circadian acrophases in peak expiratory flow rate and urinary electrolyte excretion of asthmatic children: Phase-shifting of rhythms by prednisone given in different circadian system phases. *Rassegna di Neurologia Vegetativa*, 1970. In press.

Reis, D. J.; Rifkin, M.; and Corvelli, A. Effects of morphine on cat brain norepinephrine in regions with daily monoamine rhythms. *European Journal of Pharmacology*, 8(1):149–152, 1969.

Richter, C. P. Lasting after-effects produced in rats by several commonly used drugs and hormones. *Proceedings of the National Academy of Sciences*, 45:1080, 1959.

Scheving, L. E. Circadian rhythms in plasma organic phosphorus and sulfur of the rat: Also in susceptibility to strychnine. *Japanese Journal of Physiology*. In press.

Scheving, L. E. Daily circadian rhythm in rats to d-amphetamine sulphate: The effect of blinding and continuous illumination on the rhythm. *Nature*, 219(5154):621–622, 1968.

Scheving, L. E.; Vedral, D. F.; and Pauly, J. E. A circadian susceptibility rhythm in rats to pentobarbital sodium. *Anatomical Record*, 160:741–750, 1968.

Schildkraut, J. J.; Schanberg, S. M.; and Kopin, I. J. The effects of lithium ion on H^3-norepinephrine metabolism in brain. *Life Sciences*, 5:1479–1483, 1966.

Sicuteri, F.; Del Bianco, P. L.; and Anselmi, B. Migraine as a cyclic disease with latent and overt components—effects with an antiaminic drug. *Headache*, 10:53–62, July 1970.

Smith, I.; Kellow, A. H.; and Hanington, E. A clinical and biochemical correlation between tyramine and migraine headache. *Headache*, 10:43–52, July 1970.

Smolensky, M. Reduction of side effects and induction of phase shifts by circadian timing of daily or alternate-day single-pulsed solumedrol injections. Dissertation Report to the University of Minnesota, 1969.

Stroebel, C. F. Biochemical, behavioral, and clinical models of drug interactions. *Proceedings of the Fifth International Collegium of Neuropsychopharmalogicum,* Washington, D.C. Excerpta Medica, 1967.

Suter, R. B., and Rawson, K. S. Circadian activity rhythm of the deer mouse, Peromyscus: Effect of deuterium oxide. *Science,* 160:1011–1014, 1968.

Tsai, R. H.; Scheving, L. E.; and Pauly, J. E. Circadian rhythms in plasma inorganic phosphorus and sulfur in rat: Also in susceptibility to strychnine. *Japanese Journal of Physiology.* In press.

Wahlstrom, G. The circadian rhythm of self-selected rest and activity in the canary and the effects of barbiturates, reserpine, monoamine oxidase inhibitors and enforced dark periods. *Acta Physiologica Scandinavia,* 65(supplementum 250):67, 1965.

Wahlstrom, G. Drugs which interfere with the metabolism of monoamines and biological cycles. In: de Ajuriaguerra, J. (ed.), *Cycles Biologiques et Psychiatrie.* Paris: Masson et Cie., 1968, pp. 355–372.

Walker, C. A.; Speciale, S. G., Jr.; and Friedman, A. H. The influence of drug treatment on the ultrastructure of rat hypothalamus and caudate nucleus synaptic vesicles during a programmed light-dark cycle. *International Journal of Neuropharmacology,* 1970. In press.

Wooley, D. E., and Timiras, P. S. Estrous and circadian periodicity and electroshock convulsions in rats. *American Journal of Physiology,* 202:379–382, 1962.

Wurtman, R. J.; Axelrod, J.; and Reis, D. J. Metabolic cycles of monoamines and their modification by drugs. In: de Ajuriaguerra, J. (ed.), *Cycles Biologiques et Psychiatrie.* Paris: Masson et Cie., 1968, pp. 373–381.

Zung, W. K. Antidepressant drugs and sleep. *Experimental Medicine and Surgery,* 27(1–2):124–137, 1969.

Zung, W. K. Effect of antidepressant drugs on sleeping and dreaming. II. On the adult male. *Excerpta Medica International Congress,* Series No. 150, pp. 1824–1826, 1968.

Zung, W. K. Effect of antidepressant drugs on sleeping and dreaming. III. On the depressed patient. *Biological Psychiatry,* 1:283–287, 1969.

Environment (Also See: Light)

Adam, J. M.; Lobban, J. C.; and Tredre, B. Diurnal rhythms of renal excretion and of body temperature in Indian subjects after a sudden change of environment. *Journal of Physiology*, 177(1):18–19, March 1965.

Aschoff, J. Exogenous and endogenous components in circadian rhythms. *Symposium on Quantitative Biology*, Cold Spring Harbor, 25:11–27, 1960.

Aschoff, J. Human circadian rhythms in activity, body temperature and other functions. In: Brown, A. H., and Favorite, F. G. (eds.), *Life Science and Space Research V, International Space Science Symposium, 7th, Vienna, Austria, May 10–18, 1966, Papers.* Amsterdam: North Holland Publishing Company, 1967, pp. 159–173.

Aschoff, J. Time-givers of 24-hour physiological cycles. In: Schaefer, K. E. (ed.), *Man's Dependence on the Earthly Atmosphere.* New York: Macmillan, 1962, pp. 373–380.

Aschoff, J., and Wever, R. Circadian rhythms of finches in light-dark cycles with interposed twilights. *Comparative Biochemistry and Physiology*, 16:507–514, 1965.

Barnwell, F. H., and Brown, F. A., Jr. Response of planarians and snails. In: Barnothy, M. F. (ed.), *Biological Effects of Magnetic Fields.* New York: Plenum Press, Chapter I, 1964.

Boriskin, V. V. Diurnal periodicity of basic physiological functions in personnel stationed in Antarctica. *Biologicheskiye ritny i voprosy razrabotki rezhimov truda i otdykha.* Materialy. Moscow, 1967, 18–19.

Brown, F. A., Jr. Propensity for lunar periodicity in hamsters and its significance for biological clock theories. *Proceedings of the Society for Experimental Biology and Medicine*, 120:792–797, 1965.

Brown, F. A., Jr. Effects and after-effects on planarians of reversals of the horizontal magnetic vector. *Nature*, 209 (5022):533–535, 1966.

Brown, F. A., Jr. Endogenous biorhythmicity reviewed with new evidence. *Scientia*, 103 (5–6):245–259, 1968.

Brown, F. A., Jr. A hypothesis for extrinsic timing of circadian rhythms. *Canadian Journal of Botany*, 47(2):287–298, February 1969.

Brown, F. A., Jr., and Park, Y. H. Association-formation between photic and subtle geophysical stimulus patterns— a new biological concept. *Biological Bulletin*, 132(3): 311–319, 1967.

Brown, F. A., Jr., and Park, Y. H. Synodic monthly modulation of the diurnal rhythm of hamsters. *Proceedings of the Society for Experimental Biology and Medicine*, 125:712–725, 1967.

Brown, F. A., Jr.; Park, Y. H.; and Zeno, J. R. Diurnal variation in organismic response to very weak gamma radiation. *Nature*, 211(5051):830–833, 1966.

Bruce, V. G. Environmental entrainment of circadian rhythms.

In: *Cold Spring Harbor Symposia on Quantitative Biology*. New York: Long Island Biological Association, 25:29–48, 1960.

Bruce, V. G., and Pittendrigh, C. S. An effect of heavy water on the phase and period of the circadian rhythm in Euglena. *Journal of Cellular and Comparative Physiology*, 56:25–31, 1960.

Bruce, V. G., and Pittendrigh, C. S. Temperature independence in a unicellular "clock." *Proceedings of the National Academy of Sciences*, 42:676–682, 1956.

Bünning, E. *The Physiological Clock*. Revised second edition. New York: Springer-Verlag, 1967.

Emlen, S. T. Bird migration: Influence of physiological state upon celestial orientation. *Science*, 165:716–718, August 1969.

Enright, J. T. Entrainment of a tidal rhythm. *Science*, 147 (3660):864–867, February 1965.

Farner, D. S. The photoperiodic control of reproductive cycles in birds. *American Scientist*, 52:137–156, 1964.

Garcia, J.; Buchwald, N. A.; et al. Electroencephalographic responses to ionizing radiation. *Science*, 140(3564):289–290, 1963.

Garcia, J.; Buchwald, N. A.; Feder, B. H.; and Koelling, R. A. Immediate detection of X-rays by the rat. *Nature*, 196 (4858):1014–1015, 1962.

Grigoryev, Yu. G.; Darenskaya, N. G.; Druzhinin, Yu. P.; Kuznetsova, S. S.; and Serya, V. M. Diurnal rhythms and ionizing radiation effects. 12th COSPAR Meeting: Prague, *Life Sciences*, 8:1969.

Halberg, F.; Nelson, W.; et al. Reproducibility of circadian temperature rhythm in the rat kept in continuous light of 30 lux intensity. *Physiologist*, 9(3):196, August 1966.

Hamner, K. C.; Finn, J. C., Jr.; Sirohi, G. S.; Hoshizaki, T.; and Carpenter, B. H. The biological clock at the South Pole. *Nature*, 195:476–480, 1962.

Hayden, P., and Lindberg, R. G. Circadian rhythm in mammalian body temperature entrained by cyclic pressure changes. *Science*, 164:1288–1289, 1969.

Holmquest, D. L.; Retiene, K.; and Lipscomb, H. S. Circadian rhythms in rats: Effects of random lighting. *Science*, 152:662–664, April 1966.

Kerr, F. R., and Waisman, H. A. Environmental control of ovarian development in mosquitoes of the culex pipens complex. *Science*, 151:824–825, February 1966.

Lobban, M. C. Human renal diurnal rhythms in an Arctic mining community. *Journal of Physiology*, 165:75, 1966.

Lobban, M. C. Daily rhythms of renal excretion in Arctic-dwelling Indians and Eskimos. *Quarterly Journal of Ex-*

perimental Physiology and Cognate Medical Sciences,
52:401–410, October 1967.

Lobban, M. C., and Simpson, H. W. Diurnal excretory rhythms
in man at high altitudes. *Journal of Physiology,* 155:
64–65, 1961.

Matova, M. A. Studying shifts in biorhythms when there is an
abrupt change in the geographic zone of habitation.
*Biologicheskiye ritmy i voprosy razrabotki rezhimov truda
i otdykha.* Materialy. Moscow, 1967, 50–51.

Menaker, M. Summer-winter differences in the circadian
rhythms and the arousability of bats at low body temperatures. *Anatomical Record,* 137:381, 1960.

Menaker, M. The free-running period of the bat clock: Seasonal variations at low body temperature. *Journal of
Cellular and Comparative Physiology,* 57:81–86, 1961.

Pittendrigh, C. S., and Minis, D. H. The entrainment of circadian oscillations by light and their role as photoperiodic
clocks. *American Naturalist,* 98(902):261–294, 1964.

Randall, W. Sunshine rhythms, a possible Zeitgeber for multi-
phasic biological rhythms during a year. *Journal of
Interdisciplinary Psycho-research,* 1(4):389–404, December 1970.

Rocard, Y. Actions of a very weak magnetic gradient. The re-
flex of the dowser. In: Barnothy, M. F. (ed.), *Biological
Effects of Magnetic Fields.* Vol. I. New York: Plenum
Press, 1964, pp. 279–286.

Rosenthal, J. D.; Sullivan, W. N.; Adler, V. E.; and McGuire,
J. U. Influence of temperatures and light regimens on
diapause of samia cynthia pryeri. *Journal of Economic
Entomology,* 61(2):578–579, 1968.

Swade, R. H., and Pittendrigh, C. S. Circadian locomotor
rhythms of rodents in the Arctic. *American Naturalist,*
101(922):431–466, 1967.

Wever, R. The influence of weak electromagnetic fields on the
circadian rhythm in man. *Zeitschrift für Vergleichende
Physiologie,* 56:111–128, 1967.

Wever, R. Principles of circadian rhythms in men, studied by
the effects of a weak alternating electric field. *Pflügers
Archiv für die gesamte Physiologie,* 302:97–122, 1968.

Wever, R. The effects of electric fields on circadian rhythms in
men. *Proceedings of Twelfth COSPAR Meetings.* In
press.

Wever, R. Influence of electric fields on some parameters of
circadian rhythms in man. *Proceedings of Friday Harbor Symposium on Chronobiology.* In press.

Zimmerman, W. F.; Pavlidis, T.; and Pittendrigh, C. S. Temperature compensation of the circadian oscillation in
Drosophila pseudoobscura and its entrainment by tem-

perature cycles. *Journal of Insect Physiology*, 14:669–684, 1968.

General and Review

Aschoff, J. Time-givers of 24-hour physiological cycles. In: Schaefer, K. E. (ed.), *Man's Dependence on the Earthly Atmosphere*. New York: Macmillan, 1962, pp. 380–383.

Aschoff, J. Circadian rhythms in man. *Science*, 148:1427–1432, 1965.

Aschoff, J. The biological clock. *Abbott Tempo*, Book 1:14–17, 1968.

Biorhythms in Clinical and Experimental Endocrinology. Sayers, G., and Lunedei, A. (eds.), Proceedings of the First International Symposium, Florence, May 1969. *Rassegna di Neurologia Vegetativa*. In press.

Brown, F. A., Jr. Periodicity in organisms. *McGraw-Hill Encyclopedia of Science and Technology*. New York: McGraw-Hill, 1967.

Brown, F. A., Jr. Rhythms, Biological. *Encyclopedia Britannica*. Vol. 19:292–294, 1968.

Brozek, J. Psychorhythmics: A special review. *Psychophysiology*, 1(2):127–141, October 1964.

Cloudsley-Thompson, J. L. Recent work on the adaptive functions of circadian and seasonal rhythms in animals. *Journal of Interdisciplinary Cycle Research*, 1(1):5–19, May 1970.

Dewan, E. M. Rhythms. *Science and Technology*, 20–28, January 1969.

Halberg, F. Chronobiology. *Annual Review of Physiology*, 31:675–725, 1969.

Harker, J. E. Diurnal rhythms and homeostatic mechanisms. *Symposia of the Society for Experimental Biology*, 18:283–300, 1964.

Mills, J. N. Human circadian rhythms. *Physiological Review*, 146(1):128–171, 1966.

Pittendrigh, C. S. Adaptation, natural selection and behavior. In: Roe, A., and Simpson, G. G. (eds.), *Behavior and Evolution*. New Haven: Yale University Press, 1958, pp. 390–415.

Pittendrigh, C. S. Circadian rhythms and the circadian organization of living systems. *Symposia on Quantitative Biology*, 25:159–182. New York: Long Island Biological Association, 1960.

Pittendrigh, C. S. On temporal organization in living systems. *The Harvey Lectures*, 56:93–125, January 1961.

Pittendrigh, C. S. Biological clocks, the functions, ancient and modern, of circadian oscillations. In: *Science in the*

Sixties. Proceedings of the 1965 Cloudcroft Symposium. Air Force Office of Scientific Research, 1965, pp. 96–111.

Pittendrigh, C. S. The biologist in the solar system. *Bulletin of the Atomic Scientists*, 23:4–10, 1967.

Reinberg, A., Chronopharmacology. In: Mills, J. N. (ed.), *Biological Aspects of Circadian Rhythms*. London: Plenum Press, 1971.

Reinberg, A. Biorythmes et chronobiologie. *Presse Médicale*, 77:877, 1969.

Hormones and Metabolism

Abrams, R. L.; Parker, L.; et al. Hypothalamic regulation of growth hormone secretion. *Endocrinology*, 78(3):605–613, 1966.

Ader, R. Early experiences accelerate maturation of the 24-hour adrenocortical rhythm. *Science*, 163:1225–1226, 1969.

Ader, R.; Friedman, B.; and Grota, L. J. "Emotionality" and adrenal cortical function: Effects of strain, test, and the 24-hour corticosterone rhythm. *Animal Behavior*, 15: 37–44, 1967.

Ader, R., and Friedman, S. B. Plasma corticosterone response to environmental stimulation: Effects of duration of stimulation and the 24-hour adrenocortical rhythm. *Neuroendocrinology*, 3:378–386, 1968.

Agadzhanyan, N. A., and Rafikov, A. M. Diurnal variations in altitude tolerance and the role of the adrenocortical function. *Biologicheskiye ritmy i voprosy razrabotki rezhimov truda i otdykha*. Materialy. Moscow, 1967, 8–9.

Anton-Tay, F.; Chou, C.; and Anton, S. Brain serotonin concentration: Elevation following intraperitoneal administration of melatonin. *Science*, 162:277–278, 1968.

Barnum, C. P., and Halberg, F. Enhancement of DNA metabolism and mitotic activity by pituitary growth hormone in immature intact mouse liver. *Physiologist*, 1:3–4, 1958.

Barnum, C. P.; Jardetzky, C. D.; and Halberg, F. Time relations among metabolic and morphologic 24-hour changes in mouse liver. *American Journal of Physiology*, 195: 301–310, 1958.

Bartter, F. C.; Delea, C. S.; and Halberg, F. A map of blood and urinary changes related to circadian variations in adrenal cortical function in normal subjects. *Annals of the New York Academy of Sciences*, 98:969–983, 1962.

Beisel, W. R.; Feigin, R. D.; and Klanier, A. S. Factors affecting circadian periodicity of blood amino acids in man. *Metabolism*, 17:764–775, September 1968.

Black, I. B., and Axelrod, J. Elevation and depression of hepatic tyrosine transaminase activity by depletion and repletion of norepinephrine. *Proceedings of the National Academy of Sciences*, 59(4):1231–1234, 1968.

Black, I. B., and Axelrod, J. Inhibition of tyrosine transaminase activity by norepinephrine. *Journal of Biological Chemistry*, 244:6124–6129, 1969.

Bunney, W. E., Jr., Fawcett, J. A.; Davis, J. M.; and Gifford, S. Further evaluation of urinary 17-hydroxycorticosteroids in suicidal patients. *Archives of General Psychiatry*, 21:138–150, 1969.

Bunney, W. E., Jr., and Hartmann, E. L. Study of a patient with 48-hour manic-depressive cycles, I & II. *Archives of General Psychiatry*, 12:611, 1965.

Canary, J. J.; Hellman, D. E.; and Mintz, D. H. Effect of altered thyroid function on calcium and phosphorous circadian rhythms. *Journal of Clinical Endocrinology and Metabolism*, 28:399–411, March 1968.

Clayton, G. W.; Librik, L.; et al. Studies on the circadian rhythm of pituitary adrenocorticotropic release in man. *Journal of Clinical Endrocrinology and Metabolism*, 23:975–980, 1963.

Curtis, G. C.; Fogel, M. L.; et al. The effect of sustained affect on the diurnal rhythms of adrenal cortical activity. *Psychosomatic Medicine*, 28:696–713, 1966.

Curtis, G. C.; Fogel, M. L.; McEvoy, D.; and Zarate, C. Effects of weight, sex and diurnal variation on the excretion of 17-hydroxycorticosteroids. *Journal of Clinical Endocrinology and Metabolism*, 28(5):711–713, 1968.

Daughaday, W. L.; Othmer, E.; and Kipnis, D. M. Hypersecretion of growth hormone following REM deprivation. Report to the Fifty-First Annual Meeting of the Endocrine Society, New York, June 1969.

Deschamps, I.; Heilbronner, J.; and Canivet, J. Les variations de l'insuline chez le sujet normal au cours du nycthémeré. *Annales d'Endocrinologie*, 30:589–596, 1969.

Dewar, H. A.; Menon, I. S.; Smith, P. A.; and White, R. W. B. Diurnal variations of fibrinolytic activity and plasma-11-hydroxycorticosteroid levels. *Lancet*, 2:531–532, September 1967.

Di Raimondo, V. C., and Forsham, P. H. Some clinical implications of the spontaneous diurnal variation in adrenal and cortical secretory activity. *American Journal of Medicine*, 21(3):321–323, September 1956.

Doe, R. P.; Vennes, J. A.; and Flink, E. B. Diurnal variation of 17-hydroxycorticosteroids, sodium, potassium, magnesium and creatinine in normal subjects and in cases of treated adrenal insufficiency and Cushing's syndrome. *Journal of Clinical Endocrinology and Metabolism,* 20:253–265, February 1960.

Dossetor, J. B.; Gorman, H. M.; and Beck, J. C. The diurnal rhythm of urinary electrolyte secretion. *Metabolism,* 12(12):1083–1099, December 1963.

Durrell, J. Biological rhythms and psychiatry: Psycho-endocrine mechanisms. In: de Ajuriaguerra, J. (ed.), *Cycles Biologiques et Psychiatrie.* Paris: Masson et Cie., 1968, pp. 321–328.

Durrell, J.; Libow, L. S.; Kellam, S. G.; and Shader, R. I. Interrelationships between regulation of thyroid gland function and psychosis. *Endocrines and the Central Nervous System,* Association for Research in Nervous and Mental Diseases, 1966, Vol. 43, Chapter XXI.

Eisinger, R. P. Influence of posture and diurnal rhythm on the renal excretion of acid—observations in normal and adrenalectomized subjects. *Metabolism,* 15:76–87, January 1966.

Eling, W. The circadian rhythms of nucleic acids. In: Mayersbach, H. von (ed.), *The Cellular Aspects of Biorhythms.* New York: Springer-Verlag, 1967.

Engel, R.; Halberg, F.; Dassanayake, W. L. P.; and De Silva, J. Adrenal effects on time relations between rhythms of microfilariae and eosinophils in the blood. *American Journal of Tropical Medicine and Hygiene,* 11(5):653–663, September 1962.

Engeli, M., and Halberg, F. Spectral analysis of steroid rhythms in data at equal or unequal intervals. *Federation Proceedings,* 23(2):250, March–April, 1964.

Eskin, I. A., and Mikhailova, N. V. Photoperiodicity and the function of the hypophysis and the adrenal cortex. *Bulletin of Experimental Biology and Medicine U.S.S.R.* (English translation), 46:999–1002, 1958.

Everett, J. W., and Sawyer, C. H. A 24-hour periodicity in the "LH-release apparatus" of female rats, disclosed by barbiturate sedation. *Endocrinology,* 47:198–218, September 1950.

Feigin, R. D.; Dangerfield, H. G.; and Beisel, W. R. Circadian periodicity of blood amino acids in normal and adrenalectomized mice. *Nature,* 221:94–95, 1969.

Feigin, R. D.; Klainer, A. S.; and Beisel, W. R. Circadian periodicity of blood amino acids in adult men. *Nature,* 215(5100):512–514, 1967.

Feigin, R. D.; Klainer, A. S.; and Beisel, W. R. Factors affecting circadian periodicity of blood amino acids in man. *Metabolism,* 17(9):764–775, 1968.

Forsham, P. H., and Di Raimondo, V. C. Some clinical implications of the spontaneous diurnal variation in adrenocortical secretory activity. *American Journal of Medicine,* 21:321–323, 1956.

Franks, R. C. Diurnal variation of plasma 17-hydroxycorticosteroids in children. *Journal of Clinical Endocrinology and Metabolism,* 27:75–78, 1967.

Friedman, S. B., and Ader, R. Adrenocortical response to novelty and noxious stimulation. *Neuroendocrinology,* 2:209–212, 1967.

Fullerton, D. T. Circadian rhythm of adrenal cortical activity in depression. *Archives of General Psychiatry,* 19(6): 674, 1968.

Galicich, J. H.; Halberg, F.; French, L. A.; and Ungar, F. Effect of cerebral ablation on a circadian pituitary adrenocorticotropic rhythm in C mice. *Endocrinology,* 76:895–901, 1965.

Giusti, G.; Taccorondi, R.; et al. Nycthemeral rhythm of plasma cortisol levels in the Cushing syndrome associated with hyperplasia of the adrenal cortex. *Acta Neurovegetativa Rassegna,* 30:129–136, 1967.

Graber, A. L.; Cerchio, G. M.; and Abrams, R. L. Circadian variation of intravenous glucose tolerance in man. *Metabolism.* In press.

Halberg, F. Discussion of glycogen metabolism. In: *Mechanisms of Regulation of Growth. Report of the Fortieth Ross Conference on Pediatric Research.* Columbus, Ohio: Ross Laboratories, 1962, pp. 31–32.

Halberg, F. Rhythmic interactions of steroidal and neural functions. In: Martini, L. et al. (eds.), *Hormonal Steroids.* Amsterdam: Excerpta Medica Foundation, 1967, pp. 966–979.

Halberg, F.; Barnum, C. P.; and Vermund, H. Hepatic phospholipid metabolism and the adrenal. *Journal of Clinical Endocrinology and Metabolism,* 13:871, 1953.

Halberg, F.; Frank, G.; Harner, R.; Matthews, J.; Aaker, H.; Gravem, H.; and Melby, J. The adrenal cycle in men on different schedules of motor and mental activity. *Experientia,* 17:282, 1961.

Halberg, F., and Hamburger, C. 17-ketosteroid and volume of human urine: Weekly and other changes with low frequency, *Minnesota Medicine,* 47:916–925, August 1964.

Halberg, F.; Peterson, R. E.; and Silber, R. H. Phase relations of 24-hour periodicities in blood corticosterone. Mitoses in cortical adrenal parenchyma, and total body activity. *Endocrinology,* 64:222–230, 1959.

Halberg, F.; Vermund, H.; Halberg, E.; and Barnum, C. P. Adrenal hormones and phospholipid metabolism in liver cytoplasm of adrenalectomized mice. *Endocrinology,* 59:364–368, 1956.

Halberg, F.; Vestergaard, P.; and Sakai, M. Rhythmometry on

urinary 17-ketosteroid excretion by healthy men and women and patients with chronic schizophrenia; possible chronopathology in depressive illness. *Archives d'Anatomie, d'Histologie et d'Embryologie Normales et Expérimentales,* 51:301–311, 1968.

Hastings, J. W. Biochemical mechanisms involved in biological rhythms and cycles. In: de Ajuriaguerra, J. (ed.), *Cycles Biologiques et Psychiatrie.* Paris: Masson et Cie., 1968, pp. 127–140.

Hellman, L.; Nakada, F.; Curti, J.; Weitzman, E. D.; et al. Cortisol is secreted episodically by normal man. *Journal of Clinical Endocrinology and Metabolism,* 30(4):411–422, 1970.

Hendricks, S. B. Metabolic control of timing. *Science,* 141:21–27, 1963.

Henkin, R. I. Presence of corticosterone and cortisol in the central and peripheral nervous system of the cat. *Endocrinology,* 82(5):1058–1061, May 1968.

Henkin, R. I. Auditory detection and perception in normal man and in patients with adrenal cortical insufficiency: Effect of adrenal cortical steroids. *Journal of Clinical Investigation,* 47(6):1269–1280, June 1968.

Henkin, R. I.; Gill, J. R.; and Bartter, F. C. Studies on taste thresholds in normal man and in patients with adrenal cortical insufficiency: The role of adrenal cortical steroids and of serum sodium concentration. *Journal of Clinical Investigation,* 42(5):727–735, 1963.

Henkin, R. I.; McGlone, R. E.; et al. Studies on auditory thresholds in normal man and in patients with adrenal cortical insufficiency: The role of adrenal cortical steroids. *Journal of Clinical Investigation,* 46(3):429–435, 1967.

Holmgren, H., and Swensson, A. Der Einfluss des Lichtes auf den 24-Stunden. Rhythms der Aktivitat des Leberglykogens und der korpetemperatur. *Acta Medica Scandinavica* (Supplement 278):71–76, 1953.

Honda, Y. Biological clock and the endocrine rhythm. *Advances in Neurological Science* (Tokyo), 14(1):203–207, 1970.

Honova, E.; Miller, S. A.; et al. Tyrosine transaminase: Development of daily rhythm in liver of neonatal rat. *Science,* 162:999–1001, November 1968.

Ishihara, I., and Komori, Y. Diurnal variations in the urinary excretion of corticosteroids in aging persons. Annual Report on Research Institute of Environmental Medicine, Nagoya University, 1957.

Jacey, M., and Schaefer, K. E. Circadian cycles of lactic dehydrogenase in urine and blood plasma. *Aerospace Medicine,* 39:410, April 1968.

Jardetzky, C. D.; Barnum, C. P.; and Halberg, F. Physiologic 24-hour periodicity in nucleic acid metabolism and mitosis of immature growing liver. *American Journal of Physiology*, 187:608, 1956.

Johnson, L. Diurnal patterns of metabolic variations in chick embryos. *Biological Bulletin*, 131(2):308–322, 1966.

Kahana, L.; Lebovitz, H.; et al. Endocrine manifestations of intracranial extrasellar lesions. *Journal of Clinical Endocrinology and Metabolism*, 22:304–324, March 1962.

Katz, F. H. Adrenal function during bed rest. *Aerospace Medicine*, 35:849–851, September 1964.

Kirshner, N.; Sage, H. J.; and Kirshner, A. G. Release of catecholamines and specific protein from adrenal glands. *Science*, 154:529–531, October 1966.

Klevecz, R. R., and Ruddle, F. H. Cyclic changes in enzyme activity in synchronized mammalian cell cultures. *Science*, 159:634–636, February 1968.

Knapp, M. S.; Keane, P. M.; and Wright, J. G. Circadian rhythm of plasma 11-hydroxycorticosteroids in depressive illness, congestive heart failure and Cushing's syndrome. *British Journal of Psychiatry*, 2:27–30, 1967.

Krieger, D. T., and Krieger, H. P. The effects of intrahypothalamic injections of drugs on ACTH release in the cat. *Excerpta Medica International Congress Series*, 83:640–645, 1964.

Krieger, D. T., and Krieger, H. P. Adrenal function in central nervous system disease. *Endocrines and the Central Nervous System*, 43:400–417, 1966.

Krieger, D. T., and Krieger, H. P. The circadian variation of the plasma 17-OHCS in central nervous system disease. *Journal of Clinical Endocrinology and Metabolism*, 26:939, 1966.

Krieger, D. T., and Krieger, H. P. The effect of short-term administration of CNS-acting drugs on the circadian variation of the plasma 17-OHCS in normal subjects. *Neuroendocrinology*, 2:232, 1967.

Krieger, D. T., and Krieger, H. P. Circadian pattern of plasma 17-hydroxycorticosteroid: Alteration by anticholinergic agents. *Science*, 155:1421–1422, March 1967.

Krieger, D. T., and Rizzo, F. Circadian periodicity of plasma 17-OHCS: Mediation by serotonin-dependent pathways. *American Journal of Physiology*, 217:1703, 1969.

Krieger, D. T.; Silverberg, A. I.; Rizzo, F.; and Krieger, H. P. Abolition of circadian periodicity of plasma 17-OHCS levels in the cat. *American Journal of Physiology*, 215:915, 1968.

Laatikainen, T., and Vihko, R. Diurnal variation in the concentrations of solvolyzable steroids in human plasma.

Journal of Clinical Endocrinology and Metabolism, 28: 1356–1360, September 1968.

Levine, S. The psychophysiological effects of infantile stimulation. In: Bliss, E. (ed.), *Roots of Behavior*. New York: Hoeber, 1962.

Lohrenz, F. N.; Fullerton, D. T.; et al. Adrenocortical function in depressive states, study of circadian variation in plasma and urinary steroids. *International Journal of Neuropsychiatry*, 4:21–25, 1968.

Malek, J.; Gleich, J.; and Malý, V. Characteristics of the daily rhythm of menstruation and labor. *Annals of the New York Academy of Sciences*, 98:1042–1055, 1962.

Marotta, S. F., and Linwong, M. Excretion of urinary 17-ketosteroids and 17-ketogenic steroids: I. Effects of age, time of day and season. *Chiengmai Medical Bulletin*, 5:167–181, 1966.

Meites, J. Direct studies of the secretion of hypothalamic hypophysiotropic hormones (HHH). In: Meites, J. (ed.), *Hypophysiotropic Hormones of the Hypothalamus*. Baltimore: Williams and Wilkins Co., 1970.

Mintz, D. H.; Hellman, D. E.; and Canary, J. J. Effects of altered thyroid function on calcium and phosphorus circadian rhythms. *Journal of Clinical Endocrinology and Metabolism*, 28:399–411, 1968.

Montalbetti, N.; Ghiringhelli, F.; Bonini, P. A.; and Bonanomi, L. Adrenal rhythms during human senescence. *Acta Endocrinologica*, Supplement 119:44, 1967.

Nelson, W. Aspects of circadian periodic changes in phosphorus metabolism in mice. *American Journal of Physiology*, 206(3):589–598, 1964.

Nichols, T.; Nugent, C.; and Tyler, F. H. Diurnal variation in suppression of adrenal function by glucocorticoids. *Journal of Clinical Endocrinology and Metabolism*, 25:343–349, 1965.

Nichols, T., and Tyler, F. H. Diurnal variation in adrenal cortical function. *Annual Review of Medicine*, 18:313–324, 1967.

Ojemann, F. A., and Henkin, R. I. Steroid dependent changes in human visual evoked potentials. *Life Sciences*, 6:327–334, 1967.

Oppenheimer, J. H.; Fisher, L. V.; and Jailer, J. W. Disturbance of the pituitary-adrenal interrelationship in diseases of the central nervous system. *Journal of Clinical Endocrinology and Metabolism*, 21(a):1023–1036, 1961.

Orth, D. N., and Island, D. P. Light synchronization of the circadian rhythm in plasma cortisol (17-OHCS) concentration in man. *Journal of Clinical Endocrinology*, 29:479–486, 1969.

Orth, D. N.; Island, D. P.; and Liddle, G. W. Experimental

alteration of the circadian rhythm in plasma cortisol (17-OHCS) concentration in man. *Journal of Clinical Endocrinology and Metabolism,* 27:549–555, 1967.

Parker, D. C.; Sassin, J. F.; Mace, J. W.; Gotlin, R. W.; and Rossman, L. G. Human growth hormone release during sleep: Electroencephalographic correlation. *Journal of Clinical Endocrinology and Metabolism,* 29(6):871–874, 1969.

Pauly, J. E., and Scheving, L. E. Circadian rhythms in the blood glucose and the effect of different lighting schedules, hypophysectomy, adrenal medullectomy and starvation. *Journal of Anatomy,* 120:627–636, 1967.

Perkoff, G. T.; Eik-Nes, K.; et al. Studies of the diurnal variation of plasma 17-hydroxycorticosteroids in man. *Journal of Clinical Endocrinology and Metabolism,* 19:432–443, 1959.

Pincus, G. A diurnal rhythm in the excretion of urinary ketosteroids by young men. *Journal of Clinical Endocrinology,* 3(4):195–199, 1948.

Rapoport, M.; Feigin, R. D.; Bruton, J.; and Beisel, W. R. Circadian rhythm for tryptophan pyrrolase activity and its circulating substrate. *Science,* 153:1642–1644, 1966.

Reinberg, A. Rythmes circadiens du metabolisme du potassium chez l'homme. *Le Potassium et la Vie.* Paris: Presses Universitaires de France, 1969, pp. 103–104.

Retiene, K.; Zimmermann, W. J.; Schindler, C. J.; and Lipscomb, H. S. A correlative study of resting endocrine rhythms in rats. *Acta Endocrinologica,* 57:615–622, 1968.

Richter, C. P. Hormones and rhythms in man and animals. In: Pincus, G. (ed.), *Recent Progress in Hormone Research,* Vol. 13. New York: Academic Press, 1957, pp. 105–159.

Rust, C. C., and Meyer, R. K. Hair color, molt, and testis size in male short-tailed weasels treated with melatonin. *Science,* 165:921–922, 1969.

Sassin, J. F.; Parker, D. C.; Mace, J. W.; et al. Human growth hormone release: Relation to slow-wave sleep and sleep-waking cycles. *Science,* 165:513–515, August 1969.

Scheving, L. E., and Pauly, J. E. Effect of adrenalectomy, adrenal medullectomy and hypophysectomy on the daily mitotic rhythm in the corneal epithelium of the rat. In: Mayersbach, H. von (ed.), *The Cellular Aspects of Biorhythms,* New York: Springer-Verlag, 1967.

Scheving, L. E., and Pauly, J. E. Circadian phase relationships of thymidine-^{3}H uptake, labeled nuclei, grain counts, and cell division rate in rat corneal epithelium. *Journal of Cell Biology,* 23(3):677–683, 1967.

Scrimshaw, N. S.; Habicht, J. P.; Pellet, P.; Piché, M. L.; and

Cholakos, B. Effects of sleep deprivation and reversal of diurnal activity on protein metabolism of young men. *American Journal of Clinical Nutrition*, 19:313–319, 1966.

Serio, M.; Tarquini, B.; Contini, P.; Bucalossi, A.; and Toccafondi, R. Plasma cortisol response to insulin and circadian rhythm in diabetic subjects. *Diabetes*, 17(3):124–127, 1968.

Sharp, G. W. G.; Slorach, S. A.; and Vipond, H. J. Diurnal rhythms of keto and ketogenic steroid excretion and the adaptation to changes of the activity-sleep routine. *Journal of Endocrinology*, 22:377–385, 1961.

Shenkin, H. The effect of pain on the diurnal pattern of plasma corticoid levels. *Neurology*, 14(2):1112–1117, 1964.

Sholitan, L. J.; Werk, E. E., Jr.; and Marnell, R. T. Diurnal variation of adrenocortical function in non-endocrine disease states. *Metabolism*, 10:632–646, 1961.

Silverberg, A. I.; Rizzo, F.; and Krieger, D. T. Nycthemeral periodicity of plasma 17-OHCS levels in elderly subjects. *Journal of Clinical Endocrinology*, 28:1666, 1968.

Simpson, H. W., and Lobban, M. C. Effects of a 21-hour day on the human circadian excretory rhythms of 17-hydroxcorticosteroids and electrolytes. *Aerospace Medicine*, 38:1205–1213, 1967.

Simpson, H. W.; Lobban, M. C.; and Halberg, F. Near 24-hour rhythms in subjects living on a 21-hour routine in the Arctic summer at 78°N, revealed by circadian amplitude ratios. *Rassegna di Neurologia Vegetativa*. In press.

Smith, W. R.; Ulvedal, F.; and Welch, B. E. Steroid and catecholamine studies in pilots during prolonged experiments in space cabin simulator. *Journal of Applied Physiology*, 18:1257–1263, 1963.

Southren, A. L.; Gordon, G. G.; et al. Mean plasma concentration, Metabolic clearance and basal plasma production rates of testoterone in normal young men and women using a constant infusion procedure: Effect of time of day and plasma concentration on the metabolic clearance rate of testosterone. *Journal of Clinical Endocrinology and Metabolism*, 27(5):686–694, 1967.

Southren, A. L.; Tochimoto, S.; Carmody, N. C.; and Isurugi, K. Plasma production rates of testosterone in normal adult men and women and in patients with the syndrome of feminizing testes. *Journal of Clinical Endocrinology and Metabolism*, 25:1441, 1965.

Szczepanska, E.; Preibisz, J.; Drzewiecki, K.; and Kozlowski, S. Studies on the circadian rhythm of variations of the blood antidiuretic hormone in humans. *Polish Medical Journal*, 7:517–523, 1968.

Takahashi, Y.; Kipnis, D. M.; and Daughaday, W. H. Growth

hormone secretion during sleep. *Journal of Clinical Investigation,* 47(9): 2079–2090, 1968.

Ungar, F., and Halberg, F. Circadian rhythm in the in vitro response of mouse adrenal to adrenocorticotropic hormone. *Science,* 137:1058–1060, 1962.

Vestergaard, P., and Leverett, R. Excretion of combined neutral urinary 17-ketosteroids in short-term collection periods. *Acta Endocrinologica,* 25(1):45–53, 1957.

Vestergaard, P.; Leverett, R.; and Douglas, W. R. Spontaneous variability in the excretion of combined neutral 17-ketosteroids in the urine of chronic schizophrenic patients. Psychiatric Research Reports, No. 6, American Psychiatric Association, October 1956, pp. 74–89.

Weitzman, E. D.; Goldmacher, D.; Kripke, D.; MacGregor, P.; Kream, J.; and Hellman, L. Reversal of sleep-waking cycle-effect on sleep-stage pattern and certain neuroendocrine rhythms. *Transactions of the American Neurological Association,* 93:153–157, 1968.

Weitzman, E. D. (investigator), and Luce, G. (author). Biological rhythms—indices of pain, adrenal hormones, sleep, and sleep reversal. Mental Health Program Reports-3, National Institute of Mental Health, PHS Publication No. 1876, 1969, pp. 319–332.

Weller, L. A.; Margen, S.; and Calloway, D. H. Variation in fasting and postprandial amino acids of men fed adequate or protein-free diets. *American Journal of Clinical Nutrition,* 1577–1583, 1969.

Wurtman, R. J., and Axelrod, J. The physiologic effects of melatonin and the control of its biosynthesis. *Problèmes Actuels d'Endocrinologie et de Nutrition,* 10:189–200, 1966.

Wurtman, R. J., and Axelrod, J. Daily rhythmic changes in tyrosine transaminase activity of the rat liver. *Proceedings of the National Academy of Sciences,* 57(6):1594–1599, 1967.

Wurtman, R. J.; Chou, C.; and Rose, C. M. Daily rhythm in tyrosine concentration in human plasma: Persistence on low-protein diets. *Science,* 158:660–663, 1967.

Wurtman, R. J.; Rose, C. M.; Chou, C.; and Larin, F. F. Daily rhythms in the concentrations of various amino acids in human plasma. *New England Journal of Medicine,* 279(4):171–175, 1968.

Wurtman, R. J.; Shoemaker, W. J.; and Larin, F. F. Mechanisms of the daily rhythm in hepatic tyrosine transaminase activity: Role of dietary tryptophan. *Proceedings of the National Academy of Sciences,* 59(3):800–807, 1968.

Young, V. T.; Hussein, M. A.; Murray, E.; and Scrimshaw, N. S. Tryptophan intake, spacing of meals, and diurnal fluctuations of plasma tryptophan in men. *American Journal of Clinical Nutrition*, 22(12):1563–1567, 1969.

Illness

Ader, R. Behavioral and physiological rhythms and the development of gastric erosions in the rat. *Psychosomatic Medicine*, 29(4):345–353, 1967.

Biorhythms in clinical and experimental endocrinology. In: Sayers, G., and Lunedei, A. (eds.), Proceedings First International Symposium, Florence, May 1969. *Rassegna di Neurologia Vegetativa*. In press.

Chipman, D. M., and Sharon, N. Mechanism of lysozyme action. *Science*, 165(3892):454–465, August 1969.

Di Raimondo, V. C., and Forsham, P. H. Some clinical implications of the spontaneous diurnal variation in adrenal and cortical secretory activity. *American Journal of Medicine*, 21(3):321–323, September 1956.

Engel, R.; Halberg, F.; Dassanayake, W. L. P.; and De Silva, J. Adrenal effects on time relations between rhythms of microfilariae and eosinophils in the blood. *American Journal of Tropical Medicine and Hygiene*, 11(5):653–663, September 1962.

Engel, R.; Halberg, F.; and Gully, R. J. The diurnal rhythm in EEG discharge and in circulating eosinophils in certain types of epilepsy. *Electroencephalography and Clinical Neurophysiology*, 4:115–116, 1952.

Engel, R.; Halberg, F.; Tichy, R. Y.; and Dow, R. Electrocerebral activity and epileptic attacks at various blood sugar levels (with a case report). *Acta Neurovegetativa*, 9:147–167, 1954.

Engel, R.; Halberg, F.; Ziegler, M.; and McQuarrie, I. Observations on two children with diabetes mellitus and epilepsy. *Lancet*, 72:242–248, 1952.

Falliers, C.; Purcell, K.; and Hahn, W. (investigators); and Luce, G. (author). Psychodynamics of asthmatic children. Mental Health Programs Reports-2, National Institute of Mental Health, PHS Publication 1743, pp. 149–162, 1966.

Feigin, R. D.; San Joaquin, V. H.; Haymond, M. W.; and Wyatt, R. G. Daily periodicity of susceptibility of mice to pneumococcal infection. *Nature*, 224:379–380, 1969.

Forsham, P. H., and Di Raimondo, V. C. Some clinical implications of the spontaneous diurnal variation in adrenocortical secretory activity. *American Journal of Medicine*, 21:321–323, 1956.

Fremont-Smith, D.; Harter, J. G.; and Halberg, F. Circadian rhythmicity of proximal interphalangeal joint circumference of patients with rheumatoid arthritis. *Rheumatism and Arthritis,* 12:294, 1969.

Garcia-Sainz, M., and Halberg, F. Mitotic rhythms in human cancer reevaluated by electronic computer programs—evidence for temporal pathology. *Journal of the National Cancer Institute,* 37:279–292, 1966.

Giusti, G.; Taccorondi, R.; et al. Nycthemeral rhythm of plasma cortisol levels in the Cushing syndrome associated with hyperplasia of the adrenal cortex. *Acta Neurovegetativa Rassegna,* 30:129–136, 1967.

Goldman, R. Studies in diurnal variation of water and electrolyte excretion: Nocturnal diuresis of water and sodium in congestive cardiac failure and cirrhosis of the liver. *Journal of Clinical Investigation,* 30:1192–1199, 1951.

Graber, A. L.; Cerchio, G. M.; and Abrams, R. L. Circadian variations of intravenous glucose tolerance in man. *Metabolism.* In press.

Halberg, F. Organisms as circadian systems; temporal analysis of their physiologic and pathologic responses, including injury and death. *Medical Aspects of Stress in the Military Climate,* Walter Reed Army Institute of Research, April 1964, pp. 1–36.

Halberg, F. Some physiological and clinical aspects of 24-hour periodicity. *Journal Lancet,* 73:20–32, 1953.

Halberg, F.; Bittner, J. J.; and Smith, D. Mitotic rhythm in mice, mammary tumor milk agent, and breast cancer. *Proceedings of the American Association for Cancer Research,* 2:305, 1958.

Halberg, F., and Falliers, C. J. Variability of physiologic circadian crests in groups of children studied "transversely." *Pediatrics,* 68:741–746, 1966.

Halberg, F.; Good, R. A.; and Levine, H. Some aspects of the cardiovascular and renal circadian systems. *Circulation,* 34:715–717, 1966.

Hamerston, O.; Elveback, L.; Halberg, F.; and Gully, R. J. Correlation of absolute basophil and eosinophil counts in blood from institutionalized human subjects. *Journal of Applied Physiology,* 9:205–207, 1956.

Hawking, F. The clock of the malaria parasite. *Scientific American,* 6:123–131, 1970.

Henkin, R. I. Auditory detection and perception in normal man and in patients with adrenal cortical insufficiency: Effect of adrenal cortical steroids. *Journal of Clinical Investigation,* 47(6):1269–1280, June 1968.

Henkin, R. I.; Gill, J. R.; and Bartter, F. C. Studies on taste thresholds in normal man and in patients with adrenal cortical insufficiency: The role of adrenal cortical steroids and of serum sodium concentration. *Journal of Clinical Investigation*, 42(5):727–735, 1963.

Henkin, R. I.; McGlone, R. E.; et al. Studies on auditory thresholds in normal man and in patients with adrenal cortical insufficiency: The role of adrenal cortical steroids. *Journal of Clinical Investigation*, 46(3):429–435, 1967.

Hildebrandt, G. von. Balneologie und Rhythmusforschung. *Allgemeine Therapeutik*, 6(7), July-September 1961.

Hildebrant, G. von. Storungen der rhythmischen Koordination und ihre balneotherapeutische Beeinflussing. *Bade- und Klimaheilkunde*, 4, August 1963.

Holmes, T. H., and Rahe, R. H. The social readjustment rating scale. *Journal of Psychosomatic Research*, 11:213–218, 1967.

Kahana, L.; Lebovitz, H.; et al. Endocrine manifestations of intracranial extrasellar lesions. *Journal of Clinical Endocrinology and Metabolism*, 22:304–324, March 1962.

Kraft, I. A.; Alexander, S.; et al. Circadian rhythms in human heart homograft. *Science*, 169:694–695, August 1970.

Krieger, D. T., and Krieger, H. P. Adrenal function in central nervous system disease. *Endocrines and the Central Nervous System*, 43:400–417, 1966.

Libow, L. S., and Durrell, J. Interrelationships between thyroid function and psychosis: I. A case of periodic psychosis with coupled alterations in thyroid function. *Psychosomatic Medicine*, 27:369, 1965.

McDaniel, W. B. The moon, werewolves and medicine. *College of Physicians of Philadelphia. Transactions and Studies*, 18:113–122, 1950.

Menzel, W. Langwellige Rhythm bei inneren Krankheiten. *Verhandlungen der Deutschen Gesellschaft für innere Medizin*, 73:962–973, 1967.

Menzel, W. Perturbations des rythmes circadiares chez l'homme, y compris aspect psychosomatique. In: de Ajuriaguerra, J. (ed.), *Cycles Biologiques et Psychiatrie*. Paris: Masson et Cie., 1968, pp. 205–221.

Möllerstrom, J., and Sollberger, A. The 24-hour rhythm of metabolic processes in diabetes; citric acid in the urine. *Acta Medica Scandinavica*, 160:25, 1958.

Möllerstrom, J., and Sollberger, A. Fundamental concepts underlying the metabolic periodicity in diabetes. *Annals of the New York Academy of Sciences*, 98(4):984–994, 1962.

Oppenheimer, J. H.; Fisher, L. V.; and Jailer, J. W. Disturbance of the pituitary-adrenal interrelationship in diseases of the central nervous system. *Journal of Clinical Endocrinology and Metabolism*, 21(a):1023–1036, 1961.

Rahe, R. H.; McKean, J. D., Jr.; and Arthur, R. J. A longitudinal study of life-change and illness patterns. *Journal of Psychosomatic Research,* 10:355–366, 1967.

Reimann, H. A. *Periodic Diseases.* Oxford: Blackwell Scientific Publications, 1963.

Reinberg, A. The hours of changing responsiveness or susceptibility. *Perspectives in Biology and Medicine,* 11(1): 111–128, 1967.

Reinberg, A.; Ghata, J.; and Sidi, E. Nocturnal asthma attacks: Their relation to the circadian adrenal cycle. *Journal of Allergy,* 34:323–330, 1968.

Reinberg, A.; Sidi, E.; and Ghata, J. Circadian reactivity rhythms of human skin to histamine or allergen and the adrenal cycle. *Journal of Allergy,* 36(3):273–283, 1965.

Serge, G.; Turco, G.; and Ceresa, F. Assay of a compartmental analysis of blood glucose and insulin relationships in man. *Acta Diabetologica Latina,* 5:242–243, October 1968.

Serio, M.; Tarquini, B.; Contini, P.; Bucalossi, A.; and Toccafondi, R. Plasma cortisol response to insulin and circadian rhythm in diabetic subjects. *Diabetes,* 17(3):124–127, 1968.

Shilov, V. M., and Kozar, M. I. Changes in the immunological reactivity of man exposed to various day schedules in a sealed chamber. *Biologicheskiye ritmy i voprosy razrabotki rezhimov truda i otdykha.* Materialy. Moscow, 1967, 71–72.

Sholitan, L. J.; Werk, E. E., Jr.; and Marnell, R. T. Diurnal variation of adrenocortical function in non-endocrine disease states. *Metabolism,* 10:632–646, 1961.

Sicuteri, F.; Del Bianco, P. L.; and Anselmi, B. Migraine as a cyclic disease with latent and overt components—effects with an antiaminic drug. *Headache,* 10:53–62, July 1970.

Smith, L.; Kellow, A. H.; and Hanington, E. A clinical and biochemical correlation between tyramine and migraine headache. *Headache,* 10:43–52, July 1970.

Stephens, G., and McGaugh, J. L. Retrograde amnesia—effects of periodicity and degree of training. *Communications in Behavioral Biology,* Part A, 1:267–275, 1968.

Stephens, G.; McGaugh, J. L.; and Alpern, H. P. Periodicity and memory in mice. *Psychonomic Science,* 8(5):201–202, 1967.

Tarquini, B.; Della Corte, M.; and Orzalesi, R. Circadian studies on plasma cortisol in subjects with peptic ulcer. *Journal of Endocrinology,* 38:475–476, 1967.

Wilson, C. W. M. The occurrence of circadian histamine rhythms in the rat. *International Archives of Allergy,* 28:32–34, 1965.

Wyler, A. R.; Minoru, M.; and Holmes, T. H. Seriousness of

illness rating scale. *Journal of Psychosomatic Research,* 11:363–374, 1968.

Isolation: Free-Running

Apfelbaum, M., and Nillus, P. Evolution de la conductance physiologique chez les femmes vivantes a 11°C pendant quinze jours. *Revue Française d'Etudes Cliniques et Biologiques,* 12:80–85, 1969.

Apfelbaum, M.; Reinberg, A.; Nillus, P.; and Halberg, F. Rythmes circadiens de l'alternance veille-sommeil pendant l'isolement souterrain de sept jeunes femmes. *Presse Médicale,* 77:879–882, 1969.

Aschoff, J. Circadian rhythms in man. *Science,* 148:1427–1432, 1965.

Aschoff, J. Human circadian rhythms in activity, body temperature and other functions. In: Brown, A. H., and Favorite, F. G. (eds.), *Life Science and Space Research V, International Space Science Symposium, 7th, Vienna, Austria.* Amsterdam: North Holland Publishing Company, 1967, pp. 159–173.

Aschoff, J. Time-givers of 24-hour physiological cycles. In: Schaefer, K. E. (ed.), *Man's Dependence on the Earthly Atmosphere.* New York: Macmillan, 1962, pp. 373–380.

Aschoff, J.; Gerecke, U.; and Wever, R. Desynchronization of human circadian rhythms. *Japanese Journal of Physiology,* 17:450–457, 1967.

Bayevskiy, R. M.; Chernyayeva, S. A.; et al. Investigation of the physiological condition of men exposed to isolation and hypodynamia during the shift to a new work and rest schedule. *Biologicheskiye ritmy i voprosy razrabotki rezhimov truda i otdykha.* Materialy. Moscow, 1967, 12–13.

Chipman, D. M., and Sharon, N. Mechanism of lysozyme action. *Science,* 165(3892):454–465, August 1969.

Clegg, B. R., and Schaefer, K. E. Studies of circadian cycles in human subjects during prolonged isolation in a constant environment using 8-channel telemetry systems. Memorandum Report No. 66–4 (NASA), February 19, 1966.

Colin, J.; Noudas, Y.; Boutelier, C.; Timbal, J.; and Siffre, M. Etude du rythme circadien de la température centrale d'un sujet au cours d'isolement souterrain de 6 mois. *XVI International Congress of Aviation Space Medicine,* Lisbon, September 11–15, 1967.

Colin, J.; Timbal, J.; et al. Rhythm of the rectal temperature during a 6-month free-running experiment. *Journal of Applied Physiology,* 25(2):170–176, August 1968.

Dushkov, B. A. Change in rhythmic activity and in motor coordination during confinement to a small-capacity closed chamber. *Biologicheskiye ritmy i voprosy razrabotki rezhimov truda i otdykha*. Materialy. Moscow, 1967, 27.

Ghata, J.; Halberg, F.; et al. Rythmes circadiens desynchronisés du cycle (17-hydroxycorticosteroides, température rectale, veille-sommeil) chez deux sujets adultes sains. *Annales d'Endocrinologie*, 30(2):245–260, 1969.

Halberg, F.; Nelson, W.; et al. Reproducibility of circadian temperature rhythm in the rat kept in continuous light of 30 lux intensity. *Physiologist*, 9(3):196, August 1966.

Halberg, F.; Siffre, M.; Engeli, M.; Hillman, D.; and Reinberg, A. Etude en libre-cours des rythmes circadiens du pouls de l'alternance veille-sommeil et de l'estimation du temps pendant les deux mois de séjour souterrain d'un homme adulte jeune. *Comptes Rendus de l'Académie des Sciences*, 260:1259–1262, 1965.

Litsov, A. N. Daily dynamics of some physiological functions and human work capacity in isolation. *Space Biology and Medicine*, 2(4):142–148, November 1968.

Lowe, C. H.; Hinds, D. S.; et al. Natural free-running period in vertebrate animal population. *Science*, 156:531–534, 1967.

Meddis, R. Human circadian rhythms and the 48-hour day. *Nature*, 218:964–965, June 1968.

Mills, J. N. Circadian rhythms during and after three months in solitude underground. *Journal of Physiology*, 174:217–231, 1964.

Mills, J. N. Sleeping habits during four months in solitude. *Journal of Physiology*, 189:30–31, March 1967.

Myasnikov, V. I. Circadian rhythm of physiological functions in man under conditions of isolation. *Aerospace Medicine*, 39:73–78, October 1968.

NASA. The effects of confinement on long-duration manned space flights. Proceedings of the NASA Symposium, November 17, 1966.

Pöppel, E. Desynchronization of circadian rhythms within an isolated group. *Pflügers Archiv für die gesamte Physiologie*, 299:364–370, March 1968.

Reinberg, A. Eclairement et cycle menstruel de la femme. Rapport au Colloque International du CRNS: La photorégulation de la réproduction chez les oiseaux et les mammifères, Montpellier, 1967.

Reinberg, A.; Halberg, F.; Ghata, J.; and Siffre, M. Spectre thermique (rythmes de la température rectale) d'une femme adulte saine avant, pendant, après un isolement souterrain de trois mois. *Comptes Rendus de l'Académie des Sciences*, 262:782–785, 1966.

Siffre, M.; Reinberg, A.; Halberg, F.; Ghata, J.; Perdriel, G.;

and Slind, R. Studies on two healthy human subjects isolated for several months underground. *La Presse Médicale*, 74:915–919, 1966.

Simpson, H. W., and Lobban, M. C. Effects of a 21-hour day on the human circadian excretory rhythms of 17-hydroxycorticosteroids and electrolytes. *Aerospace Medicine*, 38:1205–1213, 1967.

Simpson, H. W.; Lobban, M. C.; and Halberg, F. Near 24-hour rhythms in subjects living on a 21-hour routine in the Arctic summer at 78°N, revealed by circadian amplitude ratios. *Rassegna di Neurologia Vegetativa*. In press.

Smith, W. R.; Ulvedal, F.; and Welch, B. E. Steroid and catecholamine studies on pilots during prolonged experiments in a space cabin simulator. *Journal of Applied Physiology*, 18:1257–1263, 1963.

Light: Photoperiodism, Reproduction, and Circadian Rhythms

Axelrod, J.; Snyder, S. H.; Heller, A.; and Moore, R. Y. Light-induced changes in pineal hydroxyindole-*O*-methyltransferase: Abolition by lateral hypothalamic lesions. *Science*, 154:898–899, November 1966.

Axelrod, J.; Wurtman, R. J.; and Winget, C. M. Melatonin synthesis in the hen pineal gland and its control by light. *Nature*, 201(4924): 1134, 1964.

Axelrod, J.; Wurtman, R. J.; and Snyder, S. H. Control of hydroxyindole-*O*-methyltransferase activity in the rat pineal gland by environmental lighting. *Journal of Biological Chemistry*, 240(2):949–954, 1965.

Benoit, J., and Assenmacher, I. The control by visible radiations of the gonadotropic activity of the duck hypophysis. *Recent Progress in Hormone Research*, 15:143–164, 1959.

Benoit, J., and Assenmacher, I. (eds.) La Photorégulation de la réproduction chez les oiseaux et les mammifères, Colloquium Internationale du CNRS, 1967.

Blaney, L. T.; and Hamner, K. C. Interrelations among effects of temperature, photoperiod, and dark period on floral initiation of Biloxi soybean. *Botanical Gazette*, 119(1): 10–24, 1957.

Bruce, V. G., and Minis, D. H. Circadian clock action spectrum in a photoperiodic moth. *Science*, 163:583–585, 1969.

Bruce, V. G., and Pittendrigh, C. S. Resetting the Euglena clock with a single light stimulus. *American Naturalist*, 92:295–305, 1958.

Bruce, V. G.; Weight, F.; and Pittendrigh, C. S. Resetting the sporulation rhythm in Pilobolus with short light flashes of high intensity. *Science,* 131(3402):728–730, 1960.

Bünning, E. Known and unknown principles of biological chronometry. In: Fischer, R. (ed.), Interdisciplinary Perspectives of Time. *Annals of the New York Academy of Sciences,* 138:515–524, 1967.

Bünning, E. *The Physiological Clock.* Revised second edition. New York: Springer-Verlag, 1967.

Coulter, M. W., and Hamner, K. C. Quantitative assay of photoperiodic floral inhibition and stimulation in Biloxi soybean. *Plant Physiology,* 40(5):873–881, September 1965.

Dewan, E. M. On the possibility of a perfect rhythm method of birth control by periodic light stimulation. *American Journal of Obstetrics and Gynecology,* 99(7):1016–1019, December 1967.

Dewan, E. M. Rhythms. *Science and Technology,* 20–28, January 1969.

Emlen, S. T. Bird migration: Influence of physiological state upon celestial orientation. *Science,* 165:716–718, August 1969.

Eskin, I. A., and Mikhailova, N. V. Photoperiodicity and the function of the hypophysis and the adrenal cortex. *Bulletin of Experimental Biology and Medicine U.S.S.R.* (English translation), 46:999–1002, 1958.

Everett, J. W., and Sawyer, C. H. A 24-hour periodicity in the "LH-release apparatus" of female rats, disclosed by barbiturate sedation. *Endocrinology,* 47:198–218, September 1950.

Farner, D. S. The photoperiodic control of reproductive cycles in birds. *American Scientist,* 52:137–156, 1964.

Fiske, V. M., and Huppert, L. C. Melatonin action on pineal varies with photoperiod. *Science,* 162:279, October 1968.

Fox, H. M. Lunar periodicity in reproduction. *Proceedings of the Royal Society of Britain,* 95, 1923.

Gerritzen, F. Influence of light on human circadian rhythms. *Aerospace Medicine,* 37:66–70, 1966.

Gerritzen, F.; Strengers, T.; et al. Studies on the influence of fast transportation on the circadian excretion pattern of the kidney in humans. *Aerospace Medicine,* 40:264–271, March 1969.

Goff, M. L. R., and Finger, F. W. Activity rhythms and diurnal light-dark control. *Science,* 154:1346–1348, 1966.

Halberg, F.; Halberg, E.; Barnum, C. P.; and Bittner, J. J. Physiologic 24-hour periodicity in human beings and mice, the lighting regimen and daily routine. In: Withrow, R. B. (ed.), *Photoperiodism and Related Phenomena in Plants and Animals.* Washington, D.C.:

Publication of the American Association for the Advancement of Science, 1959, pp. 803–878.

Halberg, F., and Visscher, M. B. Temperature rhythms in blind mice. *Federation Proceedings*, 13:65, 1954.

Hamner, K. C., and Takimoto, A. Circadian rhythms and plant photoperiodism. *American Naturalist*, 98(902):295–322, September–October 1964.

Harker, J. E. The effect of photoperiod on the developmental rate of Drosophila pupae. *Journal of Experimental Biology*, 43:411–423, 1965.

Haus, E.; Lakatua, D.; and Halberg, F. The internal timing of several circadian rhythms in the blinded mouse. *Experimental Medicine and Surgery*, 25:7–45, 1967.

Hayes, D. K.; Sullivan, W. N.; et al. Photoperiod manipulation of insect diapause: A method of pest control? *Science*, 169:382–383, July 1970.

Hollwich, F. Der Einfluss des Augenlichtes auf Stoffwechselvorgänge. *Acta Neurovegetativa*, 30(1–4):201–215, 1967.

Hollwich, F. The influence of light via the eye on the endocrine system. *Anales del Instituto Barraquer*, IX (1, 2):133–142, 1969.

Hollwich, F., and Dieckhues, B. Augenlicht und Nebennierenrindenfunktion. *Deutsche Medizinische Wochenschrift*, 1–17, December 22, 1967.

Hollwich, F., and Dieckhues, B. Eosinopeniereaktion und Sehvermögen. *Sonderdruck aus Klinische Monatsblätter für Augenheilkunde*, 152(1):11–16, 1968.

Hollwich, F., and Tilgner, S. The influence of light via the eyes on the thyroid and testes. *Deutsche Medizinische Wochenschrift*, 87:2674, 1962.

Holmgren, H., and Swensson, A. Der Einfluss des Lichtes auf den 24-Stunden. Rhythmus der Activitat des Leberglykogens und der Korpertemperatur. *Acta Medica Scandinavica* (Supplement 278): 71–76, 1953.

Holmquest, D. L., and Lipscomb, H. S. The response of thermal and activity rhythms in the rat to cyclic variations in adrenocortical function and environmental lighting. *Proceedings of the International Union of Physiological Sciences*, 7:197, 1968.

Holmquest, D. L.; Retiene, K.; and Lipscomb, H. S. Circadian rhythms in rats: Effects of random lighting. *Science*, 152:662–664, April 1966.

Honjo, S.; Fujiwara, T.; Takasaka, M.; Suzuki, Y.; and Imaizumi, K. Observations on the diurnal temperature variation of cynomolgus monkeys (Macaca irus) and on the effect of changes in the routine of lighting upon this variation. *Japanese Journal of Medical Science and Biology*, 16:189–198, 1963.

Hoshizaki, T.; Brest, D. E.; and Hamner, K. C. Xanthium leaf movements in light and dark. *Plant Physiology*, 44:151–152, 1969.

Hoshizaki, T., and Hamner, K. C. Circadian leaf movements: Persistence in bean plants grown in continuous high-intensity light. *Science*, 144:1240–1241, 1964.

Hoshizaki, T., and Hamner, K. C. Interactions between light and circadian rhythms in plant photoperiodism. *Photochemistry and Photobiology*, 10:87–97, 1969.

Kaiser, I. H. Effect of a 28-hour day on ovulation and reproduction in mice. *American Journal of Obstetrics and Gynecology*, 99:772–784, 1967.

Kaiser, I. H., and Halberg, F. Circadian aspects of birth. *Annals of the New York Academy of Sciences*, 98:1056–1068, 1962.

Kerenyi, N. A., and Sarkar, K. The postnatal transformation of the pineal gland. *Acta Morphologia Academia Scientia Hungaria*, 16:223, 1968.

Kopell, B. S.; Lunde, D. T.; Clayton, R. B.; and Moos, R. H. Variations in some measures of arousal during the menstrual cycle. *Journal of Nervous and Mental Disease*, 148:180–187, 1969.

Lincoln, R. G., and Hamner, K. C. An effect of gibberellic acid on the flowering of xanthium, a short day plant. *Plant Physiology*, 33(2):101–104, 1958.

Lisk, R. D. Direct effects of light on the hypothalamus. (Symposium on Hypothalamic Control of the Anterior Pituitary.) American Association for the Advancement of Science, December 27, 1965.

Lisk, R. D., and Sawyer, C. H. Induction of paradoxical sleep by lights-off stimulation. *Proceedings of the Society of Experimental Biology and Medicine*, 123:664–667, 1966.

Lobban, M. C., and Tredre, B. E. Renal diurnal rhythms in blind subjects. *Journal of Physiology*, 170:29–30, 1964.

Lobban, M. C., and Tredre, B. E. Perception of light and the maintenance of human renal diurnal rhythms. *Journal of Physiology*, 89(1):32–33, March 1967.

Makarova, L. G. Changes of EEG in a healthy individual with trigger light stimulation. *Bulletin of USSR, Academy of Medical Science, Institute of Neurology, Moscow*, 62:6–11, November 1966.

Meites, J. Releasing factors in hypothalamic control of the anterior pituitary in mammals. (Symposium on Hypothalamic Control of the Anterior Pituitary.) American Association for the Advancement of Science, December 1965.

Meites, J. Direct studies of the secretion of hypothalamic hypophysiotropic hormones (HHH). In: Meites, J. (ed.),

Hypophysiotropic Hormones of the Hypothalamus. Baltimore: Williams and Wilkins Co., 1970.

Menaker, M., and Eskin, A. Circadian clock in photoperiodic time measurement: A test of the Bünning Hypothesis. *Science,* 157:1182–1184, 1967.

Menaker, W. Lunar periodicity with reference to live births. *American Journal of Obstetrics and Gynecology,* 98(7): 1002–1004, August 1967.

Minis, D. H., and Pittendrigh, C. S. Circadian oscillation controlling hatching: Its ontogeny during embryogenesis of a moth. *Science,* 159:534–536, 1968.

Moore, R. Y.; Heller, A.; Wurtman, R. J.; and Axelrod, J. Visual pathway mediating pineal response to environmental light. *Science,* 155:220–223, 1967.

Oishi, T., and Kato, M. The pineal organ as a possible photoreceptor in photoperiodic testicular responses in Japanese quail. *Memoirs of the Faculty of Science, Kyoto University,* 2: Series D:12–18, 1968.

Orth, D. N., and Island, D. P. Light synchronization of the circadian rhythm in plasma cortisol (17-OHCS) concentration in man. *Journal of Clinical Endocrinology,* 29:479–486, 1969.

Pittendrigh, C. S. On the mechanism of the entrainment of a circadian rhythm by light cycles. In: Aschoff, J. (ed.), *Circadian Clocks.* Amsterdam: North Holland Publishing Company, 1965.

Pittendrigh, C. S. The circadian oscillation in Drosophila pseudoobscura pupae: A model for the photoperiodic clock. *Zeitschrift für Planzenphysiologie,* 54:275–307, 1966.

Pittendrigh, C. S., and Minis, D. H. The entrainment of circadian oscillations by light and their role as photoperiodic clocks. *American Naturalist,* 98(902):261–294, 1964.

Reid, H. B.; Moore, P. H.; and Hamner, K. C. Control of flowering on xanthium pennsylvanicum by red and far-red light. *Plant Physiology,* 42:532–540, 1967.

Reinberg, A. Eclairement et cycle menstruel de la femme. Rapport au Colloque International du CRNS, La Photorégulation de la réproduction chez les oiseaux et les mammifères, Montpellier, 1967.

Rosenthal, J. D.; Sullivan, W. N.; Adler, V. E.; and McGuire, J. U. Influence of temperatures and light regimens on diapause of samia cynthia pryeri. *Journal of Economic Entomology,* 61(2): 578–579, 1968.

Rust, C. C., and Meyer, R. K. Hair color, molt and testis size in male, short-tailed weasels treated with melatonin. *Science,* 165:921–922, 1969.

Shumate, W. H.; Reid, H. B.; and Hammer, K. C. Floral inhibition of Biloxi soybean during a 72-hour cycle. *Plant Physiology*, 42:1511–1518, 1967.

Snyder, S. H.; Zweig, M.; Axelrod, J.; and Fischer, J. E. Control of the circadian rhythm in serotonin content of the rat pineal gland. *Proceedings of the National Academy of Sciences*, 53(2):301–305, 1965.

Stephens, G. J.; Halberg, F.; and Stephens, G. C. The blinded fiddler crab: An invertebrate model of circadian desynchronization. *Annals of the New York Academy of Sciences*, 117(1):386–406, 1964.

Sullivan, W. N.; Cawley, B. M.; Oliver, M.; Hayes, D. K.; and McGuire, J. U. Manipulating the photoperiod to damage insects. *Nature*, 221(5175):60–61, 1969.

Takimoto, A., and Hamner, K. C. Studies on red light interruption in relation to timing mechanism involved in the photoperiodic response of Pharbits nil. *Plant Physiology*, 40:852–854, 1965.

Thor, D. H., and Hoats, D. L. A circadian variable in self-exposure to light by the rat. *Psychonomic Science*, 12(1):1–2, August 1968.

Timonen, S.; Franzas, B.; and Wichmann, K. Photosensibility of the human pituitary. *Annales Chirurgiae et Gynaecologiae Feminae*, 53:165–172, 1964.

Underwood, H., and Menaker, M. Photoperiodically significant photoreception in sparrows: Is the retina involved? *Science*, 167:301, 1970.

Wever, R. Autonomous circadian rhythms in men as influenced by different light conditions. *Pflügers Archiv für die gesamte Physiologie*, 306:71–91, 1969.

Winget, C. M., and Card, D. H. Daily rhythm changes associated with variations in light intensity and color. *Life Sciences and Space Research*, 5:148–158, 1967.

Winget, C. M.; Rahlman, D. F.; and Pace, N. Phase relationship between circadian rhythms and photoperiodism (Cebus albifrons). In: Rohles, F. (ed.), *Circadian Rhythms in Nonhuman Primates*. New York/Basel: Karger, 1968.

Winget, C. M.; Rosenblatt, L. S.; DeRoshia, C. W.; and Hetherington, N. W. Mechanisms of action of light on circadian rhythms in the monkey. *Life Sciences and Space Research*, 8. In press.

Wurtman, R. J. Effects of light and visual stimuli on endocrine function. In: Martini, L., and Ganong, W. F. (eds.), *Neuroendocrinology*, Chapter 13. New York: Academic Press, 1967.

Wurtman, R. J.; Axelrod, J.; Chu, E. W.; and Fischer, J. E. Mediation of some effects of illumination on the rat estrous cycle by the sympathetic nervous system. *Endocrinology*, 75:366, 1964.

Wurtman, R. J.; Axelrod, J.; Sedvall, G.; and Moore, R. Y. Photic and neural control of the 24-hour norepinephrine rhythm in the rat pineal gland. *Journal of Pharmacology and Experimental Therapeutics*, 157(3):487–492, 1967.

Menstrual Syndrome

Dalton, K. *The Premenstrual Syndrome*. Springfield, Illinois: Charles C Thomas, 1964.

Dewan, E. M. On the possibility of a perfect rhythm method of birth control by periodic light stimulation. *American Journal of Obstetrics and Gynecology*, 99(7):1016–1019, December 1967.

Janowsky, D. S.; Gorney, R.; Castelnuovo-Tedesco, P.; and Stone, C. B. Premenstrual-menstrual increases in psychiatric hospital admission rates. *American Journal of Obstetrics and Gynecology*, 103:189–191, 1969.

Kopell, B. S., Lunde, D. T.; Clayton, R. B.; and Moos, R. H. Variations in some measures of arousal during the menstrual cycle. *Journal of Nervous and Mental Disease*, 148:180–187, 1969.

Malek, J.; Gleich, J.; and Malý, V. Characteristics of the daily rhythm of menstruation and labor. *Annals of the New York Academy of Sciences*, 98:1042–1055, 1962.

Moos, R. H. Typology of menstrual cycle symptoms. *American Journal of Obstetrics and Gynecology*, 103(3):390–402, 1969.

Moos, R. H.; Kopell, B. S.; Melges, F. T.; Yalom, I. D.; Lunde, D. T.; Clayton, R. B.; and Hamburg, D. A. Fluctuations in symptoms and moods during the menstrual cycle. *Journal of Psychosomatic Research*, 13:37–44, 1969.

Reinberg, A. Eclairement et cycle menstruel de la femme. Rapport au Colloque International du CRNS, La photorégulation de la réproduction chez les oiseaux et les mammifères, Montpellier, 1967.

Smith, S. L., and Sauder, C. Food cravings, depression, and premenstrual problems. *Psychosomatic Medicine*, 31:281–287, 1969.

Swanson, E. M., and Foulkes, D. Dream content and the menstrual cycle. *Journal of Nervous and Mental Disease*, 145(5):358–363, 1968.

University of Colorado Medical School, *Symposium on Menstrual Mechanisms*, Denver, Colorado: December 6–7, 1965.

Zacharias, L., and Wurtman, R. J. Blindness: Its relation to age of menarche. *Science*, 144(3622):1154–1155, 1964.

372   BODY TIME

Mental Illness

Berendes, H. W.; Marte, E.; Ertel, R. J.; McCarthy, J. A.;
    Anderson, J. A.; and Halberg, F. Circadian physiologic
    rhythm and lowered blood 5-hydroxytryptamine in hu-
    man subjects with defective mentality. *Physiologist*,
    3:20, 1960.

Bunney, W. E., Jr.; Fawcett, J. A.; Davis, J. M.; and Gifford, S.
    Further evaluation of urinary 17-hydroxycorticosteroids
    in suicidal patients. *Archives of General Psychiatry*,
    21:138–150, 1969.

Bunney, W. E., Jr., and Hartmann, E. L. Study of a patient
    with 48-hour manic depressive cycles: I & II. *Archives
    of General Psychiatry*, 12:611–625, 1965.

Cahn, A. A.; Folk, G. E.; and Huston, P. E. Age comparison
    of human day-night physiological differences. *Aero-
    space Medicine*, 39(6):608–610, 1968.

Cookson, B. A.; Quarrington, B.; and Huszka, L. Longitudinal
    study of periodic catatonia. *Journal of Psychiatric Re-
    search*, 5:15–38, 1967.

Crammer, J. L. Rapid weight-changes in mental patients. *Lan-
    cet*, 2:259–262, August 1957.

Curtis, G. C.; Fogel, M. L.; et al. The effect of sustained affect
    on the diurnal rhythms of adrenal cortical activity.
    Psychosomatic Medicine, 26:696–713, 1966.

Curtis, G. C.; Fogel, M. L.; McEvoy, D.; and Zarate, C. Effects
    of weight, sex and diurnal variation on the excretion of
    17-hydroxycorticosteroids. *Journal of Clinical Endocri-
    nology and Metabolism*, 28(5):711–713, 1968.

Dick, P.; Tissot, R.; and Pletscher, S. Influence des médicaments
    psychotropes sur les cycles biologiques et les cycles des
    psychoses. In: de Ajuriaguerra, J. (ed.), *Cycles Bio-
    logiques et Psychiatrie*. Paris: Masson et Cie., 1968.

Durrell, J. Biological rhythms and psychiatry: Psycho-endocrine
    mechanisms. In: de Ajuriaguerra, J. (ed.), *Cycles Bio-
    logiques et Psychiatrie*. Paris: Masson et Cie., 1968,
    pp. 321–328.

Durrell, J.; Libow, L. S.; Kellam, S. G.; and Shader, R. I.
    Interrelationships between regulation of thyroid gland
    function and psychosis. *Endocrines and the Central
    Nervous System*, Association for Research in Nervous
    and Mental Diseases, Vol. 43, Chapter XXI, 1966.

Engel, R.; Halberg, F.; and Gully, R. J. The diurnal rhythm in
    EEG discharge and in circulating eosinophils in certain
    types of epilepsy. *Electroencephalography and Clinical
    Neurophysiology*, 4:115–116, 1952.

Fleeson, W.; Glueck, B. C., Jr.; and Halberg, F. Persistence of
    daily rhythms in eosinophil count and rectal tempera-

ture during "regression" induced by intensive electro-shock therapy. *Physiologist*, 1:28, 1957.

Fullerton, D. T. Circadian rhythm of adrenal cortical activity in depression. *Archives of General Psychiatry*, 19(6): 674, 1968.

Gjessing, L. R. Studies of periodic catatonia, II: The urinary excretion of phenolic amines and acids with and without loads of different drugs. *Journal of Psychiatric Research*, 2(3):149–162, 1964.

Gjessing, L. R. A review of the biochemistry of periodic catatonia. Excerpta Medica International Congress Series, No. 150, 1967.

Gjessing, R., and Gjessing, L. R. Some main trends in the clinical aspects of periodic catatonia. *Acta Psychiatrica Scandinavica*, 37(1):1–13, 1961.

Gjessing, L. R.; Jenner, F. A.; Harding, G. F. A.; and Johannessen, N. B. The EEG in three cases of periodic catatonia. *British Journal of Psychiatry*, 113(504): 1271–1282, 1967.

Glueck, B. C. The use of computers in patient care. *Mental Hospitals*, 16(4):117–120, 1965.

Glueck, B. C. (investigator), and Luce, G. (author). The computer as psychiatric aid and research tool. Mental Health Program Reports-2, National Institute of Mental Health, PHS Publication 1743, 353–363, February 1968.

Goodwin, J. C.; Jenner, F. A.; Lobban, M. C.; and Sheridan, M. Renal rhythms in a patient with a 48-hour cycle of psychosis during a period of life on an abnormal time routine. *Journal of Physiology*, 17:16–17, 1964.

Halberg, F. Physiologic considerations underlying rhythmometry with special reference to emotional illness. In: de Ajuriaguerra, J. (ed.), *Cycles Biologiques et Psychiatrie*. Paris: Masson et Cie., 1968, pp. 73–126.

Halberg, F.; Jacobson, E.; Wadsworth, G.; and Bittner, J. J. Audiogenic abnormality spectra, 24-hour periodicity and lighting. *Science*, 128:657–658, 1958.

Halberg, F.; Vestergaard, P.; and Sakai, M. Rhythmometry on urinary 17-ketosteroid excretion by healthy men and women and patients with chronic schizophrenia; possible chronopathology in depressive illness. *Archives d'Anatomie, d'Histologie et d'Embryologie Normales et Expérimentales*, 51:301–311, 1968.

Harding, G. F. A., and Jenner, F. A. The electroencephalogram in three cases of periodic psychosis. *Electroencephalography and Clinical Neurophysiology*, 21:59–66, 1966.

Hartmann, E. Longitudinal studies of sleep and dream patterns in manic-depressive patients. *Archives of General Psychiatry*, 19:312–329, September 1968.

Hatotani, N.; Ishida, C.; Yura, R.; Maeda, M.; Kato, Y.; and

Nomura, J. Psycho-physiological studies of atypical psychoses—endocrinological aspect of periodic psychoses. *Folia Psychiatrica et Neurologica Japonica*, 16 (3):248–292, 1962.

Jenner, F. A. Studies of recurrent and predictable behavior. *Proceedings: Leeds Symposium on Behavioral Disorders*, 1965.

Jenner, F. A. Periodic psychoses in the light of biological rhythm research. *International Review of Neurobiology*, 11:129–169, 1968.

Jenner, F. A. Gjessing, L. R.; Cox, J. R.; Davies-Jones, A.; Hullin, R. P.; and Hanna, S. M. A manic-depressive psychotic with a persistent 48-hour cycle. *British Journal of Psychiatry*, 113(501):895–910, 1967.

Jenner, F. A.; Goodwin, J. C.; Sheridan, M.; Tauber, I. J.; and Lobban, M. C. The effect of an altered time regime on biological rhythms in a 48-hour periodic psychosis. *British Journal of Psychiatry*, 114:213, 1968.

Knapp, M. S.; Keane, P. M.; and Wright, J. G. Circadian rhythm of plasma 11-hydroxycorticosteroids in depressive illness, congestive heart failure and Cushing's syndrome. *British Journal of Psychiatry*, 2:27–30, 1967.

Krieger, D. T.; Kolodny, H. D.; and Warner, R. R. P. Serum serotonin in nervous system disease. *Neurology*, 14(6):578–580, June 1964.

Lobban, M. C., and Tredre, B. E. Diurnal rhythms of electrolyte excretion in depressive illness. *Nature*, 199(4894):667–669, 1963.

Lohrenz, F. N.; Fullerton, D. T.; et al. Adrenocortical function in depressive states, study of circadian variation in plasma and urinary steroids. *International Journal of Neuropsychiatry*, 4:21–25, 1968.

Melges, F. T., and Fougerousse, C. E., Jr. Time sense, emotions and acute mental illness. *Journal of Psychiatric Research*, 4:127–140, 1966.

Richter, C. P. Biological approach to manic-depressive insanity. *Proceedings of the Association for Research in Nervous and Mental Disease*, 11:611, 1930.

Richter, C. P. Abnormal but regular cycles in behavior and metabolism in rats and catatonic-schizophrenics. In: Reiss, M. (ed.), *Psychoendocrinology*. New York: Grune and Stratton, 1958, pp. 168–181.

Richter, C. P. Psychopathology of periodic behavior in animals and man. In: Zubin, J., and Hunt, H. F. (eds.), *Comparative Psychopathology*. New York: Grune and Stratton, 1967.

Rubin, R. T.; Young, W. M.; Clark, B. R. 17-hydroxycorticosteroid and vanylmandelic acid excretion in a rapidly cycling manic-depressive. *Psychosomatic Medicine*, 30: 162–171, 1968.

Stroebel, C. F. Behavioral aspects of circadian rhythms. In: Zubin, J., and Hunt, H. F. (eds.), *Comparative Psychopathology*. New York: Grune and Stratton, 1967.

Stroebel, C. F. A biologic rhythm approach to psychiatric treatment. In: *Proceedings of the Seventh Medical Symposium*. New York: Yorktown Heights, IBM Press, 1967, pp. 215–241.

Stroebel, C. F. Biologic rhythm correlates of disturbed behavior in the Rhesus monkey. In: Rohles, F. H. (ed.), *Circadian Rhythms in Nonhuman Primates*. New York/Basel: Karger, 1969, pp. 91–105.

Stroebel, C. F. (investigator), and Luce, G. (writer). The importance of biological clocks in mental health. Mental Health Program Reports-2. National Institute of Mental Health, PHS Publication 1743, pp. 323–351, February 1968.

Sueda, T. Schwankungen im 24-Stunden Rhythmus bei manisch-depressiven. Kranksein Pathophysiologie des manisch-depressiven Krankseins. *Folia Psychiatrica et Neurologica Japonica*, 9:1449–1485, 1962.

Tamura, A. Changes of diurnal rhythm of Na, K, and Ca excretion in urine with disorders in brain. *Psychiatria et Neurologia Japonica*, 5:405–423, 1965.

Vestergaard, P.; Leverett, R.; and Douglas, W. R. Spontaneous variability in the excretion of combined neutral 17-ketosteroids in the urine of chronic schizophrenic patients. Psychiatric Research Reports, No. 6, American Psychiatric Association, October 1956, pp. 74–89.

Wakoh, T. Endocrinological studies on periodic psychosis. *Mie Medical Journal*, 9(2):351–390, 1959.

Wakoh, T.; Takekoshi, A.; Yoshimoto, S.; Yoshimoto, K.; Hiramoto, K.; and Kurosawa, R. Pathophysiological study of the periodic psychosis (atypical endogeneous psychosis) with special reference to the comparison with the chronic schizophrenic. *Mie Medical Journal*, 10(3): 317–396, 1960.

Yamashita, I.; Shinohara, S.; Nakazawa, A.; Yoshimura, Y.; Ito, K.; and Takasugi, K. Endocrinology study of atypical psychosis. *Folia Psychiatrica et Neurologica Japonica*, 16(3):293–298, 1962.

Methods: Data Analysis

Adey, W. R.; Kado, R. T.; and Walter, D. O. Computer analysis of EEG data from Gemini flight G-T 7. *Aerospace Medicine*, 38(4):345–359, April 1967.

Cole, L. C. Biological clock in the unicorn. *Science*, 125:874–876, 1957.

Engeli, M., and Halberg, F. Spectral analysis of steroid rhythms in data at equal or unequal intervals. *Federation Proceedings*, 23(2):250, March–April 1964.

Enright, J. T. The search for rhythmicity in biological time-series. *Journal of Theoretical Biology*, 8:426–468, 1965.

Fischer, R., and Sollberger, A. Interdisciplinary perspectives of time. In: Weyer, E. M., and Fischer, R. (eds.), *The Interdisciplinary Perspectives of Time*, Annals of the New York Academy of Sciences, 138(2):367–415, 1967.

Gabrieli, E. R., and Sollberger, A. In: Gabrieli, E. R.; Albertson, P. D.; and Krauss, M. (eds.), *The Use of Data Mechanization and Computers in Clinical Medicine*. Annals of the New York Academy of Sciences, 161(2): 371, 1969.

Garcia-Sainz, M., and Halberg, F. Mitotic rhythms in human cancer reevaluated by electronic computer programs—evidence for temporal pathology. *Journal of the National Cancer Institute*, 37:279–292, 1966.

Globus, G. G. Quantification of the sleep cycle as a rhythm. *Psychophysiology*, 1970. In press.

Glueck, B. C. The use of computers in patient care. *Mental Hospitals*, 16(4):117–120, 1965.

Glueck, B. C. (investigator), and Luce, G. (author). The computer as psychiatric aid and research tool. Mental Health Program Reports-2, National Institute of Mental Health, PHS Publication 1743, 353–363, February 1968.

Gordon, R.; Spinks, J.; Dulmanis, A.; Hudson, P.; Halberg, F.; and Bartter, F. Amplitude and phase relations of several circadian rhythms in human plasma and urine resolved by cosinor: Demonstration of rhythm for tetrahydrocortisol and tetrahydrocorticosterone. *Clinical Science*, 35:307–324, 1968.

Halberg, F. Temporal coordination of physiological function. In: *Cold Spring Harbor Symposia on Quantitative Biology*. New York: Long Island Biological Association, 1960, pp. 289–310.

Halberg, F. Physiologic rhythms. In Hardy, J. D. (ed.), *Physiological Problems in Space Exploration*. Springfield, Illinois: Charles C Thomas, 1964, pp. 298–322.

Halberg, F. Physiologic rhythms and bioastronautics. In: Schaefer, K. E. (ed.), *Bioastronautics*. New York: Macmillan, 1964, pp. 181–195.

Halberg, F. Physiologic considerations underlying rhythmometry with special reference to emotional illness. In: de Ajuriaguerra, J. (ed.), *Cycles Biologiques et Psychiatrie*. Paris: Masson et Cie., 1968, pp. 73–126.

Halberg, F. Circadian temporal organization and experimental pathology. *VII Conference Internazionale della Società per lo Studio dei Ritmi Biologici,* Siena, September 1969, pp. 52–69.

Halberg, F.; Engeli, J.; Hamburger, C.; and Hillman, D. Spectral resolution of low-frequency, small-amplitude rhythms in excreted ketosteroid; probable androgen-induced circaseptan desynchronization. *Acta Endocrinologica Supplement,* 103:1–54, 1965.

Halberg, F., and Fallliers, C. J. Variability of physiologic circadian crests in groups of children studied "transversely." *Pediatrics,* 68:741–746, 1966.

Halberg, F.; Stein, M.; Diffley, M.; Panofsky, H.; and Adkins, G. Computer techniques in the study of biologic rhythms. *Annals of the New York Academy of Sciences,* 115:695–720, 1964.

Hoffman, K. Overt circadian frequencies and circadian rule. In: Aschoff, J. (ed.), *Circadian Clocks.* Amsterdam: North Holland Publishing Company, 1965.

Hoshizaki, T., and Hamner, K. C. Computer analysis of the leaf movements of pinto beans. *Plant Physiology,* 44: 1045–1050, 1969.

Iberall, A. S., and Cardon, S. Z. Control in biological systems —physical review. *Annals of the New York Academy of Sciences,* 117:445–515, 1964.

Kripke, D. F.; Crowley, T. J.; Pegram, G. V.; and Halberg, F. Circadian rhythmic amplitude modulation of Berger-Region frequencies in electroencephalograms from Macaca mulatta. *Rassegna di Neurologia Vegetativa,* 22: 519–525, 1968.

Möllerstrom, J., and Sollberger, A. Fundamental concepts underlying the metabolic periodicity in diabetes. *Annals of the New York Academy of Sciences,* 98(4):984–994, 1962.

Pavlidis, T. A. model for circadian clocks. *Bulletin of Mathematical Biophysics,* 29:781–791, 1967.

Pittendrigh, C. S., and Bruce, V. G. An oscillator model for biological clocks. In: Rudnick, A. (ed.), *Rhythmic and Synthetic Processes in Growth.* Princeton: Princeton University Press, 1957.

Sollberger, A. Biological measurements in time: With special reference to synchronization mechanisms. *Annals of the New York Academy of Sciences,* 138(2):567–599, 1967.

Sollberger, A. Rhythms and biological cycles. In: de Ajuriaguerra, J. (ed.), *Cycles Biologiques et Psychiatrie.* Paris: Masson et Cie., 1968, pp. 43–56.

Sollberger, A. How are biological time series related to the normal values concept? *Annals of the New York Academy of Sciences,* 161(2):602–625, 1969.

Sollberger, A. Problems in the statistical analysis of short periodic time series. *Journal of Interdisciplinary Cycle Research*, 1(1):49–88, May 1970.

Sollberger, A.; Apple, H. P.; Greenway, R. M.; King, P. H.; Lindan, O.; and Reswick, J. B. Automation in biological rhythm research with special reference to Homo sapiens. *Annals of the New York Academy of Sciences*, 161(2): 184, 1969.

Wever, R. A mathematical model for circadian rhythms. In: Aschoff, J. (ed.), *Circadian Clocks*, Amsterdam: North Holland Publishing Company, 1965, pp. 47–63.

Wever, R. Mathematical models of circadian rhythms and their applicability to men. In: de Ajuriaguerra, J. (ed.), *Cycles Biologiques et Psychiatrie*. Paris: Masson et Cie., 1968, pp. 61–72.

Performance, Behavior, and Sensation

Agadzhanyan, N. A., and Rafikov, A. M. Diurnal variations in altitude tolerance and the role of the adrenocortical function. *Biologicheskiye ritmy i voprosy razrabotki rezhimov truda i otdykha*. Materialy. Moscow, 1967, 8–9.

Alluisi, E. A., and Chiles, W. D. Sustained performance, work-rest scheduling, and diurnal rhythms in man. *Acta Psychologica*, 27:436–442, 1967.

Alluisi, E. A.; Chiles, W. D.; et al. Human group performance during confinement. AMRL Technical Documentary Report, 63–87 Aerospace Medical Division, Wright-Patterson Air Force Base, November 1963.

Alluisi, E. A.; Chiles, W. D.; and Hall, T. J. Combined effects of sleep loss and demanding work-rest schedules on crew performance. AMRL Technical Documentary Report, 63–64. Aerospace Medical Division, Wright-Patterson Air Force Base, June 1964.

Bjerner, B.; Holm, A.; and Swenson, A. Diurnal variation in mental performance. *British Journal of Industrial Medicine*, 12:103–110, 1955.

Cherepakhin, M. A. Normalization of physiological functions under conditions of hypokinesia caused by a regime of motor inactivity. *Biologicheskiye ritmy i voprosy razrabotki rezhimov truda i otdykha*. Materialy. Moscow, 1967, 69–70.

Frazier, T. W.; Rummel, J. A.; and Lipscomb, H. S. Circadian variability in vigilance performance. *Aerospace Medicine*, 39(4):383–395, 1968.

Gerd, M. A. Human work capacity at various periods of wakefulness. *Biologicheskiye ritmy i voprosy razrabotki rezhimov truda i otdykha*. Materialy. Moscow, 1967, 20–21.

Gramvall, S., and Lundberg, U. Variations in pulse rate at a cycle ergometer test on Swedish Air Force pilots. *Meddelanden Fran Flygoch Navalmedicinska Naemnden*, 12(1):4–5, 1963.

Hartman, B. O., and Cantrell, G. K. Sustained pilot performance requires more than skill. *Aerospace Medicine*, 8(7):801–803, August 1967.

Henkin, R. I. Presence of corticosterone and cortisol in the central and peripheral nervous system of the cat. *Endocrinology*, 82(5):1058–1061, May 1968.

Henkin, R. I. Auditory detection and perception in normal man and in patients with adrenal cortical insufficiency: Effect of adrenal cortical steroids. *Journal of Clinical Investigation*, 47(6):1269–1280, June 1968.

Henkin, R. I.; Gill, J. R.; and Bartter, F. C. Studies on taste thresholds in normal man and in patients with adrenal cortical insufficiency: The role of adrenal cortical steroids and of serum sodium concentration. *Journal of Clinical Investigation*, 42(5):727–735, 1963.

Henkin, R. I.; McGlone, R. E.; et al. Studies on auditory thresholds in normal man and in patients with adrenal cortical insufficiency: The role of adrenal cortical steroids. *Journal of Clinical Investigation*, 46(3):429–435, 1967.

Klein, K. E.; Brüner, H.; Rehme, H.; Stolze, J.; Steinhoff, W. D.; and Wegmann, H. M. Circadian rhythms of pilots' efficiency and effects of multiple time zone travel. *Aerospace Medicine*, 41, 1970. In press.

Klein, K. E.; Brüner, H.; and Ruff, S. Investigation regarding stress on flying personnel in long-distance jet flights. *Zeitschrift für Flügwissenschaften*, 14:109, 1966.

Klein, K. E.; Wegmann, H. M.; and Brüner, H. Circadian rhythm in indices of human performance, physical fitness and stress resistance. *Aerospace Medicine*, 39:512–518, May 1968.

Kosmolinskiy, F. P., and Dushkov, B. A. (eds.); or Gurovskii, N. N. (ed.), *Papers on the Psychophysiology of the Labor of Astronauts*. Foreign Translation Division of the Clearinghouse, Department of Commerce, Springfield, Virginia, 22151: AD–684–690, 1968.

Miles, G. H. Effects of physiological rhythms on performance. North Star Research and Development Institution, Minneapolis, Minnesota, March 28, 1967. AF 49–638–1604.

Richter, C. P. Psychopathology of periodic behavior in animals and men. In: Zubin, J., and Hunt, H. F. (eds.), *Comparative Psychopathology*. New York: Grune and Stratton, 1967, pp. 205–227.

Stephens, G. J.; McGaugh, J. L.; and Alpern, H. P. Periodicity
    and memory in mice. *Psychonomic Science*, 8(5):201–
    202, 1967.

Stephens, G. J., and McGaugh, J. L. Retrograde amnesia—
    effects of periodicity and degree of training. *Communi-
    cations in Behavioral Biology*, Part A, 1(4):267–275,
    1968.

Stephens, G. J., and McGaugh, J. L. Periodicity and memory in
    mice: A supplementary report. *Communications in Be-
    havioral Biology*, Part A, 2(2):59–63, 1969.

Sterman, M. B.; Howe, R. C.; and Macdonald, L. R. Facilita-
    tion of spindle-burst sleep by conditioning of electro-
    encephalographic activity while awake. *Science*, 167:
    1146–1148, February 1970.

Stroebel, C. F. Behavioral aspects of circadian rhythms. In:
    Zubin, J., and Hunt, H. F. (eds.), *Comparative Psycho-
    pathology*. New York: Grune and Stratton, 1967.

Stroebel, C. F. A biologic rhythm approach to psychiatric
    treatment. In: *Proceedings of the Seventh Medical
    Symposium*. New York: Yorktown Heights, IBM Press,
    1967, pp. 215–241.

Stroebel, C. F. Biologic rhythm correlates of disturbed be-
    havior in the Rhesus monkey. In: Rohles, F. H. (ed.),
    Circadian Rhythms in Nonhuman Primates. New York/
    Basel: Karger, 1969, pp. 91–105.

Stroebel, C. F. (investigator), and Luce, G. (writer). The im-
    portance of biological clocks in mental health. Mental
    Health Program Reports-3. National Institute of Mental
    Health, February 1968. PHS Publication 1743, pp. 323–
    351.

Svyadoshch, A. M., and Romen, A. S. The effect of auto-
    suggestion on certain cyclic processes. *Biologicheskiye
    ritmy i voprosy razrabotki rezhimov truda i otdykha.*
    Materialy. Moscow, 1967, 60–61.

Walsh, J. F., and Misiak, H. Diurnal variation of critical flicker
    frequency. *Journal of General Psychology*, 75:167–175,
    1966.

Wilkinson, R. T. Evoked response and reaction time. *Acta Psy-
    chologica*, 27:235–245, 1967.

Wilkinson, R. T. Sleep deprivation: Performance tests for par-
    tial and selective sleep deprivation. In: Abt, L. E., and
    Riess, B. P. (eds.), *Dreams and Dreaming*, Vol. 8 of
    Progress in Clinical Psychology. New York: Grune and
    Stratton, 1969.

Wyrwicka, W., and Sterman, M. B. Instrumental conditioning
    of sensorimotor cortex EEG spindles in the waking cat.
    Physiology and Behavior, 3:703–707, 1968.

Phase Shifts and Work-Rest Schedules

Adams, O. S., and Chiles, W. D. Human performance as a function of the work-rest cycle. U.S. Air Force WADC Technical Report, No. 60–248, 1960.

Adams, O. S., and Chiles, W. D. Human performance as a function of the work-rest ratio during prolonged confinement. U.S. Air Force WADC Technical Report, No. 61–720, 1961.

Adams, O. S.; Levine, R. B.; and Chiles, W. D. Research to investigate factors affecting multiple task psychomotor performance. U.S. Air Force WADC Technical Report, No. 59–120, 1959.

Adler, K. Extraoptic phase shifting of circadian locomotor rhythm in salamanders. Science, 164:1290–1291, 1969.

Alluisi, E. A. Research in performance assessment and enhancement. U.S. Army Behavioral Science Research Laboratory and Performance Research Laboratory, University of Louisville, Louisville, Kentucky, 1969.

Alluisi, E. A., and Chiles, W. D. Sustained performance, work-rest scheduling, and diurnal rhythms in man. Acta Psychologica, 27:436–442, 1967.

Alluisi, E. A.; Chiles, W. D.; et al. Human group performance during confinement. AMR Technical Documentary Report, 63–87. Aerospace Medical Division, Wright-Patterson Air Force Base, November 1963.

Alluisi, E. A.; Chiles, W. D.; and Hall, T. J. Combined effects of sleep loss and demanding work-rest schedules on crew performance. AMRL Technical Documentary Report, 63–64. Aerospace Medical Division, Wright-Patterson Air Force Base, June 1964.

Andlauer, P., and Metz, B. Variations nychtémérales de la fréquence des accidents du travail continu. Archives de Maladies Professionnelles, 14(6):613, 1953.

Andrezheyuk, N. I. Effects of different work and rest routines on subjects kept in relative isolation. Medicine, 52:631, October 1968.

Bayevskiy, R. M.; Chernyayeva, S. A.; et al. Investigation of the physiological condition of men exposed to isolation and hypodynamia during the shift to a new work and rest schedule. Biologicheskiye ritmy i voprosy razrabotki rezhimov truda i otdykha. Materialy. Moscow, 1967, 12–13.

Blake, M. J. F. Relationship between circadian rhythm of body temperature and introversion-extroversion. Nature, 215 (5103):896–897, 1967.

Blake, M. J. F.; Colquhoun, W. P.; and Edwards, R. S. Experimental studies of shift work, a comparison of rotating and stabilized four-hour shift systems. *Ergonomics,* 2:437–453, September 1968.

Bonjer, F. H. Physiological aspects of shiftwork. *Proceedings of the International Consortium on Occupation Health,* 13:848–849, 1960.

Cantrell, G. K., and Hartman, B. O. Crew performance on demanding work/rest schedules compounded by sleep deprivation. Brooks Air Force Base, Texas: School of Aerospace Medicine, November 1967.

Chiles, W. D.; Alluisi, E. A.; and Adams, O. S. Work schedules and performance during confinement. *Human Factors,* 10:143–146, 1968.

Chipman, D. M., and Sharon, N. Mechanism of lysozyme action. *Science,* 165(3892):454–465, August 1969.

Colquhoun, W. P. Biological rhythms and shift work. *Spectrum,* December 1967.

Colquhoun, W. P.; Blake, M. J. F.; and Edwards, R. S. Experimental studies of shift-work. I: A comparison of "rotating and stabilized" 4-hour shift systems. *Ergonomics,* 11(5):437–453, 1968.

Colquhoun, W. P.; Blake, M. J. F.; and Edwards, R. S. Experimental studies of shift-work. II: Stabilized 8-hour shift systems. *Ergonomics,* 11(6):527–546, 1968.

Colquhoun, W. P.; Blake, M. J. F.; and Edwards, R. S. Experimental studies of shift-work. III: Stabilized 12-hour shift systems. *Ergonomics,* 12(6):865–882, 1969.

Dehart, R. L. Work-rest cycle in aircrewmen fatigue. *Aerospace Medicine,* 38(2):1174–1179, November 1967.

Dirken, J. M. Industrial shift work: Decrease in well-being and specific effects. *Ergonomics,* 9(2):115–124, 1966.

Dushkov, B. A., and Kosmolinskiy, F. P. Rational establishment of cosmonaut work schedules. In: Gurovskii, N. N. (ed.), *Papers on the Psychophysiology of the Labor of Astronauts* (a collection of Russian articles). Foreign Translation Division, Clearinghouse, Department of Commerce, Springfield, Virginia, 22151: AD–684–690, 1968.

Eranko, O. 25-hour day: One solution to the shift-work problem. *International Congress on Occupation and Health,* 3:134, 1967.

Flink, E. B., and Doe, R. P. Effect of sudden time displacement by air travel on synchronization of adrenal function. *Proceedings of the Society for Experimental Biology and Medicine,* 100:494–501, 1959.

Galler, S. R. Relevance of biological orientation research to the field of bioastronautics. *Aerospace Medicine,* 32:535, 1961.

Gerritzen, F. The diurnal rhythm in water, chloride, sodium and potassium excretion during a rapid displacement from East to West and vice versa. *Aerospace Medicine,* 33:697–701, 1962.

Gerritzen, F. Influence of light on human circadian rhythms. *Aerospace Medicine,* 37:66–70, 1966.

Gerritzen, F.; Strengers, T.; and Esser, S. The behavior of the circadian rhythm in water and electrolyte excretion before, during and after a flight from Amsterdam to Anchorage and Tokyo, and on secondary influences on circadian kidney function. XVI International Congress on Aviation and Space Medicine, Lisbon, September 11–15, 1967.

Gerritzen, F.; Strengers, T.; et al. Studies on the influence of fast transportation on the circadian excretion pattern of the kidney in humans. *Aerospace Medicine,* 40:264–271, March 1969.

Ghata, J.; Fourn, P.; and Borrey, F. Application de l'étude des variations circadiennes a l'analyses des vols comportant le passage de fuseaux horaires. XVI International Congress on Aviation and Space Medicine, Lisbon, 11–15, September 1967.

Halberg, F.; Albrecht, P. G.; and Barnum, C. P. Phase-shifting of liver-glycogen rhythm in intact mice. *American Journal of Physiology,* 199:400, 1960.

Hartman, B. O., and Cantrell, G. K. Sustained pilot performance requires more than skill. *Aerospace Medicine,* 8(7):801–803, August 1967.

Haus, E., and Halberg, F. Phase-shifting of circadian rhythms in rectal temperature, serum corticosterone, and liver glycogen of the male C-mouse. *Rassegna di Neurologia Vegetativa,* 23(3–4):83–110, 1969.

Hauty, G. T. Relationship between operator proficiency and effected changes in biological circadian periodicity. *Aerospace Medicine,* 34:100–105, February 1966.

Hauty, G. T. Individual differences in phase shifts of the human circadian system and performance deficit. In: Brown, A. H., and Favorite, F. G. (eds.), *Life Sciences and Space Research V.* Amsterdam: North Holland Publishing Company, 1967, pp. 135–147.

Hauty, G. T., and Adams, T. Phase shifts of the human circadian system and performance deficit during the periods of transition. I: East-West flight. *Aerospace Medicine,* 37(7):668–674, July 1963.

Hauty, G. T., and Adams, T. Phase shifts of the human circadian system and performance deficit during the periods of transition. II: West-East flight. *Aerospace Medicine,* 37:1027–1033, 1966.

Hauty, G. T., and Adams, T. Phase shifts of the human circadian system and performance deficit during the periods of transition. III: North-South flight. *Aerospace Medi-*

cine, 37(12):1257–1262, 1966.

Hauty, G. T.; Steinkamp, G. R.; Hawkins, W. R.; and Halberg, F. Circadian performance rhythms in men adapting to an 8-hour day. *Federation Proceedings,* 19:54, 1960.

Holmquest, D. L.; Retiene, K.; and Lipscomb, H. S. Circadian rhythms in rats: Effects of random lighting. *Science,* 152:662–664, April 1966.

Howitt, J. S.; Balkwill, J. S.; Whiteside, T. C. D.; and Whittingham, P. D. G. V. Flight deck work loads in civil air transport aircraft. *FPRC Reports* 1240, August 1965, and 1264, December 1966. Ministry of Defense, Great Britain.

Kharabuga, S. G. Study of the effect of the daily schedule on daily periodics. *Biologicheskiye ritmy i voprosy razrabotki reshimov truda i otdykha.* Materialy. Moscow, 1967, 67–68.

Klein, K. E.; Brüner, H.; Rehme, H.; Stolze, J.; Steinhoff, W. D.; and Wegmann, H. M. Circadian rhythms of pilots' efficiency and effects of multiple time zone travel. *Aerospace Medicine,* 41: 1970. In press.

Klein, K. E.; Brüner, H.; and Ruff, S. Investigations on stress imposed on air crew in civil jet aircraft during long-range flight: Report on results on the northern Atlantic route. German Experimental Institute for Aeronautics and Astronautics, Research Report 65–44, October 1965.

Klein, K. E.; Brüner, H.; and Ruff, S. Investigation regarding stress on flying personnel in long-distance jet flights. *Zeitschrift für Flügwissenschaften,* 14:109, 1966.

Klein, K. E.; Wegmann, H. M.; and Brüner, H. Circadian rhythm in indices of human performance, physical fitness and stress resistance. *Aerospace Medicine,* 39:512–518, May 1968.

Kleitman, N. Sleep wakefulness cycle in submarine personnel. *Human Factors in Undersea Warfare.* Baltimore: Waverly Press, 1949, pp. 329–341.

Kosmolinskiy, F. P. Biological rhythms and development of work and rest regimes for cosmonauts. *Aerospace Medicine,* 1(5):136–141, February 1967.

Kosmolinskiy, F. P., and Kozar, M. I. Some indices of the stress reaction during chamber experiments with various work and rest schedules. *Biologicheskiye ritmy i voprosy razrabotki rezhimov truda i otdykha.* Materialy. Moscow, 1967, 37–39.

Kripke, D. F.; Cook, B.; and Lewis, O. F. Sleep in nightworkers: Electroencephalographic recordings. *Psychophysiology,* 1970. In press.

Kuznetsov, O. N.; Lebedev, O. N.; and Litsov, A. N. Concerning individual psychological features of human adaptation to altered daily regimes. *Biologicheskiye ritmy i voprosy razrabotki rezhimov truda i otdykha.* Materialy. Moscow, 1967, 40–41.

Lafontaine, E.; Lavernhe, J.; Courillon, J.; Medvedoff, M.; and Ghata, J. Influence of air travel on circadian rhythms. *Aerospace Medicine,* 38(9):944–947, September 1967.

Lafontaine, E.; Lavernhe, J.; and Pasquet, J. Subjective and objective responses to disruptions in the circadian rhythms during long-distance commercial flights East-West and vice versa. *Revue de Médecine Aéronautique et Spatiale,* 7(26):121–123, 1968.

Lipscomb, H. S.; Rummel, J. A.; et al. Circadian rhythms in simulated and manned orbital space flight. Paper presented at the 37th Annual Aerospace Medical Meeting, Las Vegas, Nevada, April 1966.

Litsov, A. N. Daily dynamics of some physiological functions and human work capacity in isolation. *Space Biology and Medicine,* 2(4):142–148, November 1968.

Meddis, R. Human circadian rhythms and the 48-hour day. *Nature,* 218:964–965, June 1968.

Medvedeff, E.; Barre, Y.; and Lavernhe, J. Les rythmes circadians des activités cortico-surrénale et medullo-surrénale influencés des décalages horaires. Service Médical d'Air France, 1, Square Max Hymans, Paris, 15e.

Menzel, W. Perturbations des rythmes circadiares chez l'homme, y compris aspect psychosomatique. In: de Ajuriaguerra, J. (ed.), *Cycles Biologiques et Psychiatrie.* Paris: Masson et Cie., 1968, pp. 205–221.

Mills, J. N. Circadian rhythms and shift workers. *Transactions of the Society of Occupational Medicine,* 17(1):5–7, 1967.

Mohler, S. R. Fatigue in aviation activities. *Aerospace Medicine,* 37:722–732, 1966.

Mohler, S. R.; Dille, J. R.; and Gibbons, H. L. The time zone and circadian rhythms in relation to aircraft occupants taking long-distance flights. *American Journal of Public Health,* 58(8):1404–1409, 1968.

Myasnikov, V. I. The importance of sleep in organizing the cosmonaut's schedule of daily activity. *Biologicheskiye ritmy i voprosy razrabotki rezhimov truda i otdykha.* Materialy. Moscow, 1967, 52–53.

Nicholson, A. N. Sleep patterns of an airline pilot operating worldwide East-West routes. *Aerospace Medicine,* 41 (6):626–632, 1970.

Ray, J. T.; Martin, O. E., Jr.; and Alluisi, E. A. Human performance as a function of the work-rest cycle: A review of selected studies. *National Academy of Sciences Research Council Publication* No. 882, 1961.

Reinberg, A. Evaluation of circadian dyschronism during trans-meridian flights. *Life Sciences and Space Research*, 12th COSPAR, Prague. In press.

Roberts, S. K. Circadian activity rhythms in cockroaches. II. Entrainment and phase shifting. *Journal of Cellular and Comparative Physiology*, 59:175–186, 1962.

Saito, H. Some considerations on reduction of working hours in Japan from the viewpoint of science of labour. *Journal of the Science of Labour*, 40:469–486, 1964.

Sasaki, T. Effect of rapid transposition around the earth on diurnal variation in body temperature. *Proceedings of the Society for Experimental Biology and Medicine*, 115:1129–1131, April 1964.

Sharp, G. W. G.; Slorach, S. A.; and Vipond, H. J. Diurnal rhythms of keto and ketogenic steroid excretion and the adaptation to changes of the activity-sleep routine. *Journal of Endocrinology*, 22:377–385, 1961.

Shilov, V. M., and Kozar, M. I. Changes in the immunological reactivity of man exposed to various day schedules in a sealed chamber. *Biologicheskiye ritmy i voprosy razrabotki rezhimov truda i otdykha*. Materialy. Moscow, 1967, 71–72.

Siegel, P. V.; Gerathewohl, S. J.; and Mohler, S. R. Time zone effects: Disruption of circadian rhythms poses a stress on the long-distance air traveller. *Science*, 164:1249–1255, 1969.

Simpson, H. W., and Lobban, M. C. Effects of a 21-hour day on the human circadian excretory rhythms of 17-hydroxycorticosteroids and electrolytes. *Aerospace Medicine*, 38:1205–1213, 1967.

Simpson, H. W.; Lobban, M. C.; and Halberg, F. Near 24-hour rhythms in subjects living on a 21-hour routine in the Arctic summer at 78°N, revealed by circadian amplitude ratios. *Rassegna di Neurologia Vegetativa*. In press.

Strughold, H. Physiologic day-night cycle after global flight. *Journal of Aviation Medicine*, 23:464, 1952.

Strughold, H. The physiological clock in aeronautics and astronautics. *Annals of the New York Academy of Sciences*, 134:413–422, November 1965.

Strughold, H. The physiological clock across time zones and beyond. *Air University Review*, 19:28–33, July-August 1968.

Thiis-Evensen, E. Shift-work and health. *Industrial Medicine and Surgery*, 27(10):493–494, 1957.

Thomas, L. Keep an eye on your inner clock. *Reader's Digest*, 61–64, August 1966.

Tune, G. S. A note on the sleep of shift workers. *Ergonomics*, 11(2):183–184, 1968.

Wever, R. The duration of re-entrainment of circadian rhythms after phase shifts of the Zeitgeber. *Journal of Theoretical Biology*, 13:187–201, 1966.

Wever, R. The influence of weak electromagnetic fields on the circadian rhythm in man. *Zeitschrift für Vergleichende Physiologie*, 56:111–128, 1967.

Wilkinson, R. T., and Edwards, R. S. Stable hours and varied work as aids to efficiency. *Psychonomic Science*, 13(4): 205–206, 1968.

Pineal Gland

Axelrod, J. Enzymatic synthesis of the skin-lightening agent, melatonin, in amphibians. *Nature*, 208(5008):306, 1965.

Axelrod, J.; Shein, H. M.; and Wurtman, R. J. Stimulation of C^{14} melatonin synthesis from C^{14} tryptophan by noradrenaline in rat pineal organ culture. *Proceedings of the National Academy of Sciences*, 62:544–549, 1969.

Axelrod, J., and Wurtman, R. J. Photic and neural control of indolamine metabolism in the rat pineal gland. In: Garolstein, S., and Moore, P. A. (eds.), *Advances in Pharmacology*. New York: Academic Press, 1968.

Axelrod, J.; Wurtman, R. J.; and Snyder, S. H. Control of hydroxyindole-*O*-methyltransferase activity in the rat pineal gland by environmental lighting. *Journal of Biological Chemistry*, 240(2):949–954, 1965.

Axelrod, J.; Wurtman, R. J.; and Winget, C. M. Melatonin synthesis in the hen pineal gland and its control by light. *Nature*, 201(4924):1134, 1964.

Cohen, R. A. Some clinical biochemical and physiological actions of the pineal gland. *Annals of Internal Medicine*, 61(6):1144–1161, 1964.

Fiske, V. M., and Huppert, L. C. Melatonin action on pineal varies with photoperiod. *Science*, 162:279, October 1968.

Gaston, S., and Menaker, M. Pineal function: The biological clock in the sparrow? *Science*, 160:1125–1127, 1968.

Kastin, A. J.; Redding, T. W.; and Schally, A. V. MSH activity in rat pituitaries after pinealectomy. *Proceedings of the Society for Experimental Biology and Medicine*, 24: 1275–1277, 1967.

Kerenyi, N. A., and Sarkar, K. The postnatal transformation of the pineal gland. *Acta Morphologia Academia Scientia Hungaria*, 16:223, 1968.

Moore, R. Y.; Heller, A.; Wurtman, R. J.; and Axelrod, J. Visual pathway mediating pineal response to environmental light. *Science*, 155:220–223, 1967.

Oishi, T., and Kato, M. The pineal organ as a possible photoreceptor in photoperiodic testicular responses in Japanese quail. *Memoirs of the Faculty of Science, Kyoto University*, 2: Series D:12–18, 1968.

Quay, W. B. Circadian and estrous rhythms in pineal and brain serotonin. *Progress in Brain Research,* 8:61–63, 1964.

Shein, H. M., and Wurtman, R. J. Cyclic adenosine monophosphate: Stimulation of melatonin and serotonin synthesis in cultured rat pineals. *Science,* 166:519–520, October 1969.

Snyder, S.; Zweig, M.; Axelrod, J.; and Fischer, J. E. Control of the circadian rhythms in serotonin content of the rat pineal gland. *Proceedings of the National Academy of Sciences,* 53(2):301–305, 1965.

Wetterberg, L.; Geller, E.; and Yuwiler, A. Harderian gland: An extra-retinal photoreceptor influencing the pineal gland in neonatal rats? *Science,* 167:884–885, February 1970.

Wurtman, R. J., and Axelrod, J. The physiologic effects of melatonin and the control of its biosynthesis. *Problèmes Actuels d'Endocrinologie et de Nutrition,* 10:189–200, 1966.

Wurtman, R. J., and Axelrod, J. A 24-hour rhythm in the content of norepinephrine in the pineal and salivary glands of the rat. *Life Sciences,* 5:665–669, 1966.

Wurtman, R. J.; Axelrod, J.; and Fischer, J. E. Melatonin synthesis in the pineal gland: Effect of light mediated by the sympathetic nervous system. *Science,* 143(3612): 1328–1330, 1964.

Wurtman, R. J.; Axelrod, J.; Sedvall, G.; and Moore, R. Y. Photic and neural control of the 24-hour norepinephrine rhythm in the rat pineal gland. *Journal of Pharmacology and Experimental Therapeutics,* 157(3):487–492, 1967.

Wurtman, R. J.; Chu, E. W.; and Axelrod, J. An inhibitory effect of melatonin on the estrous phase of the estrous cycle of the rodent. *Endocrinology,* 75(2):238–242, 1964.

Wurtman, R. J.; Kelly, D. E.; and Axelrod, J. *The Pineal.* New York: Academic Press, 1969.

Sleep

Abernethy, J. D.; Farhi, L. E.; and Maurizi, J. J. Diurnal variations in urinary-alveolar N2 difference and effects of recumbency. *Journal of Applied Physiology,* 23:875–879, 1967.

Abrams, R. L.; Parker, L.; et al. Hypothalamic regulation of growth hormone secretion. *Endocrinology,* 78(3):605–613, 1966.

Brebbia, D. R., and Altshuler, K. Z. Stage-related patterns and nightly trends of energy exchange during sleep. In: Kline, N. S., and Laska, E. (eds.), *Computers and Electronic Devices in Psychiatry.* New York: Grune and Stratton, 1968.

Brebbia, D. R.; Altshuler, K. Z.; and Kline, N. S. Lithium and the electroencephalogram during sleep. *Diseases of the Nervous System,* 30:541–546, 1969.

Brodan, V.; Brodanova, M.; Friedman, B.; and Kuhn, E. Influence of sleep deprivation on iron metabolism. *Nature,* 213:1041–1042, 1967.

Broughton, R. J. Sleep disorders: Disorders of arousal? *Science,* 159:1070–1078, 1968.

Cantrell, G. K., and Hartman, B. O. Crew performance on demanding work/rest schedules compounded by sleep deprivation. Brooks Air Force Base, Texas: School of Aerospace Medicine, November 1967.

Capek, R.; Babej, M.; and Radil-Weiss, T. Drug-induced sleep cycle impairment: A possible indicator of central nervous system side-effects. In: Baker, S. B. de C., and Tripod, J. (eds.), *Sensitization to Drugs,* Proceedings of the European Society for the Study of Drug Toxicity, Vol. 10. Excerpta Medica International Congress Series, 181:47–50, 1969.

Crowley, T. J.; Kripke, D. F.; Halberg, F.; Pegram, G. V.; and Schildkraut, J. J. Circadian rhythms in monkeys: Sleep, EEG, EMG, body and eye movement and temperature. *Psychophysiology,* 6:242–243, 1969.

Daughaday, W. H.; Othmer, E.; and Kipnis, D. M. Hypersecretion of growth hormone following REM deprivation. Report to the Fifty-First Annual Meeting of the Endocrine Society, New York, June 1969.

Dement, W. C., and Kleitman, N. Cyclic variations in EEG during sleep and their relation to eye movements, body motility and dreaming. *Electroencephalography and Clinical Neurophysiology,* 9(4):673–690, 1957.

Dewan, E. M. The P(programming) hypothesis for REMS. *Psychophysiology,* 4:365–366, 1968.

Feinberg, I. Eye movement activity during sleep and intellectual function in mental retardation. *Science,* 159:1256, 1968.

Feinberg, I. The ontogenesis of human sleep and the relationship of sleep variables to intellectual function in the aged. *Comprehensive Psychiatry,* 9(2):138–147, March 1968.

Frank, G.; Halberg, F.; Harner, R.; Matthews, J.; Johnson, E.; Gravem, H.; and Andrus, V. Circadian periodicity, adrenal corticosteroids, and the EEG of normal man. *Journal of Psychiatric Research,* 4:73–86, November 1966.

Friedman, A. H., and Walker, C. A. Rat brain amines, blood histamine and glucose levels in relationship to circadian changes in sleep induced by pentobarbital sodium. *Journal of Physiology* (London), 202:133–147, 1968.

Friedman, S., and Fisher, C. On the presence of a rhythmic diurnal, oral instinctual drive cycle in man: A preliminary report. *Journal of the American Psychoanalytic Association,* 15(2):317–343, April 1967.

Garvey, C. R. *The Activity of Young Children During Sleep: An Objective Study.* Intsitute of Child Welfare Monograph Series, No. 18. Minneapolis: University of Minnesota Press, 1939, p. 102.

Globus, G. G. Observations on sub-circadian periodicity. *Psychophysiology,* 1970. In press.

Greenberg, R., and Dewan, E. M. Aphasia and rapid eye movement sleep. *Nature,* 223:183–184, 1969.

Hansen, N. E. Sleep-related plasma hemoglobin levels. *Acta Medica Scandinavica,* 184(6):547–549, 1968.

Hartmann, E. Longitudinal studies of sleep and dream patterns in manic-depressive patients. *Archives of General Psychiatry,* 19:312–329, September 1968.

Hartmann, E. The 90-minute sleep-dream cycle. *Archives of General Psychiatry,* 18:280–286, March 1968.

Hartmann, E. (ed.). *Sleep and Dreaming.* Boston: Little, Brown, 1970.

Hayashi, T. The relationship between circadian sleep and gammahydroxybutyrate (4HB) in brain. *Experimental Medical Surgery,* 25(2–4):148–155, 1968.

Hayward, J. Brain temperature regulation during sleep and arousal in the dog. *Experimental Neurology,* 21(2):201–212, 1968.

Hobson, A. Sleep and biorhythmicity. *Science,* 165(3896):932–933, August 1969.

Huertas, J., and McMillin, J. K. Paradoxical sleep: Effect of low partial pressure of atmospheric oxygen. *Science,* 159:745–746, February 1968.

International Symposium of Electrotherapeutic Sleep and Electroanesthesia, *Excerpta Medica International Congress Series,* 128, 1966.

Johnson, J. H.; Adler, N. T.; and Sawyer, C. H. Effects of various photoperiods on the temporal distribution of paradoxical sleep in rats. *Experimental Neurology,* 27(1):162–171, 1969.

Jouvet, M. The states of sleep. *Scientific American,* 216:62–72, 1967.

Jouvet, M. Insomnia and decrease of cerebral 5-hydroxytryptamine after destruction of the RAPHE system in the cat. *Advances in Pharmacology,* 6B:265–279, 1968.

Jouvet, M. Biogenic amines and the states of sleep. *Science,* 163(3862):32–41, 1969.

Kales, A. (ed.). *Sleep: Physiology and Pathology.* Philadelphia: Lippincott, 1969.

Kales, A.; Preston, T. A.; Tan, T.; and Allen, C. Hypnotics and altered sleep-dream patterns. *Archives of General Psychiatry*, 23:211–218, September 1970.

Karacan, I.; Finley, W. W.; Williams, R. L.; and Hursch, C. J. Changes in stage 1-REM and stage-4 sleep during naps. *Biological Psychiatry*, 1970. In press.

Karadzic, V., and Mrsulja, B. Deprivation of paradoxical sleep and brain glycogen. *Journal of Neurochemistry*, 16(1): 29–34, January 1969.

Kleitman, N. *Sleep and Wakefulness*. Revised edition. Chicago: University of Chicago Press, 1963.

Koukkou, M., and Lehmann, D. EEG and memory storage in sleep experiments with humans. *Electroencephalography and Clinical Neurophysiology*, 25:455–462, November 1968.

Kripke, D. F., and O'Donoghue, J. P. Perceptual deprivation, REM sleep, and an ultradian biological rhythm. *Psychophysiology*, 5:231–232, 1968.

Lewis, J. Some observations on narcolepsy. *Psychophysiology*, 5:237, 1968.

Luby, E. D.; Grisell, J. L.; Frohman, C. E.; et al. Biochemical, psychological, and behavioral responses to sleep deprivation. *Annals of the New York Academy of Sciences*, 96:71–78, 1961.

Luby, E. D.; Frohman, C. E.; Grisell, J. L.; Lenzo, J. E.; and Gottlieb, J. S. Sleep deprivation: Effects on behavior, thinking, motor performance, and biological energy transfer systems. *Psychosomatic Medicine*, 22:182–192, 1960.

Luce, G. *Current Research on Sleep and Dreams*. U.S. Department of Health, Education, and Welfare, National Institute of Mental Health, Public Health Service Publication No. 1389, 1965.

Luce, G., and Segal, J. *Sleep*. New York: Coward-McCann, 1966.

Magora, F.; Assael, M. I.; and Ashkenazi, A. Some aspects of electrical sleep and its therapeutic values. *Excerpta Medica International Congress Series*, 136, September 1966.

Mink, W. D.; Best, J.; and Olds, J. Neurons in paradoxical sleep and motivated behavior. *Science*, 158:1335–1337, 1967.

Monroe, L. J. Psychological and physiological differences between good and poor sleepers. *Journal of Abnormal Psychology*, 72:255–264, 1967.

Mouret, J.; Bobillier, P.; and Jouvet, M. Insomnia following parachlorphenylalanine in the rat. *European Journal of Pharmacology*, 5:1, 1968–1969.

Nicholson, A. N. Sleep patterns of an airline pilot operating
    worldwide East-West routes. *Aerospace Medicine,* 41
    (6):626–632, 1970.

Parker, D. C.; Sassin, J. F.; Mace, J. W.; Gotlin, R. W.; and
    Rossman, L. G. Human growth hormone release during
    sleep: Electroencephalographic correlation. *Journal of
    Clinical Endocrinology and Metabolism,* 29(6):871–874,
    1969.

Passouant, P. Périodicité nychthémérale du sommeil rapide au
    cours de la narcolepsie. In: de Ajuriaguerra, J. (ed.),
    Cycles Biologiques et Psychiatrie. Paris: Masson et Cie.,
    1968, pp. 223–225.

Passouant, P.; Halberg, F.; Genicot, R.; Popoviciu, L.; and
    Baldy-Moulinier, M. La périodicité des accès narcolepti-
    ques et le rythme ultradien du sommeil rapide. *Revue
    Neurologique,* 121(2):155–164, 1969.

Pujol, J. F.; Hery, F.; Durand, M.; and Glowinski, J. Increase
    in serotonin synthesis in the brainstem of the rat after
    selective deprivation of paradoxical sleep. *Comptes Ren-
    dus de l'Académie des Sciences,* 267(3):371–372, 1968.

Reis, D. J.; Corvelli, A.; and Connors, J. Circadian and ultra-
    dian rhythms of serotonin regionally in cat brain. *Jour-
    nal of Pharmacology and Experimental Therapeutics,*
    167(2):328–333, 1969.

Richter, C. P. Sleep and activity: Their relation to the 24-hour
    clock. Sleep and altered states of consciousness. *Asso-
    ciation for Research in Nervous and Mental Disease,*
    45:8–29, 1967.

Roffwarg, H. P.; Muzio, J. N.; and Dement, W. C. Ontogenetic
    development of the human sleep-dream cycle. *Science,*
    152:602–619, 1966.

Rubin, R. T.; Kales, A.; and Clark, B. R. Decreased 17-hy-
    droxycorticosteroid and VMA excretion following glu-
    tethimide administration in man. *Life Sciences,* Part I,
    8(17):859–964, 1969.

Sassin, J. F.; Parker, D. C.; Mace, J. W.; et al. Human growth
    hormone release: Relation to slow-wave sleep and sleep-
    waking cycles. *Science,* 165:513–515, August 1969.

Shurley, J. T.; Pierce, C. H.; Natani, K.; and Brooks, R. E.
    Sleep and activity patterns at South Pole station: A pre-
    liminary report. *Archives of General Psychiatry,* 22(5):
    385–389, 1970.

Steriade, M., and Iosif, G. Opposite changes in responsiveness
    of the motor and somaesthetic cortex during natural
    sleep and arousal. *Electroencephalography and Clinical
    Neurophysiology,* 25(3):299, 1968.

Sterman, M. B. Sleep in the infant? In: Clemente, C. D.,
    Lindsley, D. B., and Purpura, D. (eds.), *Development*

of Sleep Mechanisms in Relation to Brain Maturation.
New York: Academic Press, 1972. In press.

Sterman, M. B.; Howe, R. C.; and Macdonald, L. R. Facilitation of spindle-burst sleep by instrumental conditioning of waking EEG activity. *Science,* 167:1146–1148, February 1970.

Sterman, M. B.; Wyrwicka, W.; and Roth, S. Electrophysiological correlates and neural substrates of alimentary behavior in the cat. *Annals of the New York Academy of Sciences,* 157(2):723–729, 1969.

Stern, E.; Parmelee, A. H.; Akiyama, Y.; Schultz, M. A.; and Wenner, W. H. Sleep cycle characteristics in infants. *Pediatrics,* 43(1):65–70, 1969.

Stoyva, J.; Zimmerman, J.; and Metcalf, D. Distorted visual feedback and augmented REM sleep. Association for the Psychophysiological Study of Sleep—Santa Fe, 1970.

Takahashi, Y.; Kipnis, D. M.; and Daughaday, W. H. Growth hormone secretion during sleep. *Journal of Clinical Investigation,* 47(9):2079–2090, 1968.

Tart, C. T. Waking from sleep at a preselected time. *Journal of the American Society of Psychosomatic Dentistry and Medicine,* 17(1):3–16, 1970.

Tepas, D. I. Evoked brain response as a measure of human sleep and wakefulness. *Aerospace Medicine,* 38:148–153, 1967.

Webb, W. B., and Agnew, H. W., Jr. Sleep cycling within twenty-four hour periods. *Journal of Experimental Psychology,* 64(2):158–160, 1967.

Weitzman, E. D.; Goldmacher, D.; Kripke, D.; MacGregor, P.; Kream, J.; and Hellman, L. Reversal of sleep-waking cycle-effect on sleep-stage pattern and certain neuroendocrine rhythms. *Transactions of the American Neurological Association,* 93:153–157, 1968.

Weitzman, E. D.; Kripke, D. F.; Goldmacher, D.; MacGregor, P.; and Nogeire, C. Acute reversal of the sleep-waking cycles in man: Effect on sleep-stage patterns. *Archives of Neurology,* 22(6):483–489, 1970.

Weitzman, E. D.; Schaumburg, H.; and Fishbein, W. Plasma 17-hydroxycorticosteroid levels during sleep in man. *Journal of Endocrinology and Metabolism,* 26:121–127, 1966.

Wulfsohn, N. L., and Sances, A. (eds.). *Proceedings of the Third Annual National Conference of the Neuroelectric Society.* New York: Plenum, 1970.

Zung, W. K. Antidepressant drugs and sleep. *Experimental Medicine and Surgery,* 27(1–2):124–137, 1969.

Zung, W. K. Effect of antidepressant drugs on sleeping and dreaming. III. On the depressed patient. *Biological Psychiatry,* 1:283–287, 1969.

Space

Altukhov, G. V.; Belai, V. E.; Egorov, A. D.; and Vasilev, P. V. Federation of American Societies for Experimental Biology, Washington, D.C. Diurnal rhythm of autonomic functions in cosmic flight. *Izvestia Akademiia Nauk SSSR, Ser. Biol.*, (Moscow), 30(2):182–187, 1965.

Alyakrinsiy, B. S. The ways and principles of the development of biorhythm studies and its importance in the organization of space-flights. *Biologicheskiye ritmy i voprosy razrabotki rezhimov truda i otdykha.* Materialy. Moscow, 1967, 3–7.

Analysis of Crew Performance in the Apollo Command Module, Phase II, Vol. 2, Appendix. Baltimore, Maryland: Martin Company, October 1966.

Aschoff, J. Significance of circadian rhythms for space flight. In: Bedwell, T. C., and Strughold, H. (eds.), *Proceedings of the Third International Symposium on Bioastronautics and the Exploration of Space*. San Antonio, 1964.

Berry, C. A.; Coons, D. O.; Catterson, A. D.; and Kelly, G. F. Man's response to long-duration flight in the Gemini spacecraft. Gemini Midprogram Conference, including experiment results, NASA, Washington, D.C., 1966, pp. 235–261.

Brown, F. A., Jr. The biological rhythm problem and its bearing on space biology. In: Kaufman, W. C. (ed.), *Advances in the Astronautical Sciences*. North Hollywood, California: Western Periodicals Company, 1963.

Dietlein, L. F., and Vallbona, C. Experiment M-4, inflight phonocardiogram measurements of the duration of the cardiac cycle and its phases during the orbital flight of Gemini V. Gemini Midprogram Conference, including experiment results, NASA, Washington, D.C., 1966, pp. 397–402.

Duke, M. B. Biosatellite III: Preliminary findings. *Science*, 166:492–493, 1969.

Dushkov, B. A., and Kosmolinskiy, F. P. Rational establishment of cosmonaut work schedules. In: Gurovskii, N. N. (ed.), *Papers on the Psychophysiology of the Labor of Astronauts* (a collection of Russian articles). Foreign Translation Division, Clearinghouse, Department of Commerce, Springfield, Virginia, 22151: AD–684–690, 1968.

Fedotov, Y., and Yudin, Y. Biological rhythms and astronautics. *Krasnaya Zvezda*, 212(11817):6, September 1962. Translated into English at Foreign Technology

Division, Air Force Systems Command, Wright Field, Patterson Air Force Base, Ohio, March 1964.

Halberg, F. Physiologic rhythms. In: Hardy, J. D. (ed.), *Physiological Problems in Space Exploration.* Springfield, Illinois: Charles C Thomas, 1964, pp. 298–322.

Halberg, F. Physiologic rhythms and bioastronautics. In: Schaefer, K. E. (ed.), *Bioastronautics.* New York: Macmillan, 1964, pp. 181–195.

Halberg, F.; Vallbona, C.; Dietlein, L. F.; Rummel, J. A.; Berry, C. E.; Pitts, G.; and Nunnely, S. Human circadian circulatory rhythms during weightlessness in extraterrestrial flight or bedrest with and without exercise. United States Public Health Service, NASA, Texas Medical Center, 1969.

Hoshizaki, T.; Adey, W. R.; Meehan, J. P.; Walter, D. O.; Berkout, J. I.; and Campeau, E. Central nervous, cardiovascular and metabolic data of a Macaca nemestrina during a 30-day experiment. In: Rohles, F. H. (ed.), *Circadian Rhythms in Nonhuman Primates.* New York/Basel: Karger, 1969, pp. 8–38.

Katovskii, B. S., and Pilyavskii, O. A. Effect of prolonged hypokinesia on human resistance to physical labor. *Biologicheskiye ritmy i voprosy razrabotki rezhimov truda i otdykha.* Materialy. Moscow, 1967, 32–33.

Lebedev, V. I. Scientist reviews problems of space psychology. *Science and Life* (U.S.S.R.), 3:25–29, September 1968.

Pittendrigh, C. S. Circadian rhythms, space research, and space flight. *Life Sciences and Space Research.* Amsterdam: North Holland Publishing Company, 1967, pp. 122–134.

Rummel, J.; Sallin, E.; and Lipscomb, H. Circadian rhythms in simulated and manned orbital space flight. *Rassegna di Neurologia Vegetativa,* 21(1–2):41–56, 1967.

Strughold, H. Solved and unsolved space medical problems. *Aerospace Medicine,* 38(5):520–535, 1967.

Wheden, G. D.; Lutwak, L.; Neuman, W. F.; and LaChance, P. A. Experiment M-7, calcium and nitrogen balance. Gemini Midprogram Conference, including experiment results, NASA, Washington, D.C., 1966, pp. 405–415.

Time Sense and Time Estimation

Baldwin, R. O., and Thor, D. H. Time of day estimates at six times of day under normal conditions. *Perceptual and Motor Skills,* 21:904–906, 1965.

Crawford, M. L. J., and Thor, D. H. Circadian activity and noise comparisons of two confined groups with and without reference to clock time. *Perceptual and Motor Skills,* 19:211–216, 1964.

Denner, B.; Wapner, S.; and Werner, H. Rhythmic activity and the discrimination of stimuli in time. *Perceptual and Motor Skills*, 19:723–729, 1964.

Erickson, M. H., and Cooper, L. F. *Time Distortion in Hypnosis.* Baltimore: Williams and Wilkins, 1959.

Fischer, R. The biological fabric of time. In: Fischer, R. (ed.). *The Interdisciplinary Perspectives of Time,* Annals of the New York Academy of Sciences, 138:440–488, 1967.

Fraisse, P. *The Psychology of Time.* London: Eyre and Spottiswoode, 1964.

Fraisse, P.; Siffre, M.; Oleron, G.; and Zuili, N. Le rythme veille-sommeil et l'estimation du temps. In: de Ajuriaguerra, J. (ed.), *Cycles Biologiques et Psychiatrie.* Paris: Masson et Cie., 1968, pp. 257–265.

Grossman, J. S., and Hallenbeck, C. E. Importance of time and its subjective speed. *Perceptual and Motor Skills,* 20:1161–1166, 1965.

Levinson, J. Z. Flicker fusion phenomena. *Science,* 160:21–28, 1968.

Lockhart, J. M. Ambient temperature and time estimation. *Journal of Experimental Psychology,* 73:286–291, February 1967.

Melges, F. T., and Fougerousse, C. E., Jr. Time sense, emotions, and acute mental illness. *Journal of Psychiatric Research,* 4:127–140, 1966.

Ornstein, R. E. *On the Experience of Time.* Harmondsworth, England: Penguin Books Ltd., 1969.

Pfaff, D. Effects of temperature and time of day on time judgments. *Journal of Experimental Psychology,* 76:419–422, March 1968.

Stephens, G. J., and Halberg, F. Human time estimation. *Nursing Research,* 14(4):310–317, 1965.

Surwillo, W. W. Time perception and the "internal clock": Some observations on the role of the electroencephalogram. *Brain Research,* 2:390–392, 1966.

Tepas, D. I. Evoked brain response as a measure of human sleep and wakefulness. *Aerospace Medicine,* 38:148–153, 1967.

Thor, D. H. Diurnal variability in time estimation. *Perceptual and Motor Skills,* 15:451–454, 1962.

Thor, D. H. Time perspective and time of day. *Psychological Record,* 12(4):417–422, 1962.

Treisman, M. The psychology of time. *Discovery,* 26:40–45, October 1965.

Walsh, J. F., and Misiak, H. Diurnal variation of critical flicker frequency. *Journal of General Psychology,* 75:167–175, 1966.

Wilkinson, R. T. Evoked response and reaction time. *Acta Psychologica,* 27:235–245, 1967.

INDEX

A

Abrams, Robert, 162–3
accidents, circadian
rhythm of, 27, 35
acquired characteristics,
circadian rhythms as, 48
Addison's disease, 138–40, 186
Ader, Dr. Robert, 99, 106
adrenal glands and hormones
in animals, 128–9
blindness and, 271–2
blood hormone rhythms,
128–9
depression and, 153–6
development, 97, 99–100
emotional conditioning and,
209–10
fatigue and, 138, 141
hearing and, 139–41
heart disease and, 156
in infants, 97–8, 99–100
light, effects of, 270–2
metabolism and, 75
periodic illness and, 246
sleep and, 28, 73, 78, 129
stress illnesses and, 150–2
taste sensitivity and, 138–9
age
circadian rhythms and, 108–9,
111–12
hearing and, 139–40
sleep and, 40, 107–9
aging, sleep phase shifts as factor in, 36
Agnew, Harmon, 69, 86
airline pilots and crews
aging, premature, 36
jet fatigue, 35–6
performance testing, 33–4
stability maintenance, 45
air pressure (see also Atmospheric conditions), 4

circadian rhythms and, 48
alcohol sensitivity, 180
alertness, cycles of, 89
allergies, 186–9, 256, 278
alpha rhythm (see also Brain
waves), 142
in sleep, 68, 142
time judgment and, 32
amines, biogenic, 142–4
amino acids, 8, 134–7, 175
amnesia, retrograde, 201–2
amphetamine, 183
amplitude, defined, 29
Androsthenes, 266
anesthetics, 180, 181–2
Angst, Dr. J., 252, 256
animals
alcohol, suspectibility to, 37–8
atmospheric conditions, sensitivity to, 51
biological hour in, 88
blood constituents, 129
brain waves, 141–2
cancer in, 165
cell division in, 157
circadian rhythms, 7–8, 48–51,
106–7
cosmic radiation and, 50
drugs, susceptibility to, 173–4,
180–1
enzyme rhythms, 185
estrus, effect of light on, 280–1
food utilization, 133–4
handling of, and development,
99–100
hearing, 140
learning, stress, and psychosomatic symptoms, 201–2
light and development of, 36,
268–70, 273–7, 280–1
magnetic fields, sensitivity to,
51–2, 59

397

animals (*continued*)
  pain tolerance, 178
  seasonal rhythms, 268–9
  sleep, 71, 73, 74, 80, 85–6, 92
  time sense, 11, 16
Antarctica, sleep in, 90
antibiotics, 184, 188–91
antimetabolites, 168
anxiety, *see* Emotions; Mental illness; Stress
appetite, 10, 132, 137–8
Arborelius, Dr. M., 149
Arctic hysteria, 257–9
Aretaeus, 256
Aristotle, 130
arteriosclerosis, 257
arthrosis, periodic, 245
Aschoff, Dr. Jürgen, 44, 56–8, 270
Aserinsky, Eugene, 66, 71
asthma, 150, 186–9, 259
astronauts, *see* Space exploration
astronomy and astrology, 18–19, 20–1, 263–4
atmospheric conditions
  biological rhythms and, 4, 6, 48, 50–1
  psychiatric patients' sensitivity to, 51
Axelrod, Dr. Julius, 135, 275–6
Aztecs, 263

B

Babylonians, 263
balneology, 10
Banschchikov, V. M., 82n.
barbiturates, 180, 182–4, 189
barometric pressure (*see also* Atmospheric conditions), 4
  circadian rhythms and, 48
Barter, Dr. Frederick, 156, 245
Bartoli, Dr. V., 149
behavior therapy, 208
Benoit, Dr. J., 272–3
biological hour (*see also* Circadian rhythms)
  alertness cycles, 89
  health and, 89
  in infants, 96–7
  oral behavior cycles, 97–8
  in sleep, 85–6, 87
  variations, individual, 89
biopsy, 160, 168–9

biorhythms, 23–4
Birch, Herbert G., 103–4
birds
  circadian rhythms, 7, 49
  light and, 268–70, 272–3
  seasonal rhythms, 268–9
  social factors and rhythms, 56
births
  annual rhythm, 6–7
  circadian rhythm, 7, 9, 281–2
  REM sleep and, 73
blindness, 271–2
blood
  of animals, 128–9
  circadian rhythm and, 33–4, 129–37
  clotting time, 129
  hormones, 128–9
  of infants, 98–9
  infection and, 128, 129–30
  liver and, 130–5
  pressure, 8, 96, 156–7
  periodic hypertension, 245–6
  sugar, 8, 98, 126, 130–2
  white cells in, 128
body temperatures
  circadian rhythm, 8, 31–2, 52–3
  in illness, 123, 150
  of infants, 98
  performance and, 31–3
  in sleep, 8, 29, 73, 75, 78, 80–1
  sleep-waking cycle and, 43–4
  stress and illness, 215–19
  summer hormone and, 7, 257
  temporal instability, adaptability to, 42
  time sense and, 15–16
Bohlen, Dr. and Mrs. Joseph, 258–9
Borman, Frank, 90–1
Bousquet, W. F., 185
brain (*see also* Brain waves)
  chemistry, 142–5
  hormone secretion and, 76–7
  light and, 273–9, 286
  limbic system, 87
  metabolism, and learning, 15
  of sea slug, pacemaker in, 11
  temperatures, and stress, 215–19
brain waves (*see also* Brain), 9
  alpha rhythm, 32, 68, 142
  of animals, 141
  circadian pattern, 32, 141–2

brain waves (*continued*)
in epilepsy, 179–80
information revealed by, 66–7
in sleep, 66–9, 74, 78, 83–117 *passim*, 141–2
in retardation, 95
breathing (*see also* Respiration), 10
Brown, Dr. Frank, 6, 50–2, 59
Bruner, Jerome, 200
Buddhism, time concepts of, 18, 19–20
Bünning, Dr. Erwin, 27, 48, 266–7
Burton, Robert, 278–9

C

Cahn, Dr. Harold, 108–9, 155
cancer, 27, 123, 149
cell division and, 165–8, 227–8
protein synthesis and, 169
stress and, 228
X-ray treatment of, 166–8
carbohydrate metabolism, 130–3, 126, 156, 161–3, 272
cardiac, *see* Heart
Carson, Rachel, 288
Casey, Robert, 226–7
catatonia, periodic, 247–50
cave or mine dwelling, *see* Isolation
cell division, 157–60
arrhythmic, and malignancy, 163–8
X-rays, effect of, 166–8
chemistry, body, *see* Metabolism; specific body areas (brain, kidneys, liver), and subjects (as enzymes, hormones)
Chess, Stella, 103–4
children (*see also* Infants)
circadian rhythms, 103–7
development, influence of experience on, 200
"difficult" and "easy," 104–7, 110–11
illnesses, 105, 187
learning in, 15, 109–12, 200
metabolism, 15–16
rearing of, rhythmicity and, 109–14
rhythms for orientation, 102

sleep, 69, 70, 112–15
time sense, 12–13, 17, 112–13
China, 18–19, 263
Christianity, time concepts of, 19
circadian rhythms (*see also* specific subjects), 7–9
as acquired characteristics, 48
age and, 108–9, 111–12
in animals, 7–8, 48–51, 106–7
biological hour, 85–90
of births, 7, 9, 281–2
child-rearing and, 109–14
of children, 103–7
Chinese awareness of, 18
daily living and, 145–6, 228, 287–95
day lengths, 8, 42, 52–4, 59–60
deaths, 8–9
desynchronization, individual internal, 42
drugs and medication and, 8–9, 162
education and, 109–10, 112
endogenous vs. socially conditioned, 53
forecasting, 23–4, 44–5
free-running, 53–5, 81
genetic theories of, 47–50
geophysics and, 48, 50–2, 57–59
in infants, 93, 97–107
infections and, 8
insects, 6, 7, 8, 163–4
length of, psychological stability and, 53
lunar influence, 54
maturation and, 97–8, 99–100
plants, 7–8, 265–8
of symptoms, 149–70
physiology and (*see also* specific subjects, *such as* Blood pressure; Pulse; Respiration; etc.), 8, 121–46
radiation sensitivity and, 8
social life and, 49, 56–7, 108, 109–10
stress and, 197–229
symptoms, physiological, 8
time guides necessary to, 8, 14, 55, 61
circulation, blood, 9–10
circulatory diseases, 149, 156
cirrhosis, 130
color vision, 13

Colquhoun, Dr. Peter, 32
confinement
  reaction against, 41
  work-rest schedules in, 38
contraceptives, 191
Cooper, Dr. Linn, 14–15
coordination
  circadian rhythm of, 31, 33–4
  child, learning by, 200
  work-rest schedules and, 40
cosmic periodicity (see also
  Lunar cycles)
  ancient beliefs, 234–5
  circadian rhythms and, 47–52
cosmic rays, 48, 50
crimes, rhythmicity of, 7, 283
crustaceans, rhythms of, 5–6,
  50–1
culture, and time concepts, 17–20
Curtis, George, 41–2
cycle, defined, 28–30

D

Daily rhythms, see Circadian
  rhythms; specific subjects
Dalton, Dr. Katharina, 236–7
Darwin, Charles, 266
Davis, Adelle, 240
death
  biorhythm and determination
    of day of, 23
  circadian rhythm, 8
  seasonal rhythm, 257
Declaration of Independence, 24
definitions, 28–30
Delea, Catherine S., 156
Dement, William C., 71, 74
depression, 152–6, 199, 255–6
  adrenal hormones and, 153–5
  desynchronization and, 109,
    152, 156
  electrosleep therapy, 81–2
  hypoglycemia, 131
  insomnia and, 83–4
  kidney functioning and, 154–5
Dewan, Dr. Edmond, 283–5
diabetes, 40, 160–3, 186
direction, sense of, see Orientation
DNA synthesis, 158–9
dopamine, 142
dowsing, 51–2
Dray, Dr. Fernand, 167

dreams and dreaming (see also
  Sleep)
  analyzing, 67
  in color, 72
  content of, 72
  external events, response to,
    69, 72
  learning and, 78–80
  problem solving, 67
  recollection of, 66, 72
  REM (rapid eye movement)
    (paradoxical) sleep and, 66,
    70–5
drugs and medication, 173–94
  alcohol, 180–1
  allergies and, 186–9
  anesthetics, 180–2
  animals and, 173–4, 180–1, 182
  antibiotics, 184, 188–91
  contraceptives, 191
  enzymes and, 184–6, 190, 191–
    193
  hormones, 44, 186–94
  learning cycles and, 209–10
  menstruation and, 191–3
  mental illness and, 184, 216,
    220, 223, 252–6
  narcotics, 183–4
  parasitic infections, 176–7
  phase shifts and, 44–5, 189–91
  psychedelic, and time sense,
    14
  response variations, 8–9, 173–
    194
  sedatives and sleeping pills,
    180, 182–4, 189–90
  stimulants, 180, 182–4
  strategies, therapeutic, 184–94
  time estimation for timing
    treatment, 178–9
  toxicity, changing, 173–4
  tranquilizers, 180, 183, 189–90,
    216, 220

E

Eating, see Foods
ecology, 288
economics, reform and, 287–8
edema, periodic, 239, 244
educational system, and circadian rhythms, 109–10, 112,
  202–4

Egypt, ancient, 20, 263–4, 269, 283

Einstein, Albert, 14

electroencephalography (EEGs), see Brain waves

electromagnetism, see Magnetic fields

electrosleep (electrotherapy), 81–3, 223

elephantiasis, 176

embryo, see Fetus

Emlen, Dr. Stephen T., 273

emotions (see also Psychology, individual)
behavior therapy, 208
conditioning and timing, 204–8
hormones and, 126
liver functioning and, 130–1
male cycles, 240–3
premenstrual tension, 236–40
psychotherapy, 207, 208–9
REM sleep and, 79
stress and psychosomatics, 204–29

encephalitis, 123

encephalomyelitis, equine, 175

endocrine glands, see Hormones; specific glands

energy, liver functioning and, 130–8

Engelmann, T. G., 94

enuresis, 126

enzymes, 134–6
drugs and, 184–6, 190, 191–3

epilepsy, 40, 105, 179–80

Erickson, Dr. Milton, 14–15

errors, circadian rhythm in making of, 27, 31, 34–5

Erskine, Donald R., 54–5

Eskimos, 257–9, 269

Everett, Dr. John W., 280–1

evolution, Chinese concept of, 19

exercise, physiological effects of, 38, 134

F

Falliers, C., 187

fatigue
adrenal level and, 141
rhythmic, 66
sleep-waking cycle and, 35, 43–4, 77–8

fear
free running and, 212–13
learning, timing and, 204–8
psychotherapy and unlearning of, 208–9

Feigin, Dr. Ralph D., 136–7, 175

fetus
activities of, 94–5
external sounds, response to, 102–3
in vitro gestation, 102–3, 287
rhythms of, 96–7, 102–3
sleep-like phase, 94–5

fevers, 122–3
time sense and, 15–16

Finns, 257, 279, 286

Fischer, Roland, 13–14

Fisher, Dr. Charles, 74, 87–8

fish, rhythms of, 7, 50

Fliess, Wilhelm, 23–4

Fogel, Max, 41–2

Folk, Dr. Edgar, Jr., 108–9, 155

foods
dieting, 133–4
hunger, 132
infants, feeding schedules of, 93, 104–5
isolation and eating cycles, 87–88
meal timing, 133–4, 136–7
metabolism, 132–8
sleep and utilization of, 133, 136–8
traveling, choice of in, 45
utilization rhythms, 133–8

forty-eight-hour day (see also Circadian rhythm), 59–60

Fraisse, Paul, 12

Franks, Dr. Robert, 99

Frazer, Sir James, 257–8

Frazier, Dr. Thomas, 40–1

frequency of cycle, defined, 28

Friedman, Dr. Alexander, 143–4

Friedman, Stanley, 87–8

Freud, Sigmund, 23

G

Gamma globulin, 129–30, 175

Garcia-Sainz, Dr. Mauricio, 166, 168

genetics
cancer and, 168

genetics (*continued*)
  circadian rhythms and, 47–50
  DNA and RNA synthesis, 158–159
  engineering, 286–7
  mental illness and, 221
  periodic illness and, 243–4
geophysics, circadian rhythms and, 4, 48, 50–2, 57–9
Ghata, Dr. Jean, 45, 186
Gjessing, Dr. Leiv, 247–50
Gjessing, Dr. Rolv, 247–8
Globus, Gordon, 87
glycogen and glucose, metabolism of, 131–3, 160–3, 272
gonads, light and functioning of, 272–3, 275–6, 281
gravity, influence of, 4, 50
Greece, ancient, 20–3, 124–5, 130, 149–50, 197, 235, 256, 264
Greenberg, Ramon, 79
Grigoryev, Dr. Y. G., 167
growth
  annual rhythms, 9
  hormone, 69–70, 137

H

Halberg, Dr. Franz, 36–8, 44, 128–9, 131–2, 152, 156–60, 165–6, 169, 174–5, 179–82, 184–5, 187, 241, 245, 257, 270–1, 282
hallucinogens, and time sense, 14
Hamburger, Dr. Christian, 241
Hamner, Dr. Karl, 267
Harker, Dr. Janet, 163–4, 228
harmony and unity, as medical concept, 10, 20–3, 197–200
Harris, Geoffrey, 100
Hauenschild, C., 283–4
Hawking, Dr. Frank, 176
heart
  beat, 9–10
  diseases, 9, 73, 156–7
  rate, desynchronization of, and sleep-waking cycle disruption, 43–4
  rhythms, 28
  transplants, 164–5
Hellbrügge, Dr. T., 98
Hellman, Dr. Leon, 76

hemoglobin (*see also* Blood), 8
Henkin, Dr. Robert I., 138–41
Hersey, Rex B., 241–2
Hildebrandt, Dr. Gunther, 9–10
Hippocrates, 20–2, 149, 235
histamine, 142–5, 188–9
Hoagland, Dr. Hudson, 15–16
Hollwich, Dr. F., 271–2
Holmes, Dr. Thomas H., 226–7, 228
hormones, 8
  adrenal, *see* Adrenal glands and hormones
  in animals, 128–9
  blindness and, 271–2
  in blood, 128–9
  depression and, 153–5
  emotions and, 126
  fear and danger, response to, 125–6
  growth, 69–70, 137
  of infants, 98, 99–100
  learning and, 209–10
  light and, 270–86
  menstrual cycle and, 191–3, 236–7, 238–9, 283–6
  mental illness and, 257–9
  performance levels and, 31
  sex, 167, 240–1
  sleep and, 28, 69–70, 78, 128–129, 152
  stress and, 125–6, 150–2
  summer, 7, 257
  therapy, 44, 186–200
  in urine, 125–6
Houston, Dr. Jean, 14–15
hunger, 10, 132, 137–8
Huston, Dr. Paul E., 108–9, 155
hypertension, 35
  periodic, 245–6
hypnosis, and time sense, 14–15
hypoglycemia, 130–1
hypothalamus
  adrenal secretion and, 76–7, 150–1
  appetite and, 132
  body temperature and, 123
  light and, 270–1, 273–4

I

Illness (*see also* Medicine; Mental illness; specific diseases and disorders)

Illness (*continued*)
  adaptability to sleep-cycle
    changes and, 40
  blood analyses and, 128
  body temperature rhythm **and**,
    122–3
  genetics and, 221, 243–4
  geriatric, 107–8, 109
  of infants and children, **95**,
    105, 150, 187
  infections, *see* Infection, sus-
    ceptibility to
  jet fatigue, 35–6
  liver disorders, 130–1
  lunar cycles and, 234–5
  medication, *see* Drugs **and**
    medication
  pain, 149, 178
  periodic, 22, 213–15, 233–5,
    243–59
  psychosomatic (*see also* Psy-
    chosomatics), 82, 198–229
  seasonal, 256–9
  sleep cycles and, 27, 34–6
  sleep patterns and, 73, 81–5,
    95, 107–8
  stress, 150–2
  symptoms, rhythmicity of, 149–
    170
  taste sensitivity in, 138–9
immunity, *see* Infection, susceptibility to
India, 19
Indians, 197, 263–4, 269
infants (*see also* Children), care
  of, and development, 97–
  107, 200
  circadian rhythms, 93–4, 97–
    107
  "difficult" and "easy," 104–7
  genetic defects and REM ac-
    tivity, 95
  illness, rhythmicity and, 105
  isolation of vs. stress, and de-
    velopment of, 100–1
  learning in, 95–6, 200, 202–3
  maturation of body systems, 98
  mother-infant synchrony, 101–
    102
  orientation, rhythms for, 102
  parent compatibility, 100–1
  pineal gland in, 277
  rhythms of, 93–107
  sleep of, 87, 93–8, 100–2

infection, susceptibility to
  blood constituents and, 128,
    129–30
  circadian cycle of, 8, 129–30,
    175–7
  isolation and, 39
  parasitic, 176–7
  work-rest schedules and, 39,
    130
infradian rhythm, 86
insects, rhythmicity of, 6–8, 163–
  164, 268
insomnia, 80
  desynchronization in, 81
  of elderly, 107–8
  electrosleep therapy, 81–3
  mental illness and, 83–4, 219
insulin, 160–2, 272
intermeshing of cycles, 9–11
ionization, 48
IQ, and learning, 203
Island, Dr. Donald P., 271
isolation
  circadian rhythm and, 8, 46–
    48, 52–7
  development and, 100
  eating rhythm in, 87–8
  48-hour day in, 59–60
  immunity and, 39
  reaction against, 41
  sleep and, 46–7, 53–4, 55–7,
    87
  time sense and, 8, 14, 55, 61
Ivanov, Dr. D., 142–3

J

Janiger, Dr. Oscar, 237–9
Japan, time concepts in, 19–20
Jenner, Dr. F. A., 250–2
jet fatigue, 35–7, 78
Jouvet, Dr. Michel, 73, 74
Judeo-Christianity, time con-
  cepts of, 19

K

Kaiser, Dr. Irwin H., 281–2
Kales, Anthony, 151
Kato, M., 276
Kennedy, John F., 288
Kerenyi, Dr. N. A., 277
kidney functioning and urination
  age and, 108–9

kidney functioning and urination
      (*continued*)
   in children, 126–7
   circadian rhythm, 123–7
   fluctuation, rhythmic, 42, 52–3
   hormones, in urine, 125–6
   in illness, 150, 154–5
   in infants, 93–4, 98–9
   light and, 272
   sleep-waking schedule, and, 43,
      127
   stress and, 40
   urine analysis, 124–6
   urine volume, 126–7
Klein, Dr. K. E., 33–4, 41
Kleitman, Dr. Nathaniel, 52, 66,
      71, 85–6, 88, 94
Kraft, Dr. Irvin, 165
Krieger, Drs. Dorothy and How-
      ard, 77, 189
Kripke, Daniel F., 87

                      L

Lamb, Mary, 246
Lapps, 257
Laures, Josy, 52–3
learning
   adrenal cycle and, 209–10
   behavior therapy, 208
   in children, 15, 109–13, 200
   drugs, effects of, 209–10
   emotional, and psychosoma-
      tics, 204–29
   hypnosis and, 14–15
   memory and, 201–3
   psychotherapy and, 207, 208–9
   rhythmicity, 109–13, 202–4,
      204–10
   in sleep, 78–80, 95–6, 114–15
   slow learners, 203
   time sense and, 14–15
Lehmann, Dr. Heinz, 51, 184
Lester, Dr. Boyd, 101–2
Levine, Dr. Seymour, 99–100
light (*see also* Seasonal rhythms),
      4, 263–86
   activity and, 270–1
   aging, light-dark cycle and, 36
   animals and, 36, 268–70, 273–
      277, 280–1
   artificial, 265, 277–8
   birds and, 268–70, 272–3
   blindness, 271–2

   cell division and, 157–8
   color importance, 273, 276–8
   estrus and, 279–80
   hormones and, 270–86
   insects and, 6–7
   intensity and physiological
      rhythms, 56
   lunar cycle, 282–3
   menstruation and, 279–80,
      284–6
   metabolism and, 271–2, 278
   personality and, 278–9
   photoperiodism, 266–8
   plants and, 265–8
   sea creatures and, 282–3
   sexuality and, 272–6, 278–86
   sleep and, 55–6, 278
   vision and, 13, 265
   winter solstice, 269–70
Linnaeus, Carolus, 265
Lipscomb, Dr. Harry, 41
Lisk, Dr. Robert, 274
lithium, and cyclic psychoses,
      252
liver, 130–6
   blood sugar and, 130–2
   cell division in, 159
   disease and disorders of, 130–1,
      150
Lobban, Dr. Mary, 127
Loewi, Otto, 115
lunar day, length of, 8
lunar cycles, 4
   ancient times, awareness in, 18,
      263–4, 283
   circadian cycle influenced by,
      54
   crime and accidents, 283
   crustaceans and, 5–6
   menstrual cycle and, 6, 234,
      282–3
   mental illness and, 283
   periodic illnesses and, 234–5

                      M

Madsen, Willard, 203
magnetic fields, responsiveness
      to, 4, 48, 50–1, 58
   artificial fields, effects of, 58–9
   dowsing, 51–2
   mental illness and, 51
   orientation in space and, 51–9
   sleep and, 90

Mairtet, Jean-Pierre, 55
malaria, 176
Malek, Dr. Jeri, 281
malignancy, see Cancer
manic-depression, 250–3, 255–6
Masters, Dr. Robert E. L., 14–15
Masuda, Minoru, 226–7
Maya, 263
McGaugh, Dr. James L., 201–2
McGinty, Dr. Dennis, 88–9, 92
Mead, Richard, 22
medication, see Drugs and medication
medicine (see also Illness; Mental illness; Psychosomatics; specific diseases and disorders)
    biopsy, 160, 168–9
    biorhythms, 23–4
    computerization in, 224–6, 255
    cultic, 20–3
    drugs, see Drugs and medication
    Egypt, ancient, 20, 263–4
    eighteenth century, 22
    electrosleep therapy, 81–3, 223
    geriatric, 107–8, 109
    Greece, ancient, 20–3, 124–5, 130, 149–50, 197, 235, 256, 264
    hormone therapy, 44, 186–200
    Indian (American), 197
    infection (see also Infection, susceptibility to), 8, 39, 128, 129–30
    laboratory tests and diagnosis, 168–70
    narcolepsy, 84–5
    nineteenth century, 22–3
    periodic symptoms and, 233–259
    preventive, 228–9
    radiation therapy, 166–8
    schedule regularity as treatment, 10
    surgery timing, 181–2
    symptoms, rhythmicity of, and treatment, 149–70
    total, 10–11, 20–3, 197–200
Meites, Dr. Joseph, 273
melatonin, 274–6
memory, 201–2
    amnesia, retrograde, 201–2
    in animals, 201–2

    education and, 202–4
    IQ and, 203
    learning and, see Learning
    psychosomatic symptoms as, 210–12
    sleep loss and, 65
    time sense, coding and, 16–17
menstruation, 9, 36, 235–40
    birth pattern and, 282
    hormones and, 191–3, 236–7, 238–9
    light and, 279–80, 284–6
    lunar cycle and, 6, 234, 282–3
    metabolism and, 239–40
    premenstrual symptoms, 236–240
mental illness (see also specific forms)
    age and, 108–9
    behavioral stress and, 215–21
    behavior therapy, 208
    brain temperatures and, 215–19
    computer technology, medical use of, 224–6, 255
    cycles, undetected, 252–7
    desynchronization and, 109–10, 154–6, 198–9
    drugs and medication, 184, 216, 220, 223, 252–6
    electrotherapy (electrosleep), 81–3, 223
    genetics and, 221
    hormones, 152–4, 198
    hypoglycemia and, 131
    and insomnia, 81, 83–4, 219
    kidney functioning and, 154–5
    life-change rate and, 226–7
    liver functioning and, 130–1
    lunar cycle and, 283
    magnetic fields and, 51
    periodic, 246–59
    psychosis vs. neurosis, reversibility of, 220–1
    psychotherapy, 207, 208–9
    seasonal, 256–9
    security and, 216–21
    sleep and, 40, 65–6, 81, 83–4, 219
    time sense and, 16
    time structure and, 221–9
Menzel, Dr. Werner, 150, 243
Mesopotamia, 263
metabolism (see also Body temperature)

metabolism (*continued*)
  adrenal hormones and, 75–6
  amino acids, 134–7
  antimetabolites, 168
  behavior and, 122, 126, 127, 130–2, 198–200, 258–9
  blindness and, 271–2
  of carbohydrates, 130–3, 136, 156, 161–3, 272
  in children, 15–16
  glycogen and glucose, 131–3
  and hunger, 132
  light and, 271–2, 278
  liver functioning and, 130–8
  menstruation and, 239–40
  performance and, 31–3
  periodic symptoms and, 249–250, 259
  of proteins, 135–8, 168, 272
  sleep and, 75, 136–8
  time sense and, 15–16
Meyer, Dr. Roland K., 276
migraine, 254
Miller, Dr. Neal, 199
Mills, Dr. John, 53, 55, 124
mitosis, 157–60
Möllerstrom, Dr. Jacob, 161
mollusks, orientation ability of, 51
mongolism, 95
Monroe, Laurence J., 80
moon cycles, *see* Lunar cycles
mortality, Eastern and Western views of compared (*see also* Death), 18–20
mother-infant synchrony, 101–2
myoclonic jerk, 68

N

Naps, 86–7, 107–8
narcolepsy, 84–5
narcotics, 183–4
Navaho Indians, 197
Nelson, Dr. Walter, 36
neurosis, *see* Mental illness
night work, 24, 27
  accidents and errors, 27, 31, 35
  coordination and, 31, 33–4
  REM sleep and hormonal levels, 78
  rotating shifts, 27, 35–43, 45–6
  steady, preferable to rotating shifts, 46

weekends and time off, effects of phase shifts during, 34–5
noise, as trauma, 212
norepinephrine, 142–3, 275
nucleic acids, mitosis in, 158–9

O

Oishi, T., 276
oral behavior, in isolation (*see also* Foods), 87–8
orientation, sense of, 5–6
  magnetic fields and, 51–9
Ornstein, Robert, 16–17
Orth, Dr. David N., 271
Othmer, Ekkehard, 87
oxygen consumption, variations in, 33–4

P

Pain, 149, 178
Papi, Dr. Floriano, 5
parasites, infectious, 176–7
parent-infant compatibility, 100–1
Parmelee, Arthur C., 94
Pauly, Dr. John E., 129, 157–8, 175, 182–3
Pearlman, Chester, 79
penicillin, 188
perception (*see also* Time sense; Vision), 13–14
performance
  body temperature and, 31–3
  circadian rhythm of, 30–1, 33–34
period, defined, 28
periodic symptoms in sickness and health (*see also* Illness; Mental illness; Psychosomatics; specific subjects), 233–240
peritonitis, periodic, 243–4
personality, *see* Psychology, individual
phase, defined, 29–30
phenylketonuria, 95
photoperiodism, 266–8
physiology, rhythms of, *see* specific subjects (births, hormones, etc.); specific rhythms (circadian, seasonal, etc.)
Piaget, Jean, 12–13, 200

Pierce, Chester, 53–4, 90
pineal gland, 274–7
Pittendrigh, Dr. Colin, 6, 48, 133, 270
pituitary gland, 138–41, 150–2, 273–4, 279, 286
Pizzarello, Dr. Donald, 167
plants
　circadian rhythms, 7–8, 48, 265–8
　cosmic radiation and, 50
　light and, 265–8
　seasonal rhythms, 7, 267–8
　time sense, 265–6, 267–8
Plato, 22
polar expeditions, and sleep, 90
Pollack, Dr. Irwin, 12
Pöppel, Dr. Ernst, 57–8
primates, see Animals; specific subjects
protein metabolism, 135–8, 168, 272
　antimetabolites, as cancer treatment, 168
psychedelic drugs, and time sense, 14
psychology, individual (see also Emotions; Mental illness)
　child care and (see also Children; Infants), 200
　emotion cycles in men, 240–3
　isolation vs. stress and, 100
　knowledge of rhythmicity and, 113–14
　light and, 278–9
　metabolism and, 122, 126, 127, 130–2, 198–200
　premenstrual tension and, 236–40
　rhythmic and arrhythmic children, 104–7, 110–11
　sleep-waking schedules and, 41–2, 77–8
　stability, circadian cycle and, 53
　time, stress, and, 197–229
　time structure and way of life, 145–6, 227–8, 287–95
psychosis (see also Mental illness) cyclic, 246–7
psychosomatics (see also specific diseases), 82, 198–229
　conditioning and timing, 205–8, 209–10, 212–13

desynchronization and, 212–13
electrosleep (electrotherapy), 81–3
fear and emotional learning, 204–5
genetics and, 221
life-change rate and, 226–7
mental stress and, 215–21
noise and, 212
psychotherapy and, 207, 208–9
symptoms as memories, 210–12
time structure and, 221–2
psychotherapy, 207, 208–9
Public Health Service, 152, 198
pulse, 8
　fetal, 96
　respiration and, 9–10

R

Radiation, sensitivity to, 8
Radzialowski, F. M., 185
Rahe, Dr. Richard, 226–7
Reimann, Dr. Hobart, 241, 243–245, 255
Reinberg, Dr. Alain, 186–9, 279–280
Reis, Dr. Donald, 143–4
reproduction (see also Births; Menstruation)
　birds, 272–3
　genetic engineering, 286–7
　fetal development, 94–5, 96–7, 102–3, 287
　light and, 278–86
　precosity, 275
　seasonality, human, 278–9
respiration, 8
　nostrils, uneven breathing through, 10
　oxygen consumption, variations in, 33–4
　pulse and, 9–10
rest-and-activity cycle, see Biological hour; Work-rest schedules
retardation, brain waves in, 95
Richter, Dr. Curt P., 99, 138, 190–1, 213–15, 243, 250
RNA synthesis, 158–9
Rocard, Yves, 52
Rock, Dr. John, 285
Roffwarg, Dr. Howard, 79

Rowan, Dr. Vernon, 272
Rummel, Dr. John, 41
Rust, Dr. Charles C., 276
Rutenfranz, Dr. J., 98

S

Sachar, Dr. Edward, 153
Sanctorius, 9
Sander, Dr. Louis W., 100–1
Sarkar, Dr. K., 277
Sassin, Dr. J. F., 69
Sawyer, Dr. Charles H., 280–1
schedules, *see* Sleep-waking cycles
Scheving, Dr. Lawrence E., 129, 157–8, 175, 182–3
Scrimshaw, Dr. N. C., 137
sea creatures, rhythms of, 4–6, 11, 269, 282–3
seasonal rhythms (*see also* Light), 256–7, 263–80
    ancient awareness of, 18–20, 20–2, 256, 263–4, 283
    of animals, 268–9
    of birds, 268–9, 272–3
    in births, 6–7
    growth, 9
    hormonal, 7, 257–9
    human activity and attitudes, 268–70
    of insects, 6–8, 268
    mental illness, 256–9
    physiological, 259
    of plants, 7, 267–8
    sex crimes, 7
    winter solstice, 269–70
Selye, Hans, 150–1
Senni, Tony, 52–3
Senoi Indians, 114
Serio, Dr. M., 161
serotonin, 142–3, 275
sex
    characteristics, light and, 272–276, 278–86
    crimes, 7
    hormones, 167, 240–1
shift work, *see* Work-rest schedules
Shurley, Jay, 53–4, 90
Sicuteri, Dr. F., 254
Siffre, Michel, 14, 52, 55
skin
    cells, 157, 159–60

conductivity of, in infants, 98
    temperature, 8
sleep (*see also* Sleep-waking cycle), 65–117
    age and, 40, 107–9
    of animals, 71, 73, 74, 80, 85–6, 92
    in Antarctica, 90
    awakening at will, 67, 72–3, 115–17
    body temperatures in, 8, 29, 31–2
    brain waves in, 66–9, 74, 78, 83–117 *passim*, 141–2
    cell division and, 157–60
    of children (*see also* Infants), 69, 70, 112–15
    cycle, duration of (biological hour), 71, 85–6, 87
    cycles, nightly, 66, 69
    dreaming (*see also* Dreams and dreaming), 66, 70–5
    drugs and, 81–2, 84
    electrosleep, 81–3
    external events, response to, 69, 72
    fetal, 94–5, 96–7
    food, metabolism, and, 133, 136–8
    hormones and, 28, 69–70, 78, 128–9, 152
    illness, and patterns of, 80–5, 95, 107–8
    of infants, 87, 93–8, 100–2
    insomnia or poor, 77–8, 80–4, 107–8, 219
    jerk, myoclonic, 68
    learning during, 78–80, 95–6, 114–15
    light and, 55–6, 278
    loss, ability to stand, 65–6
    making up for loss of, 69
    memory, and loss of, 65
    metabolism and, 75, 136–8
    naps, 86–7, 107–8
    physiological patterns in, 69–70, 72–3, 75–6, 80–1
    problem solving in, 67, 112
    psychosis, and sleep loss, 65
    REM (rapid eye movement) (paradoxical) sleep, 66, 70–97, 102, 107–8, 113, 116–17
    REM deprivation, 73–4, 74–5
    sleepiness, cycles of, 66, 89

sleep (*continued*)
  in space, 90–1
  stages of, 68
  thought in, 67, 78–80
  time sense in, 67, 72, 115–17
  training and control of, 67, 72–73, 91–3, 115–17
sleeping pills and sedatives, 180, 182–4, 189–90
sleeping-waking cycle (*see also* Sleep)
  adaptability to changes in, 40–43, 77–8
  adrenal secretions and, 28, 78, 129
  aging and, 36
  air travel and, 27, 35–46, 75
  animal life span and, 36
  body temperature and, 29, 31–2
  circadian rhythm and, 27–61
  day lengths, biological, 8, 42
  drug effects on, 44–5, 189–91
  drug response and, 189
  fatigue and, 35, 43–4, 77–8
  fetal, 96–7
  free-running, 53–5
  illness due to disruption of, 27, 34, 35–6, 45–6, 130
  of Indians, 61
  in infants, 93–8, 100–2
  isolation and, 46–7, 53–4, 55–57, 87
  kidney functions and, 43, 127
  light and, 269–70
  mental illness and, 222–3
  night work and, 24, 27, 31, 35, 46
  protein need and, 136–8
  psychological factors, 31, 41–2
  REM sleep and reversal of, 77
  rotating shifts, 27, 35–43, 45–46
  social factors, 56–7
  on space flights, 38–9, 40–1
  terms defined, 28–30
  testing for temporal vulnerability, 42–3
  transition period following reversals of, 34, 42–4, 76–8, 128–9
smoking cycle, in isolation, 87–8
social factors as synchronizers of

rhythms, 49, 56–7, 108, 109–110
solar cycle (*see also* Circadian rhythms), 8
Sollberger, Dr. Arne, 161
sounds, 4
  age and hearing, 139–40
  fetal response to, 102–3
  hearing ranges, 13
  noise as trauma, 212
  sensitivity to, 139–41, 179–80
Southern, Dr. Louis A., 167
space exploration
  sleep, 90–1
  time structure, 60–1
  work-rest schedules, 38–9
Stephens, Dr. Gwen, 179, 201–202
Sterman, Dr. M. B., 88–9, 92, 96–7
stigmata, 244–5
stimulants, 180–1, 182–4
Stoyva, Johann, 79
stress (*see also* Emotions; Psychosomatics), 197–229
  adrenal cycle and, 209–10
  animals, effect on, 201–2
  cumulative, 226–7
  development and, 99–100
  eating cycles and, 87–8
  electrosleep therapy, 82–3
  hormone response to, 125–6
  illness, 150–2
  life-change rate and, 226–7
  loss of Stage IV sleep under, 83–4
  mental illness and, 215–21
  non-circadian day and, 40
Stroebel, Dr. Charles F., 194, 204, 207–10, 212–13, 215–226, 228
Strumwasser, Dr. Felix, 11
Stunkard, Dr. Albert J., 132
suicides, 257
sunlight, *see* Light
Syrians, ancient, 269

T

Takahashi, Dr. Y., 69–70
Taoism, 18, 263
Tart, Dr. Charles, 116
taste sensitivity, 138–9

temperature, *see* Body temperature; Skin temperature

therapy, *see* Drugs and medication; Medicine

thinking habits, and time sense, 16–17

Thomas, Dr. Alexander, 103–5, 110

Thomas, Lowell, 45

thyroid, 137, 257

tides, influence of, 4
  on crustaceans, 5–6

time sense, 11–12
  of animals, 11, 16
  body temperature and, 15–16
  brain-wave patterns and, 32
  of children, 12–13, 17, 112–13
  circadian rhythm, 30–1
  cultural time concepts, 3–4, 17–20
  conditioning and, 11–12
  isolation and, 8, 14, 55
  memory, coding, and, 16–17
  in mental illness, 16
  metabolism and, 15–16
  physiological factors, 13–14
  of plants, 265–6, 267–8
  in sleep, 67, 72, 115–17
  trance states, 14–15

time structure (*see also* Circadian rhythms; Lunar cycle; Seasonal rhythms)
  culture, influence of, 3–4, 17–20
  as shaper of life, 3–4
  in space exploration, 60–1
  stress and (*see also* Mental illness; Psychosomatics), 197–229
  and way of life, 145–6, 227–228, 287–95

Timonen, Dr. Sakari, 279

tissues, cell division in, 157–60
  arrhythmic, and malignancy, 163–8

Titov, Gherman, 91

Tobias, Dr. Milton, 105

trance states, 14–15

tranquilizers, 180, 183, 189–90, 216, 220

transplants, phase differences and, 164–5

travel, 34–46
  drug use and, 44, 189–91

east-west, 41

east-west, and jet fatigue, 35–6

eating habits, 45

motivation, jet fatigue and, 78

REM sleep and, 75

tips for adapting to, 44–6

west-east, 43–4

tyrosine and metabolism, 133–6

U

ulcers, gastric, 35, 40, 73, 149–152, 256, 259, 278

ultradian rhythm (*see also* Biological hour), 86

urine, *see* Kidney functioning and urination

V

Vision
  color, 13
  speed of, 13–14

von Mayersbach, Dr. H., 185

W

Waika Indians, 61

wakathons, 65

Walker, Dr. Charles A., 143

way of life, and time structure, 145–6, 227–9, 287–95

weather detection, by animals, 51

Webb, Wilse B., 69, 86

weight, rhythmicity of, 9

Weitzman, Elliot, 76, 77, 178

Wever, Dr. R., 58–9

Wilkinson, Dr. Robert T., 32

Williams, Robert, 69

winter madness, 257–9

winter solstice, 269–70

Wolff, Dr. Sheldon, 245–6

Wolpe, Dr. Joseph, 208

work-rest schedules
  adaptability, individual differences in, 40–2
  age, and adaptability to changes in, 40
  alcohol, vulnerability to, 37–8
  in confinement, 38
  drug use and, 44, 189–91
  efficiency, circadian rhythm of, 31, 32–5

work-rest schedules (*continued*)
  illnesses due to, 34–5, 35–6
  illnesses and adaptability to
    changes in, 40
  infection, susceptibility to, 40
  night work, 24, 27, 31, 35, 46
  REM sleep and hormonal
    levels, 77–8
  rotating shifts, 27, 35–43, 45–
    46
  on space flights, 38–9
  testing for temporal vulnera-
    bility, 42–3

Wurtman, Richard, 134–6, 275–8,
  286
Wyler, Allen, 226–7

X

X-ray treatments, 166–8

Y

Yap, Dr. R. P., 185–6

Z

Zung, Dr. William, 83–4, 189–90

ABOUT THE AUTHOR

GAY GAER LUCE was born in Berkeley, California. She studied at Juilliard School of Music and Radcliffe College, and has an M.A. from Stanford University. For the past decade she has devoted her time to writing and speaking in the field of science, and has often appeared on radio and television. She is the author of numerous articles and of two previous books.